The British Bloke DECODED

The British Bloke

DECODED

**From Banter to Man Flu.
Everything finally explained.**

GEOFF NORCOTT

monoray

First published in Great Britain in 2023 by Monoray, an imprint of
Octopus Publishing Group Ltd
Carmelite House
50 Victoria Embankment
London EC4Y 0DZ
www.octopusbooks.co.uk

An Hachette UK Company
www.hachette.co.uk

First published in paperback in 2024

ISBN 978-1-80096-130-2

A CIP catalogue record for this book is available from the British Library.

Printed and bound in Great Britain

1 3 5 7 9 10 8 6 4 2

Typeset in 11/15pt Sabon LT Pro by Jouve (UK), Milton Keynes

This FSC® label means that materials used
for the product have been responsibly sourced

This monoray book was crafted and published by Jake Lingwood,
Pauline Bache, Liz Marvin, Mel Four, David Eldridge and Peter Hunt

*I'd like to thank my lovely
wife and brilliant son for
not only accepting the bloke
I am but making me want
to become a better one.*

AUTHOR'S NOTE

In this book, you'll encounter language which, in certain circles, might be deemed a bit old-fashioned. For example, I sometimes refer to my wife as 'the Mrs'. She's fine with that, as are most women I know, but some might consider those words a relic from the seventies – possibly like the average bloke himself. In a way, that's the point of this book. I want to examine aspects of the British Bloke which have evolved dramatically in recent years, while also acknowledging that, in other senses, we might not have changed so much at all.

In thinking about 'the bloke', I've often found myself pulling apart the dynamic between straight men and straight women, which I know could be seen by modern standards as not especially inclusive. However, in a time when writers are encouraged to 'stay in their lane', the 'heteronormative' lane is the only lane I've ever known. I'm not trying to exclude any tribe, just trying to make sense of my own.

So, whoever you are, I hope this book resonates with you as we find out more about that singular enigma – the British Bloke.

'*You tried your best and you failed miserably. The lesson is never try.*'

Homer J Simpson

PROLOGUE

Last autumn, I was picking up my six-year-old son from one of his many after-school clubs. We were talking about a playground incident which had happened earlier in the day. He'd been playing a tag-based pursuit game with his mates, but a couple of the lads had such physical pace it was virtually impossible for the other boys to win. So my son, with his top-notch brain, had cleverly rejigged the rules in order to make it a bit fairer.

The act of play colliding with cold, hard bureaucracy isn't unusual for boys of this age. For a six-year-old lad, one of the great joys of playtime isn't just the game itself but a level of needless officialdom which would make local government blush.

The faster boys eventually worked out my son's game and started to tease a little, which had him rattled.

I smiled, confident my paternal wisdom could reassure him about what had occurred. 'Son, it's fine,' I reassured him, 'All that's happened is you've had your first bit of banter.'

Before I even checked his reaction in the rear-view mirror, I could hear the finely tuned cogs of his mind whirring.

'What's banter?' he asked, his brow furrowing in a way I hadn't seen before.

I warmed to my explanation, happy to help him take his first steps into a bigger world.

'Son, banter is when your mates take the mickey out of you, it's part of friendship.'

More silence. His cogs whirred louder still and I began to flounder.

'Erm, in a group of mates, one way the other lads will assess your worth as a male is by how much banter you can take. If you can take a bit of stick they'll . . . sort of . . . know you're a good guy, because they can depend on you to stand up . . . under pressure.'

He started glancing out of the window, his subtle way of letting me know I was losing him. I started to reach further.

'I think banter evolved from when men would go out hunting. They'd be a long way from the camp and would need to know the other fellas were strong, so would test them out. Maybe in the past we'd do it physically but now we do it with words . . . it's all about not showing weakness to the tribe, you see.'

There was a long pause as he digested everything I'd said and came to a conclusion.

'I don't like banter,' he said, 'it's not fun.'

He promptly returned to looking out of the window at the dark sky and amber lights whizzing by.

Presented with the first challenge of communicating one of the central pillars of blokeyness to my son, I'd fumbled it. I'd taken what should have been a simple idea and introduced needless levels of complexity and concern. Instead of allowing his playtime event to simply be an awkward moment at school, I'd used so many hunting metaphors he must've been wondering if I'd decided it was time for his first kill.

I take being a father to a son seriously, particularly at such a confusing time for boys. Being male is one of my few areas of genuine expertise. As a bloke, I've now clocked up forty-six years of unbroken service. I dress very blokily, typically in jeans and a polo shirt. My image is so middle-of-the-road that when I do my stand-up comedy shows, I look like a ticket tout for my own gig, the kind of guy who might not know much about jokes but would definitely know where to order a skip.

Furthermore, I recently discovered I literally *am* the average bloke, certainly on a statistical basis.

I'm five foot nine (OK, five foot eight and a half) (OK, a quarter). My feet are a decidedly average size nine. I weigh thirteen and a quarter stone – and yes, my other proportions are decidedly average too. In recent elections, I've voted pretty much in line with the majority of the country. My favourite food is curry. My favourite sport is football. My favourite sitcom is – you've guessed it – *Only Fools and Horses*. My favourite documentary? *The Story of Only Fools and Horses.*

I am a route-one bloke who finds comfort and distraction in simple things.

Tesco released the most popular combination of their meal deal. Guess who'd bought a ham and cheese sandwich, cheese and onion crisps, and a Diet Coke for the last fifteen years? (And, incidentally, never got bored, though I sometimes swap out the crisps for Mini Cheddars if I'm feeling reckless.)

Even on a class basis, I'm one of swathes of people who was brought up in a working-class environment but now enjoys the trappings of a more middle-class existence. In another time, I'd have been called 'Mondeo Man' (if he didn't sound like the world's shittest superhero).

All my life I've been dimly aware that I've been cursed – or blessed – with a radical form of mediocrity, so if there's one thing I know a lot about it's being a standard bloke, and a British one in particular.

It's been a testing time for the male brand of late. In the last few years, the term 'Men' (as opposed to 'blokes') has become something of a pejorative one implying privilege and power. There was a long overdue reckoning for certain kinds of toxic men who needed taking down a peg or two: men who leched, men who waged wars . . . men who were Matt Hancock. However, as I started to think about this book, I realised there was a world of difference between those guys – who never spoke for the vast majority – and the standard British Bloke. But, as feminism found renewed energy in the second half of the 2010s, all the valid discourse also created a slipstream which other things fell into.

It's true that the list of people who've crashed economies and started wars mostly contains people who could pee standing up. But meanwhile, the other 99.9 per cent of their sex were, at worst, crashing Ford Fiestas or starting DIY projects they never finished.

So forgive me if I exclude blokes from some of the wider excesses of the male species. The vast majority of us have never harboured any desire to hold political power and the nuclear codes – and if we were given them we'd probably palm them straight off to our wives. It's safer that way. She's always done a pretty good job with the passports.

I can't speak for a whole sex, but when it comes to the sub-genre of 'blokes' I've given it a lot of thought and the good news is we might not be so bad after all. I'm beginning to think that, beneath the farting, grunting and general inattentiveness, there's a lot more to us than meets the eye. The underlying complexities of explaining banter to my son illustrate that point. Once I'd realised that something as seemingly simple as ribbing your mates was underpinned by such complicated motives, I went down a rabbit hole thinking about other blokeish things which also have hidden depths (just like, I strongly believe, blokes themselves).

So the plan with *The British Bloke Decoded* is to investigate all those unexpectedly complex intricacies of the male experience and get to the bottom of them. To unpack and decode British blokes, looking at those apparently still waters and wondering what manner of mad shit is scuttling around beneath.

Over fifty or so chapters, I've taken on subjects from man flu and lager to crying and losing friends in an effort to understand what really makes the British bloke tick. There are important questions here that need answering. What is the enduring appeal of football? Is being a good bloke about mediocrity and averageness? If so, how can someone with the exceptional talents of Freddie Flintoff be seen to epitomise the idea?

And why won't we *ever* go to the bloody doctors?

WHAT IS A BLOKE?

I've already had a couple of tentative stabs, but let's try to properly define what a bloke is.

No one can agree where the word even came from. It was first recorded in 1851 by Henry Mayhew, the journalist who revealed the plight of London's poor to an indifferent Victorian nation. He said 'bloke' was replacing 'chap' as the preferred slang for any male, but the origin of that word is obscure. It could come from an Irish dialect word meaning 'likeable man'; it could also come from the Dutch word 'blok' which means 'fool', as in 'blockhead'. I think the modern meaning might fall somewhere between the two.

What a bloke definitely isn't is a 'geezer' or a 'lad'. To the untrained eye, they may appear the same but absolutely aren't. The word bloke is usually accompanied by an adjective prefix, which is often positive: 'decent' bloke, 'good' bloke, 'nice' bloke (although there is an unwritten law that if you want to tell the world a man makes you laugh then he is deemed to be a 'funny fella').

Geezers and lads don't get adjectives because their species is generally less complicated. Geezers and lads are the aardvarks and zebras of the male world: there are quite a lot of them, but they're easy to spot and narrow in range. Blokes are otters and apes, in that they're numerous, come in many different types and have a generally good temperament (so long as you don't steal their fish or bananas).

The bloke is also quintessentially British. Not as in wearing a top hat to work like Jacob Rees-Mogg or a kilt to weddings, like that half-Scottish bloke at work, but as in they don't really exist anywhere else in the world.

Germany may have *der Kerl*, Italy may be full of *ragazzi* and France can claim *le type*, but 'bloke' and all that implies belongs fully to these islands. I am willing to accept that Australia has a whiff of blokeyness about the place, but they're twenty years behind us so haven't fully developed yet (and that sort of comment, cheeky but basically affectionate, is classically blokey).

The bloke is also more emotionally complex than the alpha, geezer or lad. He is the dependable rank and file of the male species, the standard husband, father, uncle and brother who tries his best but doesn't have much agency in his own life (certainly when it comes to deciding how the house is decorated or what events will occupy the family calendar). It's a state of mind which usually occurs at a more senior stage of life, once you've had some of the headier dreams either kicked out of you or have willingly relinquished them for a quiet life. It's a mindset which descends once you've realised your main role isn't to thrust and conquer but to be a steady and dependable presence for those you love. And to carry heavy things. Blokes are inoffensive, pliable, dependable and calm, but also a bit shit at retaining any information about the people they're closest to.

A bloke knows the value of a pub quiz and the exact combination of alcohol and roast dinner which will result in a forty-minute nap. Though blokery is usually an older man's game, it's a mindset which could evolve at any age. I've had plenty of mates who were already wearing metaphorical cardigans and slippers during their GCSEs. I had a pal in Year 11 who brought a pack of biscuits to school with him every day and used to have a nap at breaktime. We didn't know whether to call him 'Hob Nob' or 'the cat', because he could sleep anywhere (on reflection, we should probably have advised him to get checked for diabetes).

Blokes are simple and yet some of our behaviour is so utterly daft and paradoxical you have to wonder if everything is as straightforward as it seems. It's tricky, though, because societally we're encouraged to think of blokes as basic creatures. For a long time, adverts have portrayed the woman as thrifty and resourceful, while the man was either confused, lazy or falling over in the background. In any sitcom you've ever seen, the dad is the comical figure. Why? Because he's a bloke and becoming a father in itself involves a fairly cataclysmic status drop.

We may be hard to define but there are certain things which characterise the British bloke.

One is that they're generally fairly content. Happy with just being. Give a bloke a dressing gown, some Twiglets and an obscure Bundesliga football match and he can sit happily for hours. He's genetically designed to find salvation in menial tasks. As children, boys will happily go to a beach only to ignore the majesty of the ocean or the beauty of the sunset and simply dig a hole. Even at that tender young age, he's just looking for a bit of peace and quiet.

If you see a man drinking a pint in an airport pub alone, that's a bloke. If you see a man driving to the tip on a Saturday morning with a smile on his face, that's a bloke. And if you see a man heading back from the tip and on the way to the pub, that's a very happy bloke.

The bloke doesn't like a fuss. The bloke is curious about the world and occasionally baffled by it. The bloke remains in touch with his inner child and retains a certain boyishness, which can be wrongly interpreted as immaturity.

Blokes will often suppress emotions, only for them to show up in the oddest of places. For example, it's OK to get a bit misty-eyed when watching *The Repair Shop*. The average bloke will be a tear-soaked mess as he watches a ninety-five-year-old woman collect the newly fixed clogs that her dead husband walked across Belgium in during the war. We tend to let our emotions out in massive bursts. We keep it all in, then binge on a big boxset of feelings. Whether that's when someone scores at the football, someone undertakes you on the motorway or when Blackadder asks his fellow soldiers to go over the top.

Blokes also have a tendency to be nostalgic – or rather, they don't so much yearn for the past as they want the future to slow down a bit and stop hurtling at them like a flying brick. Similarly, every bloke thinks that the younger generation has 'gone soft'. We'll forever lament the fact that young lads today can't even bleed a radiator or navigate without GPS. But my dad would despair that I couldn't change the oil on my own car and his great-grandad would despair that my dad bought meat in a butcher's rather than killed the animal with his bare hands.

The real bloke is *always* on the verge of giving up on modern football as each week brings further proof that the 'game is gone'. Luckily, he will never actually give up on modern football because, you know, his dad took him to his first game and he cherishes those smoky memories of angry beered-up men shouting sexual obscenities at the referee before leaving him outside a pub with a packet of crisps for three hours.

Despite how it sounds, these are happy memories. Like I keep saying about this whole bloke thing, it's a lot more complicated than it seems.

DO YOU WANT A MEDAL?

*British men do approximately half the amount
of housework of their female counterparts.*

It's fair to say that in modern heterosexual relationships, even
when the man and woman work the same number of hours,
women still do more of the housework. Many men have been
very happy for women to smash the glass ceiling, so long as they
didn't have to help clear up the mess.

How the hell have blokes blagged this continuing imbalance?
In a time when old boardroom dinosaurs are quaking and the
likes of Beyoncé have delivered finger-wagging rebukes to men
on all manner of behaviours, how have women increased their
workload outside the home but not experienced an equivalent
reduction within it?

There is one very simple reason, and it's possibly the hardest
to get past: most blokes are happier with lower levels of general
cleanliness.

I once lived in a lads' pad and it makes me shudder to think
about the state we'd let that flat fall into. One day, we decided to
have a party and it seemed, against all the odds, that there would
be actual girls present. We knew it was very unlikely they would
be getting off with any of us anyway, but especially not if the place
looked like a smackhead's bedroom.

I took the initiative and borrowed my mum's Dyson. Dysons

were new at the time and expensive, so my mum made me promise on pain of death to return it in the state it was lent.

We started vacuuming. The vacuum cleaner had completely filled up before we'd even done one quarter of the lounge (I won't burden you with what I saw in that despicable chamber, but the debris still pops up in anxiety dreams). It took another seven full loads before the Dyson, this shining evolution in cleaning, said 'fuck it' and conked out. The mess we had lived in for so many months had driven the high point of nineties British engineering to a spluttering death within half an hour.

I'd like to think I've evolved since then, that I'd avoid living in a public health hazard even if there weren't girls around – but the disparity between the mess me and my wife will put up with remains.

This lack of equality in housework isn't just confined to blokey blokes. Some of the most progressive men I know talk a good game on equality but deliver very little in domestic help. Sure, when they're on a company diversity retreat it's all 'this is what a feminist looks like' and echoing the idea that 'time's up' for out-of-touch men (in the hope that time won't be up for them), but ask them what a floor wipe looks like and they'll fumble around and mumble something positive about Caitlin Moran. On social media, they're the first to share memes saying men need to 'do better'. However, their feminism comes to a grinding halt when it comes to them 'doing better' in their own house and, in particular, cleaning the bathroom. I know a lot of blokes who do some household chores but it's very rare that any go near the bathroom. Or, indeed, are allowed near the bathroom. I guess women can live with half-hearted vacuuming, but a bad job in the bathroom could result in an outbreak of Legionnaire's disease. Weirdly, of the few blokes I know who do regularly clean the bathroom, most of them used to be in the army. That tells its own tale: all it took to instil this basic obligation was the possibility of a court martial.

I do some housework but, if I'm honest, I'm way too pleased with myself on the odd occasion that I do. This is going to piss some women off; however, I believe there can be no personal growth without full disclosure, so here comes a dangerous level of candour.

Whenever I do housework, in my mind, it counts as some sort of favour. [Winces in anticipation of blowback.] Rather than considering it a shared responsibility in the house we both live in, I see myself as a centre-forward tracking back to defend a corner and expect to be lauded to the rafters for entry-level teamwork.

I know it's not OK to think this way, but I also wonder if it might feel less like gaslighting to hear a bloke finally admit that this is how his mind works, when it's something many women will have suspected all along.

On the occasions I do housework, it will unfold in a similar way. It'll be on a day when I'm at home with less work to do than usual. In my sixth hour of watching something frivolous, like *The Mandalorian*, a thought will crop up in my head, seemingly out of nowhere: 'Geoff, you could vacuum the lounge.'

I'm initially taken with what a great guy I am for even thinking this. What a top bloke! So taken, in fact, that I almost forget to actually vacuum the lounge.

It's debatable as to whether I even do a good job of it because, for the duration of the work, I'm already anticipating my wife's return when I can share the good news.

The moment she puts her key in the door, I'm on her like a flash, barely allowing her time to put her coat on the hook before I relay my heroics.

'Babe, I vacuumed the lounge!' I proudly announce.

The look on my face must be like that of a three-year-old boy who finally did his first poo in the big toilet.

The reaction she gives is, I'd imagine, common to many women. 'What, Geoff? Do you want a medal?'

I laugh grandly, 'No, of course not – I just wanted you to know that I see this house as a shared enterprise and I'm just doing my bit and I shouldn't presume, and . . .'. I keep speaking but I'm guarding the pathetic truth that I do want a medal. I always want medals.

Men want medals. Is that so bad? This is mummy's little soldier you're talking to – as a boy, I was feted for the most limited acts of helpfulness by my indulgent mother so, yes, maybe the occasional medal wouldn't go amiss.

This is my advice to women whose blokes don't do enough housework, though I appreciate that they might not like it: purchase some medals. Go on eBay and get a job lot of cheap plastic ones, maybe a modest number to begin with, like a thousand.

Women might think, 'But why should I have to pander to his pathetic ego? He should want to empty the dishwasher.'

If he's young, there's a chance you could still train him, but be honest with yourself. Look into his eyes. Does he seem capable of change? Does he look like the kind of bloke who's ever going to 'want' to do a domestic chore when he could be watching golf? If the answer is no then follow my advice and your life will be better, albeit grudgingly.

Whenever he does a small task reward him, sometimes with more than one medal if he's done a particularly good job. Put a wash on? One medal. Took out bins without being reminded? Three medals. And if he notices that you've left that bottle of shampoo on the bottom step of the stairs in the hope he might take it up with him, give him the whole box.

FANCY A PINT?

Fancy. A. Pint.

For British blokes, this constitutes one of the greatest sentences in the English language. The 'To be or not to be' of blokery. And just like Hamlet's famous speech, the decision to have a pint can involve an aspect of moral quandary – not least 'Is 11am too early?'

But what is at the heart of this love affair with beer? Why is it so intrinsic to the blokey identity? Is it the drink itself or everything that goes with it?

Something I've always appreciated about beer is its longevity as a popular drink. In a world where every few months a new marketing campaign informs us we should be drinking espresso martinis, or something called a 'hard seltzer' (which sounds, to me, like over-the-counter medication for loose stools), the appeal of beer has endured. As far back as the Anglo-Saxon period, this country has been bang on the ale. In general, if something's been popular for that long it can't be all bad (though I say that conscious of the fact that bread had a fairly good run until the gluten-free evangelists mobilised).

Beer is a very simple drink, comprised of just four ingredients. Grain, hops, yeast and water. You can almost imagine a standard bloke at a bar crossing himself as he reverentially intones those four holy pillars: 'The grain, the hop, the barley . . . and a packet of pork scratchings please, love.'

Unlike many sugary or fizzy alcoholic drinks, a pint of beer – unless you're trying to win a bet or lose your dignity – is usually drunk at a slow, steady pace. The drink has various gravitating factors which hold you back. If you consume those gassy bubbles too quickly, you might get the hiccups or, worse still, find yourself staring into a toilet bowl. Given these restraints, the pint stands almost as a unit of time. An alcoholic hourglass. Or half-hour glass. Or fifteen-minute glass, if you've got a train to catch.

Speaking of trains, a pint can also act as a consolation. I believe it to be a fundamental British human right that when your train is cancelled or seriously delayed, you're entitled to get a bit drunk. It harnesses one of the standard functions of alcohol: drinking to forget (though admittedly I've sometimes also forgotten when the next train departs).

One key difference with other alcoholic drinks is the degree and speed at which beer dehydrates you. It depends on the ABV but the more sensible strength offerings won't dry you out as quickly as the likes of white wine and champagne. This allows longer periods of sustained drinking, hence why we have phrases like 'it's a good session lager'. No one in their right mind would think white wine is a shrewd 'session' anything. If you hunker down for a night on the Pinot Grigio you'll be crying or fighting much quicker. There's no beer equivalent to the phrase 'white wine werewolf'. Any of the changes in character which do occur from drinking beer tend to happen more gradually.

This is a selling point, especially for something like an all-dayer, which is like batting in a Test match. You have to think about tempo, intent and the crucial decision of when you first go for a piss. Even those toilet trips can be part of the ritual. The way women go for a pee means they're not familiar with standing next to someone else having their third leak in an hour and exchanging a good-humoured lamentation that they've prematurely 'broken the seal' (on the other hand, I've never known the bonding that goes with someone I've never met before giving me a tampon).

There's a nobility in being beer drunk. Any reckless muppet can sling eight shots of sambuca down their neck, but getting to the point where you're drunk on beer means you've managed your drinking time successfully. Breaks for spirits and mixers is cheating, though an old fashioned 'chaser' at the end of the night may be allowable (only if the urgency of 'last orders' has come into play). In that context, a chaser represents good time management, and you need to be suitably drunk to commence the tedium of getting home.

I realise I'm being very light-hearted about what is, after all, still an alcoholic drink. It can be tempting to paint beer as almost innocuous. There are plenty of blokes who don't even think having a beer is proper drinking. They may respond to the question of whether they're drunk by replying 'I've only had a few beers!', as though the nobility and longevity of beer somehow excuses them from the fact that they reek of ale and are stood in the garden eating yesterday's pizza straight from a bin.

The marketing lends itself to the idea of beer drinking as just a bit of fun and I've been deeply susceptible to all the big campaigns over the years. In my time, I've been Fosters guy and a Corona guy; I've drunk German beers, Czech beers and am currently dutifully consuming the widely marketed Italian brands a guy like me is supposed to enjoy.

But I've always been fascinated by the disparity between who actually drinks these lagers and the trendy types you see in their adverts – there's usually a big gulf between the two. Stella's marketing during the nineties was a prime example. The brand had a reputation as a very strong lager (with an even worse nickname) but their most memorable ad campaign depicted a struggling bohemian on his bike in rural France, stopping at a country pub and working in return for a pint of Stella and some artisan bread.

I've drunk Stella and eaten a French stick before, but it was standing alone in front of an open fridge at around 3am because I was spectacularly drunk.

The current trend is towards Italian lagers like Peroni and Moretti. The Moretti advert in particular is hilariously out of step with its core British market. We see young, sexy Italians, both male and female, enjoying a sensible Moretti or two. I'd say, at a push, most British blokes 'sensibly' enjoy the first two, after that it's anyone's guess. In fairness, advertising has to be aspirational; you can't have a commercial depicting a bloke my age sitting on a bar stool with a hand over one eye in a desperate bid to read the fifteen text messages from his wife. Nor could you show one of my mates outside a kebab shop pushing chips into his newly vacant head.

My reverence for beer hasn't always operated at its current level, but during the lockdowns being able to get a pint on draft was one of the few things I truly missed. Unlike drinks such as wine or spirits with mixers (where what you consume at home is identical to what you'd have in a pub), a draft lager is literally a different drink. And there's something about the artistry of pouring a pint which appeals to the blokey psyche. It's like a perfect golf swing or a flawless right hook. And, just like all fine art, it comes with jeopardy – mainly the mockery which can ensue when someone comes back with too much head on their pint and has to field hilarious queries as to whether he wants a 'flake in it'.

I'm not a Guinness drinker but I can understand how that drink runs even further with the artistry principle of pint pouring. There's something inexplicably beguiling about a smiling barmaid not only pulling a perfect pint but also including the pattern of a shamrock. Though some lads take the Irish connection too far, especially if they've decided you can only take your first sip facing in the general direction of Dublin.

During lockdown one, I heard a cruel rumour that some pubs were doing draft beer as carry-outs. I drove all around my area, only to find that this was either bollocks or not happening anywhere near me. It's the kind of disappointment I should keep to myself in later years when my son, whose formative childhood and schooling were fundamentally disrupted, asks me, 'Dad, what was your lowest moment during Covid?'

I'll solemnly claim it was the Delta variant but deep down the scars of several months drinking Stella exclusively from cans will still burn.

The beer you pour at home is never as good. For a start, you don't have the fancy pumps, some of which have gone from simple functionality to – in the case of Peroni – looking like an art installation by a steam-punk fanatic. Then there are the glasses. It's hard to get excited by a pint glass when it's marked by the familiar tideline of your dishwasher. The pub pint glass, however, is often branded and clean enough that it enhances that unique amber glow. A heavenly scene.

It wasn't the pouring alone which made me yearn for draft beer during those lockdowns, it was what the pouring suggested: that I was having a pint happily ensconced in a pub.

Pubs have, happily, become more accessible to women during my lifetime, but the standard features of what would still be seen as a traditional pub (beer on tap, dartboard, pool table, jukebox) suggest the grown-up version of a playground for men. And there's nothing blokes like more than growing up but staying the same.

There's also something character-building about simply walking into a pub. If you've got any sense, you'll fall into line with the general tone of the establishment. The ambience of each and every pub is its own 'house style', which if you enter disruptively you will unsettle. Going into a pub is a good exercise in adapting yourself to the needs of those around you. If you barge into a quiet pub noisily, you'll hear the unmistakeable chunter of a group of men who've all concluded you're a dickhead.

The appeal of having a pint endures. It's still the drink of choice for men in pretty much every region of Britain. This isn't just to do with those hoppy flavours.

As blokes, a lot of the social time we spend together is characterised by the incorporation of deliberate distractions. Whether we're watching sport on telly, sport in person or playing some kind of games console, the bloke often looks to factor in elements that mean we won't have to physically face each other for too long. Women don't seem to struggle as much with physical proximity. Have a look at two ladies meeting for coffee: they're often facing each other directly, shoulders almost mirror images of one another, their bodies inclined to denote full attention. For blokes, that kind of connectivity doesn't come so easy. Maybe my son's generation will arrive at a point where they can arrange themselves in front of their best mate and, from a distance of less than two yards, make full eye contact and ask, 'So, what's going on with *you*?' That kind of intimacy is some way off for blokes like me, but throw in the culturally understood disclaimer of a pint and we've got half a chance of sitting opposite one another for a time, a rare moment facing each other with our guards down.

And maybe there's something in those simple ingredients of beer, those four pillars. Something so simple and stable has obvious appeal for the average bloke. Maybe that's how he sees himself. Straightforward, uncomplicated and outside the fluctuating realms of faddy trends.

SOMETIMES YOU REALLY DO NEED TO 'MAN UP'

A few years ago, I saw an advert by Lloyds Bank which bugged me. It was a bunch of 'slebs' – no doubt being paid obscene amounts of money – who were queuing up to tell us why they hated the phrase 'man up'. It wasn't long after #MeToo and society had moved on to conducting a more general audit of the male psyche.

Watching the advert, I bristled. For one, I suspected a couple of the celebrities didn't fully believe what they were saying but had seen which way the cultural headwinds were blowing and elected to make a few quid off it. I was also suspicious of yet another big multinational riding the wave of whatever virtuous sentiment was doing the rounds that week. I have no idea whether the people who wrote, conceived of or indeed approved the ad believed 'man up' to be a genuinely harmful phrase. For all I know they could've signed off on the copy then gone on a debauched weekend in Prague firing rockets at cows. However, as we've all come to realise, corporations fear social media backlash above all else, so now we get lots of touchy-feely adverts which are the equivalent of that guy at college pretending to be a feminist so he could snog some girls.

For blokes, on a basic level, 'man up' is a useful shorthand for when you want another male to stop being fussy or simply take one for the team.

Picture a scenario: you're away on a stag-do; there's four of you in a budget hotel room. Three of the lads wish to sleep with a window open (for we are men, we *cannot* be too hot). However, your mate with the poor circulation doesn't stop wanging on about how cold it is. He's not going to win the argument, it's three against one, so eventually you just have to tell him to 'man up' and turn out the lights. There's no way you're all going to tolerate being hot just for him, plus the room needs a through breeze to dissipate the increasingly oppressive fog of man-musk.

Some people might take exception at the deployment of 'man up' in that context, but what else are we supposed to say?

'Come on Wayne, find your non-gender-specific inner fortitude!'

In such a scenario, I'm much happier to be a bloke. Simple democracy can win the day. I'd imagine the exact same scenario on a hen-do might play out a bit differently. Women, generally being more sensitive to other people's needs, might at the very least entertain soppy Claire who has suddenly declared she wishes to sleep with the light on. They know it's unworkable but they might talk through the issue, wishing to give nightmare Claire a sense that she's at least had her say. They might even explore the idea of the other three girls sleeping with blindfolds on. But I'd be hard pushed to sacrifice the simplicity of being able to tell another bloke to just belt up and crack on. It makes life easier for the tribe when you're able to play this card. Will Wayne have grown up nursing psychological traumas from being told to suck it up in this way? Possibly, but look at the upside: we as a society will spend less time sleeping in unnecessarily hot rooms.

And yet the phrase 'man up' is, in some quarters, *problematic* – possibly because there's an implied expectation that this characteristic is somehow exclusive to men. It's a fair point, especially given that the phrase involves the word 'man'. This doesn't, however, exclude women from having their own equivalent (though 'woman up' doesn't sound right . . .'Bird up'? . . .'Wench up'? It's hard to get a phrase that scans properly and doesn't sound like a sexist insult from the 1600s).

Women have plenty of words and expressions that celebrate qualities they think are unique to them. They can multitask. They can listen. They can clingfilm. They can actually find things in the house. Blokes rarely get upset when women claim all these virtues as their own.

There's even a song 'I'm Every Woman' (written by Nickolas Ashford and Valerie Simpson) which posits a litany of frankly supernatural abilities all women are believed to possess. The song incudes the belief that woman are mind readers who effectively manifest in the face of danger, then concludes with 'I ain't bragging'. No, not bragging at all. Just a clairvoyant oracle with the ability to physically appear in the face of peril and basically do everything.

But fair enough, it's a great song and only popular in the first place because women's emotional power is something we all benefit from and can identify.

But could you have a blokey equivalent of 'I'm Every Woman'? And what would it even sound like? Sadly, given the cultural tendency to think of blokes as rubbish, it would probably tend towards self-deprecation:

'I'm every geezer, it's all buried deep, deep within me.
I can't read your thoughts right now, nor do I have the inclination to.'

So, 'man up' has become a discredited phrase, even though 'balls' as a metaphor for courage has somehow continued largely uncontested. It's legitimate to query balls as a symbol of bravery because the metaphor actually correlates male biology with courage. But is it a myth?

Of the blokes I've known, the one with the biggest balls I've ever seen was a nervous wreck. Eventually he got the nickname 'Buster'. A lot of the women in our social circle got the wrong end of the stick and ended up discovering that his 'stick' wasn't the reason he was called 'Buster'.

Big balls, however, still carry with them the idea of prestige. Maybe this comes from the hokey idea that bigger testicles produce more sperm. Except it's not hokey at all: big bollocks really are more fertile (despite it seeming like one of those myths science would shrug off as bollocks). Some women prize large penises as a sign of virility, but the science suggests they should really be making potential suitors do a cough check rather than getting out the tape measure.

And what of this idea of courage coming from a man's balls? At the very least they do seem to produce more testosterone and are associated with higher levels of aggression – though aggression and bravery aren't the same thing (and as an owner of profoundly average-sized balls I would say that, right?).

One thing you can say about balls is that they're odd, the only delicate bodily organ to hang outside the body. It's a ridiculous design flaw to let something so vulnerable brave the elements in this way. That might be where the courage idea emanates from: it's not the balls which bestow bravery, it's the place they've chosen to live. Balls literally have the balls to be balls. They sit in full public view knowing they could get really cold, really hot or have a football slammed into them to the great delight of any watching males.

So I empathise a bit with queries over why balls stand as a metaphor for courage, but as society progresses in great leaps and bounds could we maybe just keep the idea that 'manning up' is a male thing? Call it 'heritage sexism'. The concept has uses we can all benefit from, especially when it comes to marshalling potentially unruly younger males.

Picture this: it's a family Christmas and you've invited too many people over (for many blokes, anything more than immediate family could be considered 'too many', but bear with me). You haven't got enough space to sleep everyone; you're a room and a blow-up mattress short. Someone in the family is going to have to sleep in the living room on a makeshift bed, made up of cushions from the couch. Who is going to take that bullet?

Definitely not Nanna.

Nor your uncle with the bad back.

Any of the middle-aged women? Nope, they won't have that.

The kids? It would feel too much like an adventure and they'd never stop talking.

So will it be the strapping twenty-five-year-old male family member?

Of *course* it will. He'll whine, sure, but you have a phrase at your disposal to eventually silence him: 'man up'. For this brief moment, he's expected to make a minor sacrifice for the good of the group.

Don't feel bad for him as he strops into the front room carrying the worst duvet in the house (often some god-awful floral relic from the seventies). This is a good moment for the lad, an opportunity for personal growth. He'll wear his morning backache as the equivalent of being daubed with blood after the first kill. He might make a fuss, but the reaction of the group will teach him that society does not care for a fussy man.

On a simple level, manning up is useful.

If the dogs need to be walked and it's raining – man up.

If the takeaway brought three Big Macs and one Filet-O-Fish, but no one really wanted the Filet-O-Fish – bloody man up and eat that fishy burger.

When a nervous flyer really wants the aisle seat but you desperately didn't want to sit in the middle so paid extra to avoid it, but this person is freaking out and, hey, it's just a twelve-hour flight, right? Man up. Sit in that seat. Everyone on the plane will benefit from you doing so, even if the large sleeping man next to you has started whimpering and nuzzling your shoulder.

There are obvious limits to 'manning up'. It is not applicable to anything in and around your actual physical health. Whatever the tough-guy gurus say, there are no viruses or cancers which can be 'sweated out'. And if being forced to sleep on couches is causing genuine mental health issues, say, if it's drifted into a sixth week, even when there are beds free, it's time to speak up.

Manning up isn't a gentleman-only club, everyone's welcome; it would just be nice if it was one phrase we could hold on to. Only time will tell. But for now, consider the merits of 'manning up', knocking your everyday sense of importance down a peg or two. Job done.

HEROES OF BLOKEDOM #1:
FREDDIE FLINTOFF

Like many blokes, the summer of 2005 largely passed me by as I was fixated on the Ashes cricket series between England and Australia. It started in late July and before I knew it, I was unceremoniously dumped into early autumn, my mental bandwidth having been dominated for weeks by a titanic tussle between an ageing but still excellent Australian side and an England team coming to pre-eminence. Not only that, England hadn't beaten Australia for seventeen years.

We'd lost so heavily and often in the preceding years that watching England play Australia had become a process of self-flagellation, where small victories had to be treated like big ones. Unremarkable end-of-series dead rubber victories were practically celebrated with ticker-tape parades. Even one of our players scoring a quick fifty could feel like a solid case for a knighthood. Learning to love cricket during this dismal era set me up for a lifetime love of the sport. To bastardise a modern meme: 'If you don't love me at my worst, you don't deserve me at my nail-biting best.'

Standing above that epic series was the formidable figure of Andrew 'Freddie' Flintoff. In all the hero worship that followed it was almost forgotten his first name sounded vaguely middle class. He never *seemed* like an Andrew. The 'Freddie' moniker was far more apt for what he represented to the general British public. It had the alliteration which always cements a name in your brain. One of my best mates is called 'Matt Marney'. Everyone remembers Matt, not least because he's a great bloke and a force of nature, but it's also fun to say his name. 'Do you know Matt Marney?' – it rolls off the tongue.

Meanwhile, 'Geoff Norcott' is a clunky stop-start affair which lacks any genuine cadence (the fact I was the second successive man in my family to go by that name is hard to fathom).

But when it came to 'Fred', everything was in place for him to climb straight into the nation's hearts and set up camp forever.

During that seesaw Ashes series, every time Australia started to re-assert their former dominance, Freddie stood up to them. Even in the first Test, though England ultimately lost that game, Fred slapped the Aussie bowlers to all parts during the second innings. At one point, he hit the ball so hard he broke his bat. Fred's own hardware couldn't stand up to the onslaught. It was like me, a comic, literally taking a roof off.

In the second Test, England had a better chance than usual as Australia's best fast bowler Glenn McGrath had stepped on a cricket ball while throwing a rugby ball around and was out injured (I'm ashamed to admit that upon hearing that news on the way to the ground I celebrated like I'd just won ten grand on a scratchcard).

England batted well in the first innings, but after a wobble we were threatening one of our trademark collapses. Freddie stepped to the Edgbaston crease and started heaving the ball around like he was trying to kill a pigeon in Wolverhampton. We scored 400 in a day, which doesn't sound like a lot amid the epic modern era of dizzying totals, but was it unheard of back then.

The Australian opening batsmen, Langer and Hayden, who I'd never seen take a backwards step, came out to bat a tricky few overs at the end of the day. However, they surprised us all by literally taking a backward step. There was only a light spot of rain in the air but those two pointed to the heavens like Noah trying to wrangle some free plywood. In days gone by, not only would tough Aussie males like them not have noticed the rain, for good measure they'd have wrestled a couple of crocodiles on their way to the middle.

The following day, with Australia rebuilding their innings, Aussie batsman Ricky Ponting was starting to look dangerous. Freddie came back on to bowl and had a couple of near misses. This seemed to be the way Ashes cricket had gone for so long, moments of English hope which eventually drift away, but Flintoff kept going and eventually got Ponting out with a peach (of a delivery . . . I'm aware most people reading this won't like cricket, bear with me).

This was the thing that didn't normally happen. Up to that point – before our nation actually started winning stuff – English sportsmen were past masters of the near miss. Whether it was losing on penalties or Tim Henman double faulting in a semi-final, we were all too familiar with the wry smile. Freddie actually prevailed. His smile was authentic.

English cricket has frequently served up all-action figures – before, in the shape of Ian Botham, and since, in figures such as Ben Stokes. But those two seem like men from another planet. Botham had a bit of eighties Hollywood glamour about him and Stokes has that otherworldly granite mentality of the modern elite performer. Fred, however, seemed ordinary in his extraordinariness. After England won that second Test by the barest of margins, while the other players were celebrating, he went over and crouched next to his crestfallen opponent Brett Lee to offer words of consolation. If that happened today I might go super-cynical and conclude that such a Corinthian gesture had been dreamed up by a team of sports image consultants, but given Freddie's temperament, it just felt like the natural action of a genuinely good bloke.

Even the way Flintoff celebrated England's series victory made him seem salt of the earth. He got drunk, very drunk, but crucially never acted like a dick. They say 'in vino veritas' and the fact that Flintoff could look like he fell asleep in a barrel of cider and still smile kindly suggested our hunches about his character were well founded. Yes, he pissed in the garden at Number Ten, but as blokey indiscretions go it could've been a lot worse. At least it wasn't in a sink. Or on the prime minister.

Growing up, every bloke knew someone a bit like Freddie – maybe not pound for pound in terms of actual ability, but someone who was ridiculously good at sport yet wore that talent lightly. Flintoff was one of those blokes who intuitively understood the relationship between man and ball. That seems to be the epitome of that kind of natural athlete – along with being good at everything else: the first time they pick up a ping-pong bat they play like a Chinese ten-time world champion. You'd think this would inspire envy but, in my experience, blokes tend to love a guy like this. In life, few are leaders; most of us are just looking for a guy to march behind.

I did eventually work in reasonably close proximity to the great man himself, writing for sports panel show *A League of their Own*. The first meeting was embarrassing. I played it super-cool . . . by reeling off a long list of stats from the 2004 South

Africa England series, speaking in rapid sporting clichés, and offering praise he must've heard a million times. This was all done in a breathless, nervous high pitch, like Kevin *and* Perry sped up and on helium. Freddie was very gracious – and when, on our second meeting, he remembered my first name I felt ten feet tall.

The standard idea is that blokes want to *be* their idols. I'm not sure that's entirely true. If I was Freddie Flintoff, who would be my Freddie Flintoff? Maybe that's Freddie's tragedy. For all his gifts of character and talent, unlike the rest of us, he doesn't have an Andrew Flintoff to look up to.

WHY WON'T MEN WEAR SUN CREAM?

*On holiday, 82 per cent of women wear sun cream,
versus only 65 per cent of men . . . who are probably
acting under strict instruction.*

SCENE

*A family on holiday on the Costa Brava. It's 39 degrees
centigrade. Grandpa looks lovingly at his daughter-in-law
applying sunblock to his two beautiful grandchildren. She
concludes the application.*

> Keith: *You missed a bit. Yeah that's right, get those little 'uns
> well and truly covered.*
> Daughter-in-law: *You should put some on, Keith. It's the
> middle of the day.*
> Keith: *Nah, not for me, love.*

*The daughter-in-law looks quizzically at Debbie, Keith's long-
suffering wife. Debbie rolls her eyes at the younger woman; she's
been trying to make Keith apply sun cream for the best part of
forty years. She can't have this discussion again.*

If your starting view of blokes is a dim one, you might pass off
their reluctance to apply sun cream as simple idiocy or even
laziness – the kind of short-sighted behaviour which helps ensure

that men continue to die younger than women. It's easy to go with the simple explanation: blokes don't use sun cream because in the short term, it's easier to *not* use sun cream. There may well be future consequence to these actions but for now, they'll just . . . leave it. Perhaps that's it, pure laziness.

Or are they not applying sun cream because such an act of self-care identifies them as a bit limp? Scared? A bit 'girly'?

Or is it just straight-up bravado?

I've thought long and hard about this and have concluded that it's none of these. The truth is much more interesting.

Until not too long ago, in terms of our relative progress as a species, men were expected to go out and hunt. To do this, they had to withstand discomfort for the good of the tribe. They literally had to 'man up' or people might not get fed.

Now, I often casually quote our more primitive past as a way of explaining male behaviour, but it can also offer too easy an answer. It should also be said that – as much as I suspect hunter-gatherer instincts still echo down our DNA – I don't think I personally would have been a very useful man during that time. I'd have been a shit hunter.

People forget the 'gatherer' part of that equation. I suspect my family would've been doing a lot of gathering. In all likelihood, I'd have rocked up back at our shoddily built hut after several weeks 'hunting' sporting only a single rabbit, whose foul stench suggested it was already long dead by the time I accidentally stepped on it. And the suspicion would linger that I'd actually used the hunting expedition as a cover for getting some peace and quiet. The Stone Age equivalent of a salesman taking a motorway Travelodge even though the 'business trip' was only fourteen miles from home. When they excavated our settlement thousands of years later and examined our fossilised shit, my family's reliance on gathered nuts and berries would have been so great they'd have dubbed us 'the muesli people'.

But, despite my likely Stone Age incompetence, I still wonder if these hunter behaviours still reside in blokes somewhere, only to pop up thousands of years later on a beach in the Costa Brava. Once upon a time, while out hunting, it would've been important to demonstrate you weren't too precious about your own personal welfare. When stalking a yak, it wouldn't have instilled much confidence in the other males if you started bleating about a nettle sting. Or got the lads looking for pumice stones because the hard skin on your feet was getting out of hand. Perhaps knocking back the offer of sun cream is one of the last remaining options the modern bloke has to demonstrate his resilience.

Nowadays, as with many aspects of modern masculinity, not applying sun screen lacks the heroic sense of self-sacrifice you might have got from toughing it out on a hunting trip. Today, there's no glory left, no sucking it up for the good of the tribe, just you thinking you can tough out the unremitting glare of the hottest thing in our solar system. For a bit, anyway, until, on day five, you give in like a sulky teenager after your third bout of sunstroke.

If my generation are hard work, the familiar stubborn grandpa at the top of the chapter represents even more of a problem. Many women make the mistake of thinking they can inform older blokes about the risks of skin cancer and that information alone will change their behaviour. It's not that simple. In the same way people who've stuck with smoking ignore the gory modern packaging of cigarettes, any man who's got to sixty thinking his body has a unique ability to withstand the radiation of the *actual sun* is unlikely to change his ways. He'd have to admit that other things he left unattended might be a problem too, like his bad back or the fact he never got a hug off his dad.

My own dad wasn't one for sun cream. He wasn't one for hugging either. It's not that he was without empathy, but he could be hilariously blunt. My parents were already long divorced by the time my mother died in 2009. My dad had been relatively attentive in the immediate aftermath of her passing. He'd checked in more often than not and was making a special effort to not remind me of other comedians with more successful careers.

About six months after she'd gone, I was a little late to meet up with him (he hated lateness above all else; he'd have rather I'd done a degree in dance and movement). He asked me where I'd been. I told him I'd been at a counselling session which had over-run.

He furrowed his brow. 'Counselling? Are you still doing all *that*?'

For once, I responded as a comedian rather than as a son. 'Well she's still dead, ain't she?'

Dad paid for lunch that day.

He wasn't one for therapy himself, just as he wasn't one for sunblock. The aversion comes from exactly the same well. That kind of self-preservation would just never occur to him. To preserve the self is to admit vulnerability.

Part of the sunblock aversion could also come down to the physical embarrassment of having to apply it. Blokes may deem the process of putting on suntan lotion to be a weird act of public self-love. In general, men aren't well versed in the maintenance of their own bodies full stop, let alone on a beach. I remember the reproachful look my dad gave me when he found out I used moisturiser on my face. I had to hold off letting him know that I'd bought a man-bag – there was only so much subversion he could handle in one day.

It's not just the perceived vanity of applying sunblock which poses a problem, it's the competence. Have you *seen* a bloke applying suntan lotion? They do it with the same conviction most men display clingfilming leftovers for the fridge. It's obvious most of us have never contemplated how to navigate that tricky bit of our middle back. There's a lack of match experience and we end up looking like cats when they sacrifice their dignity to lick that awkward spot between neck and chin.

Rather than trying to smoothly and evenly distribute the cream on their body, blokes get frustrated and resort to effectively slapping themselves across the chest and back – like a weird form of tub-thumping. It's simply not possible for them to dissociate the idea that applying any cream to the body is something women do.

So the sun cream dilemma serves as a good example for the sometimes bewildering nature of the bloke's conduct. On the face of it, there's belligerence and stubbornness, but those are the symptoms rather than the condition. The behaviour is driven by huge sliding tectonic plates of masculinity. People would rather deal with the surface level actions than acknowledge that masculinity is confusing – so confusing, in fact, that it's often easier to present it as basic.

So when you see one of us decline sunblock in forty-degree heat, it might not just be laziness or bravado, it's more likely to be an anxious, deeply felt instinct which also helps keep a lid on a whole can of psychological man-worms.

JOEY DOESN'T SHARE FOOD!

In the sitcom *Friends*, part of the appeal of the character Joey Tribbiani lay in his consummate representation of the typical bloke – the American version, but one which clearly resonated with a British audience. Joey liked sport, girls and – most importantly – food. He represented male simplicity in its most basic and loveable form.

Whenever he exhibited predictable blokey behaviours for a punchline I was always surprised by the degree to which some women in the live studio audience would offer up a whoop of endorsement. There was something about his basic manliness they approved of. Though it's highly probable that those quasi-primitive behaviours came across as sexy because the actor perpetrating them was, himself, very sexy. Eating a massive pizza by yourself is significantly less endearing when you don't look like Matt LeBlanc did in the early noughties.

The whoops were never louder than when Joey would eat voraciously. Whether it was food off the floor, food no one else wanted or sandwiches stashed in comical places, there's something about having a good appetite which seems undeniably manly.

When you're dating a woman and eat with her family for the first time there's a curious unspoken obligation that you will eat well, preferably taking in a fair portion of meat. If you're being cooked for at the family home, there's a further expectation that you will honour the chef, meaning that if you don't go for a second or, preferably, third helping, there could be furtive glances between her relatives.

Who is this man you've brought to us? Is he rude? Weak? A VEGAN???

However, if you complete a third helping – or if in a restaurant, order the biggest steak and make light work of it – you'll most likely get a pat on the back and this healthy first outing will reassure the family unit that you're not a weirdo.

The need to eat heartily diminishes once they learn to trust you, but if you become part of the family, be warned – this expectation has a habit of coming back into play, especially around festive meals.

One year, I had a third helping of Christmas dinner. This became a talking point and I realised I'd essentially done what cricket umpires do when they take a light reading as to whether it's too dark to continue play: I'd set a standard of three helpings. 'Old Geoffrey Three Helpings!' But I'm now in my mid-forties and if old Geoffrey Three Helpings continued on his roguish big-appetited path, their hope I'd put in a good shift at the dinner table may eventually be trumped by concerns that my wife had married someone with an emerging co-morbidity.

To get around this, I've had to come up with strategies to sustain this reputation without dying from high cholesterol. So here are my tips.

1. For some reason, no one really clocks how much food you're having on your first helping, so make sure you hit all the main food groups but keep it modest.

2. Get up quickly for helping two. This identifies you as a good appetite guy. 'What's he *like*?' they'll all say indulgently. However, this is where the strategy element comes in. On this helping you have more of what you skimped on in the first, but no meat this time. A couple of potatoes and loads of veg. A packed plate but not a mental number of calories.

3. The third helping is the showstopper. You want to wait until the other men are flagging, sitting back and tapping their paunches, as if food is a form of wrestling and they're happy to submit. Then, you stand up again with your plate (in my mind this is all done in slo-mo, possibly to the theme from *Gladiator*). This time you go big on the meat and – yes – another Yorkshire. A man who likes meat and Yorkshires can't be all bad. Enjoy the high fives on the way back to your seat, knowing that when you fall asleep in roughly forty minutes it's because you did God's work.

There's no obvious logic for the cultural expectation that blokes will go big at family meals. We know that men's bodies are on average larger and therefore require a higher daily calorific intake. But in a time of increasing sensitivity around women's body shapes and of equality between the genders, many restaurants and food outlets have gone for the broader idea of 2,000 daily calories for adults. But implying that men and women need the same amount of calories isn't scientific. It's like claiming you'd need as much petrol to fill up a Range Rover as you would a Kia Ceed (no shade on women; to me, the Ceed, with it's incredible MPG and warranty, represents the superior vehicle).

It seems odd to ignore the effect biology would play on your calorific needs, but it could be a reflection of a trend where many modern men find themselves in less physical jobs. These days, Derek in finance probably doesn't need his sausage baguette to be one third bigger than Pauline's in HR, because he spends exactly as much time sitting on his arse as she does.

Hunger does seem to be more of an immediate driving force for blokes though. If I think about the people I know who suffer most acutely from the 'hanger' phenomenon (the idea that some people *have* to satisfy their hunger immediately or will start throwing cutlery around), it's pretty much exclusively blokes.

I have a window of about twenty minutes from first hunger pangs to thinking I'll expire on the spot if I don't neck an emergency lump of cheese. This disposition can create anxiety, particularly when dining at restaurants.

One of my big issues with restaurants is that I'm not in control of when I'm going to eat. A lot of Turkish places cover this by immediately bringing out bread and olives. That's pretty much an automatic five-star rating from me. Even if the subsequent chicken kebab contained feather and beak, I'd still award no less than a four. Immediate bread means you can relax, settle into the environment and think about what to order with a clear head.

Otherwise, there's a lot of waiting. First for the waiter to come to the table. Even when they turn up, they might cockily (in my mind anyway) inform you that they're only doing drinks orders first. I'd have hoped the fact I was chewing the place mats was a clue I was good to go.

You might then find yourself in the situation where – when the waiter eventually deigns to come for the food order – someone in the group will grandly announce, 'Oh, we haven't even *looked* at the menu yet!' As though we're all devastating raconteurs rather than disorganised muppets who haven't made a single attempt at addressing the primary reason we're there in the first place. Then I start to fret that, having been dismissed in this off-hand manner, the waiter may never return. Ever. (It could be hanger, or something I should talk to my counsellor about.)

It can be tempting to think that men are the sex who are all about the food. We have sayings which support this idea, such as, 'The way to a man's heart is through his stomach.' But have you ever cooked a woman a good meal? They seem pretty happy about it. When blokes do eat it's often with a grim sense of duty. I've always admired the steely commitment workmen exhibit in greasy-spoon cafés as they try to cram so many food groups onto a fork that it seems like an attempt at a weird world record.

I'm not sure blokes do enjoy food more than women, but I do think we're wired to think we should 'feast' differently. In many cultures, a man who eats well sets others at ease. Like so many other things, just do it, whether you want to or not. It's just another peculiar aspect of being a bloke.

'I'm not a smart man,
but I know what love is.'

Forrest Gump

BLOKEY FILM REVISIONS #1:
JERRY MAGUIRE

In the spectrum of your life as a male, middle age represents a unique vantage point where you're still just about in touch with the boy you once were but also staring out to the horizon of the old bastard you'll soon become. I've noticed that in my own sweet spot of blokedom I've started to rewatch classic films through a slightly different lens.

When I first saw *Jerry Maguire* I simply thought it was a very good film. It had Tom Cruise (always a good start), Cuba Gooding Jr on objectively hilarious form, Renée Zellweger being lovely, and that little blonde kid being so cute I never want to see a clickbait link saying 'Do you know what the kid from Jerry Maguire looks like now?' (If it turns out that pure-faced boy eventually became a crackhead I too shall hit the pipe.)

Jerry Maguire is one of those glossy agreeable films of the mid-nineties which – even if people don't love – they rarely have anything against. Recently, as I've become more of a film buff, I've tried to work out what genre it falls into.

It's definitely not an action film, though being a Tom Cruise movie there is of course a bit where he sprints for no apparent reason.

It's funny but not explicitly a comedy – certainly not whenever Cuba is absent from a scene.

Is it a sports movie? Kind of. It does tell the tale of a jobbing pro waiting for his moment in the sun, but that doesn't form enough of a central narrative to rank alongside films like *The Way Back*, *Rocky* or *King Richard*.

Then it hit me: *Jerry Maguire* is a romcom for blokes. It's pretty much a one-movie genre.

I'm not saying that prior to *Jerry Maguire* I hadn't also enjoyed romcoms principally aimed at women. Like many blokes, I sometimes protest too much when we settle down to *Maid in Manhattan* or *Sleepless in Seattle*, only to mysteriously develop a dust allergy during the final act. However, I reserve the right to mock all the obvious tropes, such as the kooky woman with her own cottage industry who meets a handsome billionaire yet *somehow* finds a way to love him. Or the bloke making an over-the-top romantic gesture to a woman he hardly knows. Even the fact that these movies almost always suggest that opposites attract (I'd say, particularly over the last few years, that opposites repel, certainly if Brexit comes up).

Then there's the cliché of couples snogging in the rain (I don't want to stereotype . . . well, evidently I do . . . but in the real world, women and rain don't go well together – what Spiderman can do upside down in the pissing rain would have most women dashing to take cover under the entrance to Argos).

Some recent feminist discourse has made certain generic features of romcoms a little trickier to pull off. For example, persistence was always a guaranteed winner for our male romantic lead, but now there's a fine line between showing an interest and showing up at her flat unannounced (again). Previously, the leading man would usually have personality traits that would challenge the leading lady: *So you're against big corporations . . . but remind*

41

me of your favourite coffee chain? As we all know, a man who calls out a woman's low-level hypocrisies within minutes of meeting her is guaranteed to get a shag.

Even the ubiquitous mad dash to the airport is replete with modern pitfalls. If you were somehow able to crunch the usual two hours of security into a few minutes, you'd probably emerge with some Just Stop Oil protestor superglued to your leg. And if you did finally get within six feet of the stunned woman you'd be Tasered as a potential terrorist or sex pest.

So generic romcoms have become harder to pull off, but what *Jerry Maguire* did was something I hadn't seen done before or since: it articulated a common romantic fantasy of many men.

To begin with, Jerry has it all. So he's proved he can be a basic millionaire, no sweat, but he then has an attack of conscience. He doesn't just want to be rich; he wants to be rich the *right* way. At his high point of moral grandstanding, Jerry is dumped on his arse by a sports representation agency. The only person who stands by him is the impossibly lovely Dorothy who, despite being a single mum, walks out on a good job to go into business with a deranged man holding a goldfish.

In fairness to the film, it addresses the plausibility issues through Dorothy's funny yet cynical sister, but nevertheless, the plot rolls on and Jerry – in one of those mad moments of romantic mania every bloke has at least once in his life – declares that the couple should set up home together. He likes Dorothy but loves her son (who wouldn't? I would happily spend six years in a loveless marriage just to play catch with that kid).

This is a revolutionary storyline. We have a man who actively wants to be a stepfather; he feels a greater draw to that role than to romantic love. We come to realise, however, that the barrier between Jerry and Dorothy isn't that he doesn't love her, it's that he doesn't feel enough of a man to be what she needs. He's not worthy of her love. Not yet, anyway.

This is a shrewd direction for the film to go in because men can feel that their living defines them in the eyes of their other half. Whenever a bloke becomes jobless, his functional worth is judged more harshly. I've known several men get made redundant in middle age and one of the things they always wonder in their darker moments is 'Will she leave me?'

Do women have this thought when they get made redundant or fired? I honestly don't know, but it would be a very odd development in a friendship group if a woman reported that, after just six months out of work, the bloke kicked her out: 'I can't believe it, girls; he kept singing you've got to have a j-o-b if you wanna be with me. Apparently, the only thing *going on* was the rent.'

For blokes, from the moment you get your first full-time job, often aged around nineteen to twenty-one, you're expected to aim for roughly forty-five years of unbroken employment. Statistically, you might spend some time out of the workforce, but the general expectation is that may amount to only a year or two of your entire adult life. Staying employed for such a large portion of your life is a tall order and the necessity to earn can become the mother of all invention, but it can also manifest in anxiety dreams in which you're the least well-endowed bloke in *The Full Monty*.

Jerry Maguire works as a romcom because it offers a world

where everything can go horribly wrong at a crucial point in your professional life, but with a best friend who sticks by you through thick and thin, a good woman by your side, and an impossibly cute stepson, you can still find a way to be the man you want to be and the man they need.

That's why, for blokes, *Jerry Maguire* is a groundbreaking movie and a truly romantic ideal.

YOU LOOK SMART

A lot of blokes resent the obligation to dress smartly for formal social events because, broadly speaking, we don't like 'dressing up'.

It's the cause of frustration in many relationships and the process of encouraging a man to 'make an effort' is a negotiation which may start months before the actual event. There are some blokes who will push this to the limit and try to wear a T-shirt, sometimes even flipflops, to a wedding – but most of us tend to close the deal some way nearer to what our other half wants.

It's almost always the smarter move.

I have a lifelong aversion to wearing smart clothes. I don't just dislike it, I actively resent it. Whenever I'm expected to wear a suit, tie or a shirt for any occasion, I'm transported back in time, and I'm once again that little boy who was reluctantly having a brutal side-parting combed into his hair by an intent mother. Even today, as I do up a tie, I can feel the freshly salivaed thumb of senior women in my family smudging away marks on my face, like their spit was nature's anti-bacterial wipe.

When I was a teacher I did wear a suit to work, but that was only because I'd worked out that teenagers are incredibly superficial creatures and – for some weird reason – dressing like

I was from 1980s Special Branch made it marginally less likely that the pupils would stab each other with a compass.

I feel bad about this churlishness around wearing formal attire. I'm aware that my wife and many women feel great scrutiny towards their appearance at big social occasions. I've seen the stress it puts on my wife, particularly on the occasions when we've headed to an overseas wedding and our bag has been last out at baggage reclaim. I'm also conscious that I'm delving into some fairly stereotypical comments about gender and weddings, that men grudgingly fall into line while women fret about how they look.

In my defence, weddings, by definition, are incredibly gender stereotypical.

Weddings are a ritual almost exclusively based on presumptive and old-fashioned ideas about the two sexes. Yes, we tinker – sometimes the bride is 'given away' by a woman and many modern brides make speeches – but the whole day is dripping with heteronormativity (which might be why every gay wedding I've ever attended was over-subscribed).

No matter what kind of wedding it is, the pressure on women to look good is palpable. Men are expected to look 'presentable', which doesn't carry the same weight of expectation. However, there is a flipside to this: if a woman nails her look on a big day, she'll spend the whole event being told how lovely she looks. Not just that, if she *really* nails it, in years to come, female friends and relatives will literally remember what she wore.

'Oh my God, that white jumpsuit!'

'The one with the straps?' another friend will chime in.

'Amazing,' the third will conclude.

I don't need to understand why women are able to remember

other people's clothing in such detail. Equally, I can't explain why I don't remember the place settings at my own wedding but am able to tell you that Wimbledon FC's goalkeeper at the beginning of the 1988–89 season was Simon Tracey. We all have our own mysteries and at least women's recall tends to be reserved for things they were actively involved in.

So I think part of the reason women put effort into their appearances on big occasions is because they know the rewards are there. The stakes just aren't the same for blokes. The top-end outcome for us is that someone will give you a cursory up and down look then say 'Don't you look smart?' (which is not even a full compliment but a rhetorical one). Maybe they've clocked that it's the same suit you wear to weddings, funerals and the occasional job interview. Forget the fact you lost weight for the wedding or that you re-did your side parting three times (three!). Nope, it's 'You look smart'. The same compliment you get right from being that reluctant eight-year-old boy up to being a fully grown man – because God forbid you pull focus from the shimmering princess by your side.

And it's fair; you put in the hours, you get the rewards. Since make-up hasn't yet become part of mainstream male culture, we don't have the tools at our disposal to attract attention in the same way. I'm glad. Make-up would do my head in. It's a time-consuming ritual which I'm grateful most blokes aren't routinely expected to engage in.

Whoever that first woman to decorate her face was, she changed the game forever. I often picture that initial sliding-doors moment when a woman applied something to her face to enhance her attractiveness. In some prehistoric time, a woman – let's call her 'Danielle' – was out tilling the fields when she accidentally pricked her finger. She noticed a small bead of bright red blood at the tip of her index finger. In a moment of inspiration, she applied it to her lips. Immediately, she got more attention from the basic and predictable males around her, who made approving noises which roughly translated as 'Ugh, same woman look slightly different'.

I picture how the wiser women in the tribe would've reacted to this seismic development, leaning against a tree, thinking, 'You silly cow, Danielle. Do you know what you've started? You've basically instigated the beauty equivalent of a nuclear arms race in which whatever one woman does other women will have to match or exceed it. Just know that one day in thousands of years, some women will feel obliged to get up earlier than their families to paint their faces because they don't want to be judged at the school gate.'

If men do want to stand out we could take bolder choices with our outfits. At one friend's wedding – under my wife's sage advice – I wore a flamboyant pink shirt and got a lot of praise . . . actually she's just reminded me it was 'hot pink', and maybe this is part of the problem.

Blokes literally don't see the same colour spectrum women do. After twenty years of marriage, I'm convinced that women don't actually believe in the existence of the colour black. No matter how certain you are that something is black, they'll be on hand to casually correct you that it is in fact 'midnight blue'.

It turns out this is one of those biology issues; women are literally more capable when it comes to correctly assessing a colour and can detect more shades than men. That's why advertising for the Dulux colour scheme targets women, usually showing a woman on a couch protectively hugging a mug in a beautiful and recently decorated purple living room. Sorry, 'mauve'.

The different pressure on women to look good is something blokes have to just accept. I see it at close hand via my female colleagues on TV. They undergo much greater scrutiny than male comedians. Similarly, just like weddings, they also tend to get a lot more praise, to the point where they can get free clothes off the designers. I have never had a panel show appearance go out and been tweeted, 'Dude, where *did* you get that faded polo shirt?'

My son has been clever enough to remember the attention he's got for wearing a smart waistcoat or a natty hat. Where I once wriggled as my mum dressed me, he happily submits to the process because he trusts my wife's judgement. I'm sometimes envious of how sharp he looks and the praise he gets. Given our physical similarities, they are often outfits which might look alright on me too. This isn't a coincidence; I think my wife has given up trying to make me more stylish and is instead focusing her energies on him.

Me? I'm too basic and long in the tooth to become stylish. As long as I've shaved, I smell alright and am wearing matching socks, I reckon I'll be fine in polite society. I'm in my mid-forties for God's sake. When it comes to big family events, I'll take a perfunctory 'You look smart' if it means I can spend another hour watching *Soccer Saturday*, safely detached from the chaos and army of hair straighteners upstairs.

MEN'S INTUITION

More than half of British men gamble.

Throughout history, there have been a fair number of blokes who believe they can predict the future. Sometimes it's fellas like Nostradamus prophesising the end of humanity; sometimes it's politicians making ominous speeches, and sometimes it's just your dad's mate spending all day down the bookies because he thinks he can work out who has the fastest dog.

This last example represents the most common form of male soothsaying: gambling.

For most blokes, the occasional bit of gambling is a measured pastime. However, they'll often harbour the daydream that they could take it further, and talk in hushed, reverential tones of a bloke they knew who 'actually made a living by gambling'.

The need to believe in this mythical individual speaks to a particular fantasy that not only can you win the occasional cheeky twenty quid here and there, you can actually monetise your unique talent for watching sport. I'm not saying there haven't been men who have gambled and done OK – for a while – but we tend to mysteriously leave their story at the point they won thirty grand at Cheltenham, not two years later when they were selling their kid's Xbox at Cash Converters.

Serious gambling is something I'm grateful not to have the gene for. Not only do I not have it in my blood; I just don't *get* what that buzz is. I've had plenty of friends who do, but how they get their kicks has always perplexed me.

I spent a day at Cheltenham Races with one mate who 'likes to put a bet on' (a classic blokey understatement, in the same way that 'he can handle himself' usually means 'he's a violent psychopath'). He had a good day at the racecourse and won around three grand. As we were travelling back into town to start the evening's drinking, thereby moving the gambling instinct to betting on the capacity of our livers, he was checking his phone for local casinos.

I spoke to him a few days after that and asked why he'd eventually left a great night out to carry on gambling (and ultimately lose most of his winnings, it turned out). He said it was because he was chasing the rush.

But what was the 'rush' like? I didn't understand.

He explained, 'You know when you're driving and the car in front suddenly comes to a halt and you have to slam on the brakes?'

I nodded and waited.

He gestured with his hands as if to say, 'Voila! There's your buzz.'

I replied, 'That's a horrible feeling.'

He looked a bit rueful then said, 'Well, we all gamble on something.'

As a pursuit, hobby or addiction, gambling has changed a lot in my lifetime. Blokes of my vintage and above will remember the bookmakers of the eighties and early nineties: a bunch of – often – seedy-looking geezers, standing together but not together, smoking roll-ups and staring at screens. It was like a pub without the pork scratchings or the occasional sound of laughter.

Eventually, in the same way that people who ran football realised how off-putting the environment felt to women, bookmakers realised they might be leaving money on the table, what with half the population viewing entering a betting shop as being akin to walking down by the docks alone late at night. In came cleaner, well-lit bookies, with pastel shades and a welcome reduction in the general sense of sadness. I wouldn't say nipping along to the bookies has become a standard activity for most women, but it's now something they could do without feeling like they need a bodyguard.

My mum gambled, but her version tended to take place in the bingo hall. She made the smart move of calling her weekly trip 'having a flutter'. I went with her a couple of times and all her bingo buddies claimed it was the social element they craved, but once the caller started they had their dabbers brandished like weapons and stared daggers at whichever lucky cow called 'haaase' ahead of them.

The real revolution in gambling over the last fifteen years has been the online sphere. This industry has evolved to hook young men with devastating efficiency. Adverts depict impossibly handsome men, dressed like descendants of the Peaky Blinders, checking their phones while inevitably accompanied by a WAG-style trophy blonde.

Female online gambling in the form of sites like Foxy Bingo has been on the rise too. Overall participation in some form of gambling runs nearly at fifty-fifty these days, but the percentage of people who go on to become compulsive and form addictions are overwhelmingly men.

One such innovation, which was always going to be catnip to blokes, is 'cashing out', where the gambler gets to feel like Gordon Gekko, holding his nerve on deals which could make millions, as opposed to Gordon from Telford, deciding whether to take £25 winnings because Swindon have just taken the lead against Newport County.

The genius of the bookmaker's marketing is to play to the male tendency to fantasise. If they're not trying to make you think you're Tommy Shelby crossed with Jeff Bezos, the other way gambling markets itself is by suggesting that betting is akin to involvement in the sport itself.

For a while, Sky Bet ran a campaign saying, 'It matters more when there's money on it.' No shit. Everything matters more when there's money involved. Gambling, divorces – your relationships with family as they read out the will. They were trying to encourage men to find a new level of sporting meaning by leveraging their own finances.

Typically, no one would care too much about a midweek Papa John's trophy game between Portsmouth and Leyton Orient, but stick twenty quid on it ending nil–nil in normal time and *you're practically in the dug-out* (if Ray Winstone uses that slogan I will sue for royalties).

I suspect this strategy plays to the sense of wonderment at sport which many men felt in their younger years but lost as they grew older. As you age and other commitments compete for your attention, it gets harder to zero in to the same degree . . . *unless* you put money on it. If there's money involved you're believing in sport Santa again, like a thirty-year-old leaving out reindeer food in a tenth-floor flat.

Gambling addiction is a serious affliction and the online

arena does seem to have opened up new and creative ways for blokes to lose their shirts. For most of us, however, sticking the odd bet on remains a sensibly managed pastime.

The majority of my mates bet sensibly and tend to go small on something like an accumulator. They put down anything from £5 to £20 trying to predict numerous results where the odds are similarly multiplied and they could walk away with several thousand pounds.

It seems simple on paper. You pick a bunch of the odds-on favourites but bring your blokey sporting intuition to bear as you stick an unlikely 'x' by Middlesbrough for an away win. The other mortal males would never dream of backing 'Brough that weekend, but *you* have contacts (and by 'contacts' I mean you were listening to a football podcast with Micah Richards and found out their keeper has finally shaken off that troublesome wrist injury).

Pretty much no one ever wins on the big football accumulators, in the same way that no one ever wins that luxury sports car being raffled in an airport departure lounge. The footie accumulator bloke will, nevertheless, still share stories of his near misses like glorious tales of war. If it hadn't been for that last-minute equaliser by York City in the Vanarama National League he'd be a millionaire (Rodders), but the reason the odds are so long is because, in a series of ten bets, those unlikely twists are factored in. Bookmakers don't become millionaires by not knowing that, sometimes, a team of absolute donkeys might shin one into the net during the last minute of injury time.

Maybe the accumulator bloke doesn't ever want or expect to win. The real story is in the close shaves, the last-minute penalties which robbed them of that early retirement in Marbs.

At least society has a long-standing understanding of men who like to gamble. The more recent crypto phenomenon is a lot less well established and even more confusing. The crypto guy is way more tedious than the bloke posting photos of his betting slip on social media. The crypto guy is willing to invest in pretend money then spend the next six years of his life monitoring that one billionth of a Bitcoin like a male penguin nursing an egg.

It's not to say there won't be blokes who do well out of crypto, but it's unlikely to be you. My view has always been that if they're advertising to schmucks like me, the big ship has probably already sailed.

Gambling speaks to an innate sense in many blokes that we want, and sometimes need, to take risks.

Perhaps the gambling impulse is a deeper manifestation of the two sexes' relationship with the past, present and future. The phenomenon of women's intuition suggests that they fancy themselves as shrewd readers of everything that's happened before. The equivalent delusion men suffer from is the idea that they can predict everything that will happen from this point on. Maybe not floods, house prices, or even whether she'll stay with you once the kids leave home – but we do fancy ourselves to call the correct score in the upcoming Ashes series.

Gambling is and always will be a mug's game. If you need further evidence, look no further than the vibrant betting markets in and around Kim Jong Un. There are all sorts of things you can bet on regarding the North Korean dictator: when he'll leave office, how he'll leave office, when he'll die and – at one point – whether or not he would play a round of golf with the then US president, Donald Trump.

What kind of psychopath bets on the next move of a psychopath?

If you're STILL not convinced gambling's a mug's game, Paddy Power has in the past offered odds on when the world would end. If you were correct, and your estimation beat the expectations of every single respectable scientist, how the hell do you propose to collect your winnings?

Maybe the winnings aren't the point. Maybe it's getting to proudly text your mate a picture of your betting slip just before a giant meteor slams into the earth, with the caption 'Called it!'. There's no way of checking, but I'd guess every single person who has bet on the date of the world ending was a bloke. There wouldn't be too many women in their right mind who would bet on something so ridiculous.

Britain's richest woman is, after all, a bookmaker, which says it all.

PINK JOBS, BLUE JOBS

In the 2017 general election, then prime minister Theresa May gave a notorious interview (in fact she gave several during that campaign, but this is the one which didn't involve running through grass).

In an attempt to tease her out of a sometimes frosty image, Alex Jones, of *The One Show*, asked Mrs May and her husband about their domestic set-up. Her husband, Philip, revealed that he had to take the bins out but was allowed to decide when – which got a laugh of recognition from the crew.

Theresa, possibly buoyed up by the unfamiliar sound of laughter, chipped in with, 'There are boy jobs and girl jobs, you see.'

Immediately, social media – and Twitter in particular – was ablaze with indignation at this assertion of tired, lazy, sexist, patriarchal (probably fascist) propaganda.

In the skewed cultural world of mainstream media, this became the phone-in subject of choice for the next forty-eight hours: the controversial idea that, in general, men and women living together will often divide tasks along gender lines.

A couple of days later, I was writing on a topical TV show and the production crew continued the outrage at this fusty, out-dated image of the male–female dynamic that this TORY was pushing.

I kept my counsel for a while, then ventured, 'She's right though, isn't she?'

Because she was! It may not be a reality we want to acknowledge in the progressive twenty-twenties, but the idea of pink jobs and blue jobs will still resonate with many people.

So let's accept that they commonly exist, pick a few examples and dig a bit deeper.

TAKING THE BINS OUT = BLUE JOB

There are a number of reasons why blokes might be expected to do this.

Firstly, bins can be heavy, especially if your wife had friends over and the recycling is brimming with empty bottles of Whispering Angel. Bins are on wheels these days but it can take a bit of a heave-ho to shift them. Getting a wheelie bin moving can look as laboured as Granddad getting out of a chair. Almost every woman I know possesses more than enough upper-body strength to move most wheelie bins, but it would take them more effort.

Secondly, the decision to put the bins out is normally something remembered late at night when it's already dark and cold. At this point, the command for the bloke to do it isn't born of natural selection, the woman may just not *want* to venture outside at this time. She's statistically more likely to already be in some form of nightwear (I haven't researched this I just *know*, OK? I'm forty-six and don't know a single bloke who's ever left the house and got in the car still wearing slippers). She'll also still be doing a disproportionate amount of the domestic work and may feel that this late-night task is the very least the bloke can do.

The same theory applies to the evening run to the petrol

station. Sometimes, while watching *Masterchef* or *Bake Off*, you may be so inspired by the complex and artful desserts that you take the cultured decision to go out and buy a Double Decker. In this instance, that mission is almost exclusively a male one (rising to 100 per cent in the event of pregnancy).

WRAPPING PRESENTS = PINK JOB

Full disclosure: like many blokes, I find wrapping anything stressful and would happily let my wife do all of it forever. I also know that however hard I try she's going to look at my finished product askance.

Even when my wrapping is shaping up to be a disaster, I refuse to start again. Where a lot of women will correctly identify it's gone a bit curly and give it another go, I'd rather use three different of types of wrapping paper to get to the job done rather than simply admitting defeat.

The bloke's priority for wrapping is singular: can you see what's underneath the paper? If the answer is 'no', job done. Even if what's covering the present contains elements of tinfoil.

GETTING RID OF SPIDERS = BLUE JOB

Despite women kicking arse all over the employment landscape it remains the case that for many the sight of a spider can have them squealing and standing on a chair like it's the 1950s. In this instance, it's advisable for the bloke to pull the hero move, not least because it involves no bravery whatsoever, given that there aren't any British spiders which are remotely poisonous.

It's probably better for the spiders that it falls to blokes too, as I've seen otherwise gentle women turn to brutal killers the moment anything with eight legs scuttles across a rug.

LOW LEVEL MEDICAL EMERGENCIES IN
THE HOUSE = PINK JOB

If there's a cut or bruise in the house, it does seem to fall to women to attend to it. I don't know why this is. Maybe it's all those action films where the hero gets a cut and is dutifully attended to by his female sidekick, who has mysteriously mastered the art of the butterfly stitch. Plus, it also gives him a chance to flinch just a little at the antiseptic, even though he just walked away from an exploding building without flinching.

Or maybe the nursing obligation is all Florence Nightingale's fault.

All I know is that when there are kids involved, and if you ask them, they'd pretty much always prefer a woman to handle such things. They've seen how the blokes in the family approach wrapping presents and packing clothes. They're not idiots.

OK, we've dealt with a couple of age-old classics, but the jobs we do change over time so let's consider where some of the newer household tasks fit into the pink and blue scheme of things.

STAYING ON THE LINE TO A CALL CENTRE
FOR A LONG TIME = BLUE JOB

This is clearly one for the blokes.

Although women might spend more time talking on the phone, the gritty business of dispute wrangling is quite clearly the fella's work, as he is often the one blessed with an overdeveloped ego and a pioneering protective bravado. Nothing makes the neutered modern bloke feel quite as powerful as asking to speak to someone's line manager. It's the modern equivalent of pistols at dawn.

Consequently, my yearly job of getting the car insurance company to lower their standard increase back down to a slightly smaller premium is something I undertake with great relish. The guy on the other end better know who he's dealing with. That's right, I'm the legendary fella who was once upgraded by not just one but *two* iPhone models.

PUTTING WINE BOTTLES INTO THE BLUE RECYCLING BIN = BLUE JOB

Look, your neighbours know that you're a lager man but, nevertheless, there's a degree of public shame to depositing drained bottles of Gerard Cordier in recycling – so any true gentleman should happily take that clanking noisy hit. Plus there's an inherent unfairness to redress – a beer drinker could unload a whole weekend's drinking without alerting anyone to their decadence, since empty lager cans barely make a sound (another reason why lager is the best drink).

RETURNING AN UNWANTED ONLINE PURCHASE = PINK JOB

In recent years, I've made a lot of progress with birthday cards (see page 247 for more), but I'm afraid that if I've bought something online and need to return it, I hold it out to my wife pathetically, like a three-year-old boy brandishing his poopy pants.

She's generally more 'match fit' with such things, given that she orders and returns more stuff, but I also don't get how the process works. Not only is it confusing, but returning online purchases often includes the use of stickers and labels, which I deem to be technically arts and crafts and therefore outside my jurisdiction.

Basically, if it was left to me every single out-sized pair of jeans and every electrical item with European plugs would go straight in the bin.

SPORTING HOLY TRINITY #1: FOOTBALL

*Supporting the football team your dad followed is the
top reason people pick a side.*

During the 1980s and 1990s, I followed Wimbledon football
club up and down the country. Getting into football isn't unusual;
what was peculiar is that it happened despite my family having
no tradition of supporting a team whatsoever. In working-class
circles this was odd, like a posh family who has no strong feelings
about skiing.

There were reasons. My mum had been brought up in care, so
there was no partisan legacy on her side. Back then, however,
investment in the game would've typically come from your dad
anyway. Football allegiance was just one of those things you
tended to get from your old man, like eye colour or impatience.
But my dad didn't have any pastimes, full stop. If he'd ever been
asked to list his hobbies, I suspect they'd have been 'punctuality
and mortgages'.

My nan and granddad weren't into football either. Despite
living on a council estate, they were into ballroom dancing,
which was odd at the time, but you could draw a wonky line
from that to the fact that I met my wife on the dancefloor at a
nightclub.

Not only were my family not into football, when I started to
show an interest in the game they were a bit unnerved. It was the
late eighties and the game was blighted by hooliganism. The

climate then was very different to now, when stadiums routinely have their share of young goons who've watched *Football Factory*, wear their budget *Peaky Blinders* fancy dress, and spend ninety minutes with their mouth writing cheques their fists could never cash. Back then, naughty things were happening on and off the terraces. My nan, in her oddly prim and regal manner, responded to my emergent love of football in the same way I might react to my son today if he got into bareknuckle boxing.

By the age of nine, I hadn't shown much interest in sport at all, let alone football. But when we moved to a council estate, I quickly realised that I was in a much more blokey environment and needed to fit in. All the men supported teams, as did their sons, who kicked battered footballs around the estate virtually nonstop. I decided I needed to 'man up' and get with the programme. It was one thing having an oddly extended vocabulary for a boy my age, but if I didn't support a football team I could kiss any chance of making friends on the estate goodbye.

I lived every single one of my first fourteen years within spitting distance of Wimbledon FC's original stadium on Plough Lane. In a way, the Dons were a good choice for an already eccentric kid. We weren't one of the best supported teams and didn't have some of the 'nutters' other nearby clubs like Chelsea and Millwall seemed to attract. The ground itself was charmingly ramshackle. Don't get me wrong, matchday was still a manly experience, but my club had plenty of oddball supporters who brought soup in a flask and knitted their own memorabilia. Anyone who followed Wimbledon at that time would tell you that our real thugs were on the pitch, as the squad back then boasted notoriously 'uncompromising' players like Vinnie Jones and John Fashanu. We weren't the most intimidating fans, so we effectively outsourced the aggro to the playing staff. There was a curious tension between how mild our fans could be and how much pleasure we took in yet another opposition player going off on a stretcher.

Even though our fans weren't the most macho, the matchday experience was still replete with some key features of blokeyness: beer, fried food, Bovril, shouting, men standing in each other's company but not together and songs – so many songs.

One of the least understood paradoxes of football is that what's called 'toxic masculinity' sits alongside a patent desire to have a good old sing-song. Yes, some of the chants are akin to battle cries, but others are pretty gentle. Man City sing enigmatic classic 'Blue Moon'. Liverpool belt out the emotionally epic 'You'll Never Walk Alone'. In probably the most unusual case, West Ham sing 'I'm Forever Blowing Bubbles'. There's nothing quite so incongruous as tens of thousands of cockneys singing the line 'and like my dreams they fade and die' – like Doris Day dressed from head to toe in Stone Island.

The templates for terrace chants come from surprisingly un-macho sources: opera, Abba, the Pet Shops Boys. One of the most enduring and recognisable football song structures comes from the disco classic 'Go West'. For all its machismo, football also allows the blokeyest of men to sing their little hearts out like they're doing acapella at a glee club.

I got the football bug pretty bad, aided and abetted by the Wimbledon team of the late eighties punching significantly above their weight. Having only come out of non-league in 1978, we won the FA Cup against the mighty Liverpool in 1988. It was billed as one of the great giant killings of all time, not least because Liverpool had already won the league that year, but it's generally forgotten that we'd finished a not too shabby seventh place. Not only that, we'd beaten Liverpool the season before. So it was David versus Goliath, but if David was only one weight division down and had a horseshoe concealed in his boxing gloves.

Blokes can draw a sense of their character from the team they support. Being a Wimbledon fan was a good moral lesson for me. Their ability to upset the odds gave me the sense that anything was possible, especially with hard work (and a few psychos who could fracture tibias with a look).

Seeing Wembley stadium as a thirteen-year-old was an unforgettable spectacle. So much of what hooks the football fan is those sensory elements. The aesthetic beauty of stadiums themselves, the sight of that many people packed into one place, the smells of the food, the sounds of the chanting. I'd often get into the ground long before kick-off just to sit amid the experience for as long as I could.

A lot of football fans have an early taste of euphoria, which gets them hooked. My moment came watching that famous Wimbledon team upset the odds to win the cup, like a gambler whose first bet was a rank 20/1 outsider which romped home.

However, as with all gambling, unless you support the biggest clubs, the losses can eventually mount up. At 5pm on a Saturday, there will be hundreds of thousands of blokes who didn't get what they want and enter into a giant man-sulk about events beyond their control. It must seem odd that this creature who panics when asked what he's thinking and rarely expresses emotions is suddenly having a hissy fit in front of Sky Sports waving his arms around like an Italian chef. Football serves as an emotional conduit for men all around the world, but given the reputation the British have for being reserved, it's no surprise that a lot of our latent emotions come out within the confines of football stadiums and that the intense atmosphere of our domestic games is one of the reasons it's such a successful export. (Who'd have thought our dads not hugging us would ultimately help sell Premier League rights in Malaysia?)

All of which is partly why a bloke will regularly and ruminatively comment that 'the game's changed'. I suspect blokes have been claiming the 'game's changed' ever since its inception. When goalkeepers started wearing gloves. When players stopped emerging for the second half finishing a cigarette; and when you could no longer punch the opposition's best player into the foetal position. These days, my pals constantly talk about how they don't 'feel' it like they used to. Some of that is down to the way the game has undergone radical commercial change over the last twenty years, but it's also a consequence of advancing years. Middle-aged men take a while to work out that their relationship with the joy of football has fundamentally changed, like teenagers confused as to why they no longer rush downstairs on Christmas morning. Some try to keep the intensity by drinking loads or betting large sums of money, but the true wonder of football will always be felt most keenly by the young.

One tangible effect of the increasing foreign ownership of Premiership teams has been to add a further layer between the current function of the game and its original purpose. The words 'football club' have a genuine meaning. People often don't stop to think about the 'club' bit. It's a place to go, to be around friends, people to talk to, something else to focus on at the end of another hard week.

In the Birmingham area, Aston Villa and Birmingham City arose in part out of a desire to create places where the scores of antisocial young men who'd been causing mischief could go on a Saturday afternoon, to keep them out of gangs like the Peaky Blinders. In a football stadium they might still act up but at least it was contained (though far less likely to form the basis for a successful BBC drama).

In the same way that boxing clubs were a way of channelling aggression, going to the football can be like a version of primal scream therapy, where the process of venting feelings doesn't result in you feeling like a muppet. Not only that, you can take the piss out of cosseted millionaires who've owned a Bentley since they were fifteen. It's a bargain, really.

If you think that for a bloke, football is about football, you're missing the point. It's called 'the beautiful game' but as an aesthetic experience the sport doesn't really compare to the pristine look of cricket or the kinetic joy of tennis. The intensity of the game is derived from the scarcity of scoring opportunities. That's how those big emotions get released. In every fan there is a balloon waiting to pop. They're not ecstatic because they watched eighty-nine minutes of drudgery. It's that one minute, that one moment where they could truly let go, scream at the top of their lungs and hug a stranger. Consequently, men who didn't cry at their own parent's funeral can safely transfer that emotion to going out of the Carabao Cup on penalties.

When West Ham left their spiritual home of Upton Park, there were numerous videos of tough-looking working-class men crying their eyes out at the closure of their historic ground. They were mocked for shows of incongruous sentimentality, but people seemed to not get it: football is one grand analogy, and like all analogies it only works when you're throwing other, seemingly unconnected things into the mix. Those same people mocking the West Ham fans might well have been distraught when Paris's Notre-Dame cathedral burned down in 2019. You could throw the same argument back at them: 'It's just a building'. But of course Notre-Dame wasn't 'just' a building and neither was Upton Park just a stadium. It was a place where fans purged a bunch of feelings they couldn't find an outlet for elsewhere.

If those men found they couldn't let those feelings go in their real lives, then so much the better that they could do it somewhere.

CHAINED TO A MADMAN: A BLOKE'S SEXUAL LIFE

The average age at which British men lose their virginity is 18.3 years old.

Despite all the advances in gender equality, blokes still feel it's their job to take the lead on initiating things in the romance department. Asking women out on dates, going in for the first kiss, suggesting sex . . . then pretending you were only joking when all those suggestions crash and burn horribly.

You might dismiss the burden of initiation as being 'just how it is', but I refer you to a 2016 poll which revealed that men might not be so happy with the status quo. The poll explored the top five grievances the two sexes have with each other. Women's top five focused more on domestic issues, like him leaving the toilet seat up, not tidying after himself . . . continuing to draw breath. One of British men's top grievances, however, was that it always fell to them to initiate sex. I can hear some women groaning and playing tiny imaginary violins, but as men hit middle age the process of kickstarting romance becomes a harder mountain to climb (not least when you're dealing with only three solid erections per month).

It's a very different story in their youth, when blokes have a full tank of testosterone and several natural drivers which make the risk of initiating sexual activity seem like a reasonable gamble with their self-esteem. In some ways, you don't have a choice – that madman between your legs often puts your mind on autopilot (this is not to excuse men for the worst behaviours around sex – like all autopilots, the real pilot should be on hand, sober enough to make the correct calls if you hit turbulence). In your formative sexual years, the urge to have sex is an impulse created on your behalf, something your body and subconscious decided on long before you took that nervous walk towards a nice-looking woman in a pub. Like the salmon swimming back upstream, you continue walking in her direction even if it looks like she just rolled her eyes.

Seduction in general has long been a particular problem for the British bloke. Try to think of a particularly British way a man could 'seduce' a woman. What comes to mind?

The most obvious archetype is the bumbling posh bloke. Hugh Grant dithering over his words and slowly winning the woman over. This is bollocks. The only person the Hugh Grant approach works for is Hugh Grant, who has the ultimate advantage of actually being Hugh Grant. In my experience, dragging out the process of asking a woman on a date or for a kiss is rarely endearing. It makes you look indecisive and weak. I don't want to sound too Andrew Tate, but I think it's fair to say that there's no amount of gender equality which would render acting like a sap sexually attractive.

For men, rolling the dice always involves a combination of faith and – above all – energy: the sheer will to keep returning to the pontoon table of sex.

By adulthood, the average male will have experienced far more sexual rejections in his life than a woman. 'Crashing and burning' is an unavoidable rite of passage for any bloke. It's the most crushing feeling imaginable, but also the thing most likely to make your mates piss themselves laughing. The joy in the eyes of your friends when you get 'pied off' by a girl is hard to quantify. We've all known it. The only time you'll ever see your best mate happier is if you got smashed in the nuts by a cricket ball. If a man ever asks me what it's like to have a terrible comedy gig I tell him it's like getting brushed off by a girl in front of 400 people. You can see it in his eyes, he knows what I mean. He's glimpsed that void.

During your thirties, the male libido can be given an additional lease of life by the fact that the woman you're with has decided she doesn't after all want to devote her life to listening to your music recommendations and generally having a laugh, she now wants to have a kid.

Many men moan about the expectation to perform during attempts to conceive but you have to view it positively: is it 'pressure'? Or 'guaranteed shagging'? It's ironic that the bloke complaining about becoming a 'sexual object on demand' is now the exact emotional creature his partner once yearned for and at just the point she needs him to deliver the goods and stop whining like a little bitch.

By your mid-forties, however, once baby-making is largely concluded, sex is something very different: it's become an activity couples are vaguely conscious they should engage in every so often – a cross between a leisure pursuit and something on a to-do list, like getting the dog groomed or visiting relatives. Whenever you *do* get down to it, the two of you seem to have a pleasant enough time, but part of that euphoria comes from having temporarily ticked something off the list. And if you conclude the act with enough time to watch an episode of *Below Deck*, happy days. It can feel less like a hot act of steamy lovemaking and more like you've just done the big shop.

Once you've hit a certain age, it's also all the better for coming as a pleasant surprise. It's like walking home from the pub and thinking, 'Blimey, I was *not* expecting to see Halley's Comet tonight. Bonus.'

While most blokes will recognise libido as a tide which eventually has to recede – not entirely unwelcome, given all the energy it's consumed and humiliation it has caused – a declining sexual drive can lead men to do crazy things. Some blokes aren't willing to disappear into their sexual twilight without a fight. They look for ways of feeling like that mad horny teenager once more, which leads them to make all manner of Faustian pacts.

Some middle-aged men forget the happiness and additional life expectancy which a stable marriage affords and go off with a younger woman. I don't doubt that it would be exciting to have a younger lover. I'm sure your penis – that madman in charge of the Light Brigade who has led you to so many glorious defeats – would be delighted. But the question all men must ask themselves on the point of such a decision is this: 'Will the sex be so good it compensates for the trauma of a divorce?' And: 'Does my penis have a great track record when it comes to making big life decisions? Especially bearing in mind how many random erections I got during that GCSE maths exam.'

So a true British bloke will eventually arrive at a very different relationship with sex. If he does seem a lot less interested in having it these days, just bear in mind that he's the veteran of many bruising campaigns. He's crashed and burned many times. He is both Goose and Maverick . . . but mostly Goose.

And – just like a lady wearing her Bridget Jones big knickers – him wearing socks *and* sandals in the front room around bedtime may be his unique way of asking you to accept that, on this occasion, no means no.

TALL PRIVILEGE

Five foot nine is the average height for a
UK male . . . I swear to God it is!

The advent of dating apps formalised something in the male/female dynamic which we'd lost sight of over time: for most women, it's important for blokes to be tall – or at the very least, taller than them.

If you look at women's dating profiles, many are prescriptive about the kind of height they're looking for in a fella. Some say 'no short men', some will even set a benchmark figure, such as six foot, like the dating equivalent of height restrictions at theme parks (except more crushing because those rules may eventually mean you die alone).

How many times have you heard a woman not only stipulate that their bloke has to be taller than them, but go on to place the further hurdle: 'He's got to be taller than me when I'm wearing heels.' Just to make things even harder, they've artificially added anything from two to six inches to their height and declared this to be the new benchmark. Yet if a bloke turns up to a date wearing platform shoes apparently he's the weirdo.

When it comes to specificity about physical attributes, we're living in a very different time, where women are able to be fairly direct about what they're looking for while men have had to become ever more euphemistic when it comes to their aesthetic preferences. A bloke would rightly expect to get very few matches if he wrote in his bio, 'Nothing lower than a C cup'.

It's odd that the preference for men to be taller has been so persistent over time. It comes from a woman's ancient and reasonable impulse to find an effective protector. If she were significantly taller than him and there was a bear on the loose, the woman could find the guy shrugging apologetically and holding the door open for her, nodding suggestively towards the perils of the outside world.

If we're honest, on a purely aesthetic level it does look incredibly weird when you see a woman who is significantly taller than her man. It's one of life's odder images, like seeing a cat on a lead. However, in an odd way, a big height difference seems to work better than a small one: if you're going to go shorter, go a LOT shorter. Seeing a tall woman pull a very short man to her plentiful bosom is never not funny.

For blokes who haven't owned Playboy mansions or appeared in buddy comedies with Arnold Schwarzenegger, height is another crucial attribute we can do nothing about. That stark reality is made all the harder once you know the benefits that tall males enjoy.

A study published by the American National Bureau of Economic Research suggested that taller men report greater levels of contentment, and are less likely to experience sadness or, somewhat astonishingly, physical pain.

Physical pain? What the actual fuck? This isn't just a fringe benefit; their lives are better on a cellular level. It's like finding out that men with large penises have more enjoyable orgasms. (Do they? Actually, I'd rather not know.)

Tall men also statistically earn more and are more likely to impress at job interviews. They're also more likely to be respected by their male peers. The list of benefits is huge. Or 'tall'.

Until fairly recently, I had, for some reason, harboured the idea I was five foot ten. I used to mention this belief on stage and people would frown, shake their heads and sometimes openly laugh at me. In the fullness of time they were proved right – I'm five foot eight and a quarter. But the fact that I couldn't even conjure up enough inner confidence to project the idea I might be a mere inch and a half taller was disappointing.

Whatever the average male height is, the standard idea of a 'good height' for a man in Britain is six foot. This means a lot of men around my height still get called 'short' when we statistically are not (am I sounding enough like a chippy short guy yet?). In fact, if you aggregate all the male heights globally, British men of average stature would still be taller than a significant majority of everyone alive today.

I sometimes surprise my wife with this knowledge when we're on a tube train. The low ceiling of the London Underground makes relative height easier to discern. In a busy carriage, I can point out to her just how many of the thirty or so people within sight I'm taller than. It's not much of a boast, more the law of averages: once you take into account women, children and the half of all men I'm taller than, that puts me mathematically well into the top 25 per cent.

And yet audiences continue to laugh when I claim that I'm not short, like some vertically challenged Pinocchio insisting 'I'm a real boy!'

So, anyway . . . It would seem that rather than being short, not being tall is the greater Achilles heel, the worse crime. Napoleon is a prime example. Widely considered to epitomise little man syndrome, he was actually five foot five (or so he said). That was the average height for a Frenchman at the time, yet it still wasn't enough and he's considered one of history's great short arses (I moan a bit, but at least I never took revenge by invading half of Europe).

The mockery of men of below average height can be brutal. In the original *Shrek*, the running joke about Lord Farquaad is simply that he's very short. At one point, Shrek and Donkey do an extended pun-off on the subject.

How must it feel to be a genuinely short young boy watching that film for the first time? At the same time as his sister is watching animated films with brave female leads and adverts promoting body positivity, everyone is falling about laughing over a male character's genetics.

Our current prime minister (let's be honest, there might have been three more by the time this gets published) Rishi Sunak is a diminutive five foot six. He's faced a lot of open mockery for this. *The Huffington Post* ran a piece on the subject in which they sensitively republished a lot of the most hurtful insults, just to, y'know, show you how seriously they were taking male height-shaming. Though they did go on to say that it was wrong and hurtful, about two thirds of the way down, after a clutch of mocking tweets and by the time most readers had lost the will to live.

Rishi is clearly conscious of how his height affects people's perception of him. A lot of his photos have people standing distances apart not seen since the height of Covid. And who can blame him when you consider the value society puts on tall men? Tom Cruise is only too aware: it's the reason he's been practically walking on stilts since the early eighties.

Analysis has shown that, on dating sites, men who stood at around six foot three got 60 per cent more messages than blokes around five foot seven and eight.

Sixty per cent!

It's like a version of the dating show *Take Me Out* where any man under six foot who comes down that elevator not only gets buzzed off but gets fired straight into space.

So much stock is put on height, but basic differences in stature are often less stark than the optics suggest. If you compare a successful, extremely tall celebrity like Richard Osman against a much-loved shorty like Sandi Toksvig, you'd be forgiven for thinking that he's twice her height. He's not. Richard is a grand 200cm, but Sandi is 152cm. Which means, somewhat unbelievably, that he's only 24 per cent taller.

This is reassuring for a guy like me. Think of a handsome basketball player who's six foot nine. Believe it or not, he's only 14 per cent taller than me (though, for a lot of reasons, his dating site DMs would probably be much more than 14 per cent busier than mine).

Height is another thing, like penis size, which matters to a lot of women but which men can't do anything about. The superficial features of female beauty – hair, eyes, eyelashes, lips, cheeks, boobs – can all be enhanced in different ways. Blokes literally cannot make themselves taller (well, they can, but it involves some bizarre operation where they break both your legs, so your family don't know if you had self-esteem issues or defaulted on a debt to a loan shark).

Interestingly, the National Bureau of Economic Research study also found that men most likely to call their lives the 'worst possible' were an inch shorter than average. This makes sense.

It's better to die having never known of the promised land than have glimpsed it up close. This might be why I'm so exercised on the subject . . . perhaps I should reveal my hand, as there's a chance I have too much skin in this game.

At the age of twelve, I was already my current height and my doctor reckoned I would hit 'at least' six foot. There's a photo of me at the end of Year 7 standing head and shoulders above all my classmates. I got used to the comments tall guys get: 'Did you fall asleep in a greenhouse?', 'They been feeding you raw meat?', 'Have you been held back a year?'

The problem was that I suddenly stopped growing. Not just for the next year or so, but for the rest of my life. The height I'd reached at twelve was as tall as I'd ever be. This was a cruel way for my final adult height to unfold. One September, I went back to school and lads I'd lorded it over six weeks previously were now patting me on the head. I still hate getting a hug from taller men. Not only does it make me feel like less of a man; I also feel like a sibling going around the giant house of a brother who inherited everything.

So if you ever see me on stage or in print trying desperately to be taken seriously as a man of five foot nine, please bear mind that I was once destined for more – so much more.

GEOFFREY THE GIRAFFE

Question. Are you a woman reading this? If yes, are you married to a working-class bloke? If the answer to that is also 'yes' now turn to him and ask him if any of his friends have funny nicknames.

Enjoy the next two hours.

You're welcome.

Nicknames aren't the sole preserve of working-class men, but it does seem to be a cultural phenomenon where we over-represent. I'm not saying middle-class blokes spend their lives calling each other solely by Christian names, but what they call nicknames often amount to adding a 'y' at the end of a surname.

I can't recall exactly when me and my mates started dabbling with nicknames. Small children had them at school, but they tended to be route one and cruel. If you pissed your pants in assembly you probably got called 'pissy pants' (personally, I'd add a 'captain' at the beginning for creativity, but that's just me).

When I was at primary school, there was a popular book called *Geoffrey the Giraffe*. The moment I saw my teacher holding that title, I knew I was in trouble. My classmates all started singing 'Geoffrey the Giraffe' in that sarcastic, teasing way small kids have a habit of doing. I didn't even know why I was so upset, there are worse animals to be compared to than a giraffe, but as is often the case, alliteration had a persuasive power way beyond its actual function (and the irony of that taunt would be even more hurtful today given what I've already revealed about my height).

As we became teenagers, the nicknames grew a little more complex and ironic.

One day, I asked my mate Mick if he'd come with me to a football trial. He asked who was organising it and I said it was a bloke called 'Lofty'. Mick said he couldn't go because he'd already committed to attending a trial organised by a 'Danny White'. When I got to the training ground I was surprised to see Mick there. Being dumb young men, it took us far too long to work out that 'Lofty' and 'Danny White' were the same person. It was like an extremely low-rent version of the end of *Usual Suspects* when the investigating officer lets his mug fall to the floor.

Danny was our Keyser Söze.

He was also called Lofty because . . . wait for it . . . he wasn't actually tall. It all seems fairly obvious and basic now, but back then we were only just starting to explore irony (and the value of characters from *It Ain't Half Hot Mum*). As the years rolled on we got more creative, to the point where a bloke being called Lofty could just have meant he liked lofts.

One early complex nickname was born when my mate Rick threw his joypad across the room because he couldn't handle being continually beaten at Pete Sampras Tennis on the Sega Mega Drive. We called him 'Fatima', a reference to that famous athlete's supreme javelin lobbing skills and just how far that joypad travelled (it was a big lounge and the thing almost flew out the window).

The problem was that his nickname became so ingrained we stopped saying 'Fatima' with irony, so new friends were left confused when our mate, the mysterious 'Fatima', turned out to be a painfully white lad from Scarborough.

There were other legends of the nickname game. 'Fireplace Jack', so called because he had sex in a fireplace. Then there's my mate we call 'Gary'. He got that name because he looks like another of our mates called Gary, who we now call 'Original Gary'. Imagine how pissed off he is at not even being the foremost Gary in a group of mates where he's the only bloke actually called Gary.

There are plenty of nicknames born of one man showing limited and temporary expertise in a given field. There's 'Magnus', who got his name after the former *University Challenge* host Magnus Magnusson, following a semi decent run on a pub quiz machine. And 'GBJ', which is short for 'Genius Bar Jim' – who simply knew how to reset my brother-in-law's MacBook.

Nicknames can be fun, but they can also run the risk of immortalising things you'd rather forget.

Once, in Berlin, we were running low on alcohol. All we had left was sambuca, so we poured (rationed) all the remaining measures into a selection of shot glasses. There was a well-marshalled process for calling each man up for his latest dose, but things inevitably got drunken and distracted. As the man in charge of this process, however, I was hypervigilant. I got a sense from Danny's body language that, amid the drunk fog of war, he was up to no good. As he stepped up to the table in the corner of the room, he had a quick look over one shoulder, then slammed an illegal second shot. I very quickly said, 'Check out old Danny two shots!'

Danny's face fell, not least because he knew he'd been caught, but also because he realised that the nickname scanned well enough for it to have a good chance of sticking. On the plus side, it sounded pretty cool – 'Danny two shots' brought to mind one of Joe Pesci's mates in *Goodfellas*. The problem was that nothing gives blokes more pleasure than unpacking a nickname, so ever since that day, Danny has had to take repeated punishment beatings as we relay his origins story.

One of my favourite nicknames is 'Dead Steve'. Steve's moniker was a complicated one. He got it back in the early nineties when he went to Thailand for a month. Back then, we didn't know anyone who went away that far and for that long. Without mobile phones or even email, we had no idea as to Steve's welfare. As two weeks became three then three turned into four, rumours started to circulate. Once a whole month had gone by, we could only conclude that Steve was in fact dead. The rumour went around south London like wildfire.

'You heard about dead Steve?'

'What's happened?'

'There's a clue in the name.'

Luckily, Steve is still with us, but none of us is getting any younger and at some point it might make sense to give him a quick rebrand.

One thing you can never do is pick your own nickname. Over the years, I've known some who've tried. Back in the early noughties I thought (hoped) that I looked a bit like Joey from *Friends* and considered that this could be a useful comparison from the point of view of attracting ladies (and excusing my habits around food). I tried to casually insinuate that a few people had started calling me 'Joey', or whatever, and shrugged with the forced oversell of the patent liar.

The lads rounded on me pretty quickly and gave my attempted nickname a tweak. I didn't mind really. So long as they called me something. One of the great things about becoming friends with other blokes is that you feel like you've been born again into a slightly different family. The one thing any family wants to do with a new arrival is to give it its own name.

It's just a shame that, having hoped to be named after one of the sexiest men on telly, I quickly got christened 'Fat le Blanc'.

HEROES OF BLOKEDOM #2: ADRIAN CHILES

My second blokey hero is also someone I've had the privilege of working with: Adrian Chiles.

In a way, saying Adrian Chiles is my hero is a very Adrian Chiles thing to do.

In the past few years, as well as being a terrific broadcaster, he's carved out a niche writing for the *Guardian*, producing articles which are not only outside the publication's usual social and political bias, but are also unique in their celebration of mundane and noble preoccupations, something the average bloke tends towards.

Here are a few of Adrian's best titles to savour:

'If dishwashers were a sport, my dad would be world champion.'

'All you can eat? I take those words as a promise and a challenge.'

'An ear and nostril waxing is exquisitely painful – but just what I needed.'

There are so many. Chiles once extolled the virtues of having a urinal in his home toilet and, while the world was obsessing over war and pestilence, he went off on one about why he hates sand.

There are some in metropolitan circles who enjoy his low-level ranting in the same way they enjoy professional darts – ironically.

I don't. I just think he's shrewd enough to know that his everyday brand of blokery strikes a genuine chord with millions of people. It's not an 'angle'; it's a faithful reflection of the small things which can feel so big in daily life.

For a time, newspapers, populated as they largely are by urban middle-class professionals, wrongly concluded that all we want to read about is Brexit, or whether misgendering should come with a custodial sentence. Chiles knows differently. Life is already stressful, so it's preferrable to get exercised about the little things – not least because those are problems we at least stand some chance of resolving. His articles succeed for the same reason programmes about bargains and gardens succeed: in the real world, that's what people truly care about. Ask anyone who hates sand about sand. They'll get way more exercised about that than whether sports pundits should tweet about refugees. Chiles comes across as the kind of bloke who could solve most of the world's problems with a pint and a squirt of WD-40.

I'm not sure whether the act of falling into conversation with some random geezer at a pub is a thing any more. Was it ever? The kind of men who speak to strangers in pubs are usually rampant alcoholics only ever a moment away from saying something genuinely dodgy. Chiles, however, really does seem to be the bloke you might get into a good chat with: informed yet informal, giving off the reassuring vibe of a man who always has the correct Allen key to hand.

I remember the first time I saw Chiles on telly. It was in the mid-nineties and he was co-presenting a show called *Working Lunch*. Even the name 'Adrian Chiles' carried with it an air of Midlands chumminess. Post diversity targets, we're more used to hearing working-class accents on the Beeb – but back then, his broad Brummie tones stood out in a bland sea of Received Pronunciation, particularly in the world of 'serious' broadcasting. You have to remember that this was before the Midlands twang underwent a trendy rehabilitation at the hands of the Peaky Blinders. Back then, when we thought of the Midlands we were thinking of Noddy Holder rather than Tommy Shelby.

Adrian seemed confident and informed while also coming across like one of your dad's most likeable mates. The accent helped in establishing him as normal. With all respect, it's very hard to imagine anyone from this part of the country as part of the liberal elite. I had no idea what his upbringing was like but filed him away as working class. Even today, he could be sipping kombucha on the slopes at Davos and still sound like he bulk-buys from Aldi.

His common-touch expertise echoed the world I lived in at the time. My dad's mates down the pub were all fairly political and clued up. Having been adult men during the volatile 1970s, they discussed public affairs all the time, but when it came to politics on the telly or radio the glottal well and truly stopped.

One of Chiles's other great strengths is that I've never had an idea of how he might vote. It's not cool in blokey circles to get preachy. He has a knack of getting irritated rather than angry, which helps make him seem authentic to the watching public. It's refreshing at a time when, via a string of big stories like Brexit and Covid, journalism became a seriously high-status profession.

When Dominic Cummings sat in the rose garden at Number Ten behind that trestle table, like he was about to serve homemade lemonade at a country fete, the journos queued up to grill him about driving to Durham, but mostly delivered what sounded like GCSE drama monologues. The situation was crying out for someone like Chiles to chime in like an everyman and say, 'Hang on just a minute, you drove to check your *eyesight*??'

Chiles, through not over-speaking or emoting, seems both authentic and authoritative. There are no long words simply for their own sake. No showboating. Even when he wrote an excellent book on drinking habits, he didn't do the showbiz thing of lurching from over-indulgence to abstinence, he simply put forward an argument for drinking less.

This is how most people think, and though his life today may well be rarefied and fairly wealthy, Adrian Chiles, with his ability to seem exceptional in his unexceptionalism, will always feel like the quintessential British Bloke.

FANCY A CURRY?

Just like being asked if you fancy a pint, 'Wanna go for a ruby?' is up there with the best questions you could ask any bloke (not least because a curry also tends to involve several lagers).

Going for a curry skews blokey. I've seen plenty of women in curry houses over the years, but it's rare that I've witnessed a raucous group of ladies enter the Raj Douth after a day on the ale and order thirty-two poppadoms and eight Cobras before they've even sat down.

So what's the connection between blokes and going for a curry?

The first big draw is that a curry is perceived as an informal way to dine. It's often a spontaneous adjunct to a whole day spent together, usually drinking. You hit that point where things will either get really messy or you recognise food intake to be crucial (either that or several of your mates' knees are playing up and you need somewhere you can be guaranteed a seat). I'm not saying I haven't booked restaurants for a group of blokes before, but it's been rare, and canvassing opinion for food options too early on a lads' WhatsApp group can result in a whole day of ridicule (and yet another new nickname). This differs as you move through the class brackets, though. Among more middle-class blokes, it's not unheard of for people to mention TripAdvisor ratings and query who the chef trained with.

The standard curry-house experience, however, is a different beast. A lot of their trade is made up of large groups of blokes making a sudden decision to add further digestive problems to the following day. As an establishment, a curry house knows how to cope with a huge influx of men and they rarely mess about asking if you've booked (you've never booked). There's also a lack of protocols at a curry house. If I went to a fancy place with my wife she might shoot me a look if I started asking for table bread too early, but the fact you'll have poppadoms is generally a given and will be confirmed as the waiter takes your coat.

The poppadoms themselves epitomise the informal nature of the curry-house experience. Bread rolls need to be daintily buttered but poppadoms get smashed to pieces within minutes.

As blokes often communicate in analogies, how you eat a poppadom can be a good way of telling the group who you are. Any man who brings his fist down on the whole pile without first consulting the group has established himself as a wannabe alpha. Blokes who just pick up a shard of poppadom and randomly scoop it in the pots and sauces are rank-and-file heathens, but a clearly thought-out and structured approach represents peak blokery. I tend to find a decent-sized piece, normally approximately an eighth the size of the entire poppadom, and think of it more of a pizza on which to put toppings. I don't want to have so many onions that I need to spend the following day adopting Covid levels of social distancing, and nor do I want so much mango chutney that it feels like I've already started my dessert. By showing such forethought I could be easily construed as fancy or fussy, but it's neither – I just love having a curry and am confident enough in my own process not to be swept along with the herd.

When it comes to poppadoms, the only thing up for debate is the number, plus an unequivocal promise that they'll bring out the lime pickle.

Lime pickle used to be a standard feature of the poppadom condiments but somewhere in the late noughties it became a treat you had to ask for, like the curry equivalent of under-the-counter medication. This move may have been an act of charity by the restaurant itself. When you overdo a curry, a lot of the acid comes from the pickle, containing as it does a devastating combination of chilli and lime. If they really wanted to show customer care they wouldn't bring out After Eights at the end of the meal, it would be a tray of Rennies.

However, the jeopardy of spice levels opens up another element of curry's appeal to the blokey mentality: it engages with the attraction to risk.

There's something of the Vegas casino about going for a curry. You could get the balance right and have a great meal with no enduring legacy. Or you could overreach, leave with the hiccups and be up at 5am the following morning with your backside on fire, seeing if Just Eats delivers omeprazole. In the same way that car parks absolve themselves of responsibility for any thefts which happen within them, it would make sense for a curry house to remind patrons that 'All choices made within this establishment are your own. If you're pushing fifty and order anything stronger than a dopiaza, you've only got yourself to blame.'

A curry house is one of few places where the drinks order is posed more in the form of a rhetorical question. 'Nine Cobras?' That's the starting point for the waiter. If you're going to showboat and order something different it's on you to explain yourself. Cobra is such a great recent accompaniment to curry that I shudder to think of the gassier alternatives I used to wash down a jalfrezi with.

It was designed with curry in mind. When Labour leader Keir Starmer faced questions over 'Beergate' allegations in Durham, the political class obsessed over whether or not he'd broken lockdown rules. The police eventually decided he hadn't, but for a lot of the British public we'd come to our own verdict: the man drank San Miguel with a curry and was therefore a psychopath. I'm not saying you can *only* drink Cobra, but it had better be something damn similar.

With the poppadom and lager choices settled, the real opportunity for bravado begins: your choice of main.

I'm not saying a bloke should *never* have a korma, but if he does he should at the very least explain why. I just don't know why you'd go for a meal with such flavour potential as a curry but choose something so childlike as a chicken korma. It's like going to a theme park and making a beeline for the magic teacups. If you're genuinely worried about the level of spice have a bit of tandoori chicken. Even this turns out to be a bit on the flavoursome side: tandoori comes with the cucumber raita for you to dive into, like a culinary plunge-pool just outside the sauna.

Once upon a time, I'd have gone quite high up the heat scale, usually ordering a madras, and sometimes a vindaloo. I had a decent tolerance for hot curries given that, for the first nine years of my life, I had a surrogate Indian family living upstairs who I spent a lot of time with. I used to trot up there regularly and, even as a six-year-old, was dealing OK with the dopiazas and bhunas of this world.

I was, for a time, something of a novelty. When they had Indian relatives over, they would all want to see the phenomenon of this little white boy polishing off spicy dishes for themselves. They'd crowd around, marvelling at me knocking back a masala like I was a character from the director's cut of *The Greatest Showman*. Consequently, curry always meant more to me than just the dish itself – it took me back to a much-loved part of my childhood. But like anyone who gets a buzz from something, you eventually go looking for bigger kicks.

For a long time, vindaloo was the apex predator of my curry world, but some time in the late nineties there were dark murmurings about a dish called a 'phaal'.

I had to try it.

In the curry house, I made a big deal of ordering the phaal, confidently telling the waiters that I was effectively half Indian so it shouldn't pose too much of a problem.

I still remember the moment the heat kicked in. It wasn't on the first or second mouthful but somewhere around the third when my body started going into violent revolution against my foolish choices. I gave the waiter a look which must have been like the accusatory one people throw when they realise they've been poisoned. Then I got the most savage hiccups I'd ever had. The waiters started to look genuinely concerned and I ended up doing shots of cucumber raita like I was in a head-to-head drinking competition with a teetotal vegetarian.

It wasn't the last time my bravado would undo me either.

In 2013, I was doing some gigs for the British armed forces in Cyprus and we had the honour of performing for a Gurkha regiment.

The Gurkhas enjoyed the gig and invited us to dine with them afterwards. I got the sense they might try to test our capacity for Nepalese cuisine and noticed some of the soldiers cautiously watching us after each course.

I thought I'd withstood the best of what they had to offer when the chef finally brought out what looked like a very plain plate of chicken nuggets. I laughed, surprised, and held one up to a lad who'd been watching me intently, making a 'is this the best you have to offer?' gesture. His gaze didn't change, and I'd soon come to realise that it was the unbreakable glare of the stone-cold assassin.

I don't know what was in those chicken nuggets, but I'd eaten about three before I got any sense of how much trouble I was in. It wasn't just a chicken nugget; it was a sleeper cell of fire. There was a devilish delayed release from the spice within. The heat was happening not in my mouth or throat but somewhere deep in the pit of my stomach, like a culinary depth charge.

I was determined not to give away how much I was struggling but, like any man trying to throw out an immovable poker face, sweating was something I wasn't in control of. Thank God I wasn't in a Pizza Express.

With the gaze of the guy who'd taken me out still upon me, I decided to double down. I couldn't let him 'win', so, with sweat streaming down my face and a fire happening in my gizzards, I took a couple more nuggets and ate them. He cheered. The sweats got worse but I kept going and spent the whole of the following day in the bad place.

That day, I proved something to those lads. I can't tell you exactly what, or whether it was worth it, but I got the sense that my willingness to endure pain for honour had won me respect. (Though none of them ate the chicken nuggets, so I might've proved myself a reliable comrade or just been the evening's entertainment.)

This is the power of spicy food and, more specifically, a curry. Nowhere else does the simple selection of your main course offer scope for acts of true daring and heroism. For blokes, it can be not just a meal but a full-on adventure.

*'Dear, I always say,
a flawed husband is
better than none at all.'*

Mrs Doubtfire

BLOKEY FILM REVISIONS #2:
MARY POPPINS

As we know, at heart, the modern bloke is a sentimental softy and while he may publicly say that he only watches films with Tom Hardy or an aeroplane containing Samuel L Jackson and some snakes, secretly he's delighted to be watching *Frozen* again with his kids (although he may have to come up with a creative explanation for why his eyes are streaming when Olaf the Snowman starts to melt).

Accordingly, one of my top five favourite films is surprisingly soppy: *Mary Poppins*.

Don't laugh. In my defence, I should add that the other four are *The Empire Strikes Back*, *Avengers: Endgame*, *Goodfellas* and *Top Gun: Maverick* (imagine me now crushing a plastic cup like Brody in *Jaws*).

I always loved *Mary Poppins*; we used to watch it at least once a year growing up, often around Easter. In her own way, my mum had a touch of the Poppins about her – a funny and, in some ways, mystical woman who always had surprising things in her handbag.

At first, I understood the film as I was supposed to: Jane and Michael were good kids in need of more attention; the wife was a bit distracted but otherwise a nice enough lady and Mr Banks was the well-meaning villain of the piece who needed to loosen up and join in the fun. He was always coming home from work in a grump and ruining everyone's fun. The idea struck a chord at that point in my life, as my own dad could sometimes feel a little separate from the main business of the house. He too had some weird job in London I didn't fully understand. The fact that Banks was British also felt important. There have been plenty of Hollywood films since which have dealt with the issue of busy and emotionally distant dads, but the idea seems particularly resonant when merged with the British stiff upper lip.

However, as I've got older and my own responsibilities have started to mount up, I've started to view old Banks in a very different light.

Why is Mr Banks the villain of this piece at all? He's clearly grafted his whole life in a toxically masculine workplace to finance a lovely gaff slap bang in the middle of London (although presumably the estate agent knocked a few guineas off the asking price because of the daily damage done by the next-door neighbour firing an actual cannon every bloody day of the week). Is it too much to ask that when he gets home of an evening his kids aren't being collared by the local bobby and his Mrs isn't constantly out at feminist rallies like an early prototype of an Islington mother? Votes for Women is a noble cause but Banks can't be expected to be the sole breadwinner *and* stop his kids going off the rails at the same time as his wife is chaining herself to them.

Banks is clearly a decent bloke at heart; he's just slightly out of step with the rest of the family. He tries to join in, doesn't he? He even sings a song, albeit reluctantly, like an older member of staff at a company karaoke, but at least he has a go. And in his song he quite rightly points out that he'd like a bit of discipline in the family, some basic rules to live by. Who can disagree when he says he doesn't want 'disaster and catastrophe' in the house?

Surely that's the first aim of any responsible father, isn't it? Apparently not. Apparently that makes him a stick-in-the-mud who doesn't approve of a strange woman encouraging his kids to dance on a rooftop without a safety harness. And yet, when he merely tries to demonstrate the value of money his kids start acting up like he's taking them for a root canal.

All that poor sod wanted was to get home, kick off his spats, have a nice plate of liver and onions and watch a magic lantern show with the family while they ask him how his day was. And, of course, the answer to that question would be, 'The same as every other bloody day, a waking nightmare of class snobbery and excruciating boredom.' Except he would never articulate that thought because the conscientious bloke wants to protect his family from the crushing truth of reality.

Into this bargain comes Mary Poppins, who I do fully love – and was my first crush – but, let's be honest, she's a vain woman and an absolute loose cannon. She introduces a strange brand of socially acceptable voodoo into the Banks household and suddenly this poor overworked chap is having to contend with hyperactive kids, distracted staff and talking furniture.

He's already being outmanoeuvred in his own house by women and children and now has to cope with a magic nanny he didn't employ in the first place (who, let's not forget, deployed a magic gust of wind to dispatch the other candidates in a brazen act of industrial espionage). A lesser man would have gone next door and turned that cannon on his own house but no, he's a bloke, so he sucks it up and soldiers on.

Eventually, Banks's defences lower and he gets sucked into the mania of talking furniture and show tunes, and quits his high-powered job to go and fly a fucking kite!

The Poppins purists will point out that, in the final scene, he does get his job back at the Dawes Tomes Mousley Grubbs Fidelity Fiduciary Bank, but that all feels a bit Disney. It's not how Edwardian England worked at the time. The man would've become an absolute joke in polite society. The world of high finance was in no way ready for the kind of hands-on dad who'd want time off to help his kids prep for World Book Day. So no, I don't find the ending of the film to be realistic (casually leaving aside other realism issues such as cartoon penguins and magic spoons).

I'd like to see a real-world sequel to the events of *Mary Poppins*, a gritty account of the next years in the Banks family's life as they'd have been more likely to transpire. This would be my pitch:

It's two months after Mr Banks quit his job and the family savings are starting to run out. Banks has had to let the staff go and Mrs Banks has reluctantly quit the protest scene and finally got a job.

Poor young Michael Banks has had to go cap in hand to Bert to formally take up a role as chimney sweep, which he can do thanks to the lax employment rules of the time, where he finds the jaunty songs have stopped and the hard work begins.

Eventually, the whole family starts to resent Banks as they realise they did want a more empathic father, but not at the expense of a nice lifestyle.

Maybe I'm taking it too seriously. Maybe I've now become the Mr Banks who needs a bit of saving. It's possible.

I've noticed that as I've got older, there's one bit of dialogue which always makes me emotional. Jane and Michael have been in trouble with their dad and start low level trash-talking Mr Banks to Bert, but good old Bert is having none of it and drops a couple of truth bombs. He reminds Michael of the people who keep an eye on him every day, but that there's no one keeping a similar eye out for their father and that his troubles are something he works through without complaint, 'alone' and 'silent'.

It gets me every time.

It's not right to completely dismiss the emotional message of *Mary Poppins* but we could all do with watching it again and, at the very least, accept that Mr Banks – emotionally stunted though he was – was putting in a shift and trying to do the right thing for his family. I think in the language of love it's what's called an 'act of service'.

Perhaps he did get his job back at the bank, which had suddenly become a touchy-feely organisation with beanbags and dress-down Fridays, but by God, him going cuckoo in front of the board members was one hell of a risk and frankly not the action of a responsible family man.

Motherhood can benefit from being romanticised, but fatherhood can excel when it comes to the perception of taking one for the team. That's what being a bloke is all about. Flying a kite is fun, but some days the fun is for other people, especially when there's hard graft to be done.

BLOKES NEED A MAXIMUM OF THREE HAIRSTYLES IN A LIFETIME

In one of the more extreme assertions in this book I'm going to confidently state that any bloke having more than three hairstyles in his lifetime has serious psychological problems.

I'm not throwing shade on women – who can easily go from bob, to feathered to pixie cut in the space of one crazy summer – I'm saying the rules are different for blokes. For us, changing hairstyle is more like moving house: if you do it too often you'll end up lacking any sense of where to call home.

A fella's first haircuts aren't even really his choice, or they weren't when I was growing up. While girls would petition for pigtails or ponytails, wavy or crimped, I was more or less told 'you're having a crew cut, boy'. It wasn't my mum readying me for national service, more that crew cuts were cheap or that she was happy to do them herself. While my sister's visits to the hairdressers were almost ceremonial affairs, mine had the functionality of an agricultural shearing.

The fact that my hair was cut by my mum reflected how little status it held. It was just another in a long line of highly skilled things mums feel qualified to do (thank God she was working full-time when I needed a circumcision). My mum did have a go at my sister's hair from time to time, but that all stopped the time she ended up looking like Terry from *Minder*.

The three main hairstyles of my life have been: crew cut, faux hawk and side parting. There were three shocking days in the early nineties when I had not only curtains but curls in them, like I'd swung by Madchester via a tumble dryer. It was got rid of so quickly that I consider it akin to a marriage quickly annulled.

The boldest hairstyle choice I ever made was the 'faux hawk'.

It was the early noughties. I was in my mid-twenties and had decided it was time to attract a female life partner. The way I'd do that was by having a mixture of a flat top and my hair pushed forward and a bit to the middle. It was the haircut of choice for a lot of cool blokes on telly at the time, so I felt pretty confident I'd be married within the year.

Shortly after the big rug rethink, I made the mistake of imploring a female colleague who I fancied to 'Look at my hair!'. This was overheard by a mate and the phrase 'look at my hair' is still a catchphrase on the lads' WhatsApp group.

The style was called 'faux hawk' because it looks like a mohawk for the risk averse. It was part of a trend at the time, seeded by the likes of David Beckham, in which ordinary men toyed with what was formerly uber-masculine imagery. Beckham was having the kind of macho tatts once favoured by mechanics at deserted gas stations in Utah. Consequently, blokes like me, who were not quite ready to 'get inked', settled instead for T-shirts bearing this kind of artwork. Nothing says 'manly' like tattoos which are 100 per cent machine washable.

The faux hawk was, for a time, a trendy hairstyle, and it was a real departure for me. It did the job too, as within a couple of years I actually did meet the love of my life. She didn't actually say 'amazing faux hawk let's spend the rest of our lives together' but in some ways she didn't need to.

That hairstyle lasted right up until the early 2010s. The faux hawk started to wear a bit thin on thirty-year-olds and my ever-expanding spam meant it looked like I was trying to show as much forehead cleavage as possible.

I'd already sensed my lurch towards small-c conservatism, so a side parting seemed like the next and most logical step. It was good enough for my granddad to fight the Nazis with, so it should be sufficient to guide me through my forties. I wanted the kind of immaculate side parting that would make me look like a safe bet for a twenty-five-year mortgage.

To my surprise, the new hairstyle got a bit of stick on the comedy circuit; maybe they wisely realised that as my hair became small-c conservative the rest might follow. However, one of my comedy heroes, Bob Mills, gave a more positive reaction. He said I looked like a 'Spitfire pilot' and it wasn't meant as an insult.

The side parting is where my hairstyle has stayed ever since. I'm happy here; it's like a forever home. There's nothing I can do about my receding hairline, but we're nowhere near comb-over territory. Yet. I can't grumble: my spam may be getting bigger but my hair has remained reasonably dark, just like my old man's did. His stayed dark right up until the end. He barely spent any money on his hair during an entire lifetime but died with the kind of barnet modern men would pay six grand for.

It may sound a bit fusty to have decided on a haircut for life before I turned thirty but if blokery is about consistency and a lack of fuss, there's something to be said for picking a style and bloody well sticking with it.

Look at Noel Edmonds. Following the huge success of *Noel's House Party*, he spent many years in the TV wilderness. Did he start dicking around with his rug? No. When he made his triumphant return with *Deal or no Deal*, Noel emerged with the exact same hair we'd last seen him with. What a power play!

The most respected men in society aren't changing their haircuts every other week. You'd never see George Clooney bust out a skin-fade and curtains within the same year. Or Bradley Cooper lurch between his glorious brushed-back mane and a buzz cut. And what would we conclude if Boris Johnson actually started combing his hair? That he had turned over a new leaf? Or was facing a court appearance? David Beckham was simply the exception who proved the rule.

The problem with blokes constantly messing about with their hair is it represents an admission that they give a shit. You're letting everyone know you spend a long time thinking about your appearance.

I can hear a lot of women thinking 'What's wrong with that?'

You simply can't compare men and women's attitudes to hair. There's no equivalent male phrase for 'a woman's hair is her crowning glory'. Female investment in hair is exponentially higher. I've never knowingly paid fifteen quid for shampoo. Or bought shampoo (though I'm happy to use my wife's – I see it as revenge for all the over-sized hoodies which have mysteriously gone missing).

I also found out recently that pretty much every woman I know dyes her hair. Not only that, they sometimes use mad phrases like 'I'm dying it back to its natural colour'. They've got so far lost in the hair game that they can no longer detect why 'dying' something back to its 'natural' colour could be seen as an unusual concept.

You only have to look at most blokes' attitude to going to the barbers to get a sense of how functionally we view our locks.

Most men I know baulk at the idea of making an appointment and, furthermore, if they arrive and there's more than one other bloke waiting ahead of them in the queue they'll strop out like a commuter who's just seen his next three trains cancelled.

In short, I don't want hair to be something I have to think about very often. There's far more interesting stuff going on inside my head. Ideally, I'd like to make the same monthly time investment in my hair as I do remembering to buy dog food.

IT'S PROBABLY NOTHING

Women make 50 per cent more visits to the doctors per year than men.

Recently, I had the comedian Richard Herring on my podcast talking about his experience with testicular cancer. He relayed how he'd been one of those guys who'd encouraged other men to check their balls while simultaneously failing to check his own (though thankfully he still caught it in good time). I echoed his entreaty to all men to give their balls a once over while being dimly aware that I would still fail to check my own.

Why was that? What kind of madness can allow me to fully take on board an argument while subconsciously electing to not follow its obvious wisdom?

It must be particularly weird for women who see their fella absent-mindedly fondling his bits every third minute for non-medical reasons, yet when there's finally a socially acceptable, even clinical, reason to touch his privates, he suddenly goes all coy.

On a basic level – and this may not be a common thing – I just find my balls a bit weird. The design features of the actual penis aren't too bad, but the balls are just . . . odd. These tiny hypersensitive things suspended in a sack. I guess I'm worried that I'll find a lump but also grossed out by the texture. In the same way some people get freaked out by Velcro. It's odd to have an organ which has chosen to live in such a dangerous place, like those Arctic geese who bring up their young on the edge of a cliff.

There's another reason for this blind spot, one which is perhaps more common (and less weird) than my own bollock dysmorphia: blokes just aren't as dialled into their bodies as women are.

Think about it: from the moment of that first menstrual cycle, nature gives women a regular heads-up that their body is 'doing stuff'. Men only have sporadic alerts that there's anything going on at all.

Such signals don't happen that often, full stop, and most of them are weighted towards early life in any case. You go through puberty, your voice drops, your balls drop, your body odour goes up – but once that's done . . . nothing. In fact, if you're lucky enough to experience general good health, you might go decades where your body reports that it's all quiet on the western front. Any changes that do occur generally aren't good. Hair in the nose. Hair in the ears. Hair in most places apart from the one where you want it, just as if your nose and ears are taunting your forehead.

Our bodies are less vocal than women's; consequently, we have the scope to ignore any of the weird shit taking place within. It will often take high levels of discomfort before we even consider taking action.

My dad was a real martyr in this respect.

When he was in his early sixties, my sister invited my dad out to Houston for a holiday and treated him to a pedicure. Not long after she'd started, the woman performing the treatment looked up in concern, in much the same way a surgeon might glance around if an operation was going wrong. They'd noticed my dad had a very serious in-growing toenail. When questioned about it, Dad cheerfully reported back that he'd had it for about ten years. He elaborated that, rather than go to the doctors, he'd instead opted to periodically 'dig it out' himself.

The employees of the spa looked baffled.

However, for my dad, properly attending to his toenail would create a fuss, and on a daily basis the physical discomfort was preferrable to fuss. He got up every single day and compared the niggling pain in his foot to the ball ache of visiting a doctor. Every single day, he weighed up the pros and cons then came down on the side of going about his business as usual. If he'd have just teased out his logic a little and plotted another graph he might've compared overall loss of quality of life versus localised inconvenience, but that wasn't how my dad's mind worked.

I guess the further it went the more embarrassed he became. He knew he'd have to undergo the ignominy of whoever worked on his feet pulling out an industrial-sized planer while shielding their face with a welder's mask to avoid potentially lethal shards of toenail. Even so, it's undeniable that once ten years had passed, a quick visit to the doctors and the attendant treatment would've been better than the day-in, day-out soreness, but the old man took a gamble and on one level I respect that – partly because the apple doesn't fall far from the tree.

In the mid-noughties I got a verruca. I'd had it about a year and thought I should probably mention it to my wife, who suggested a bunch of things which sounded like a massive pain in the arse, so I googled what to do.

I found one article which suggested that the best thing to do was to just leave it.

So I did.

Don't get me wrong, there were plenty of other articles suggesting all manner of treatments, including freezing part of my foot and making various dietary adjustments involving almonds, but I opted to observe the one article I found which allowed me to do sod all.

That verruca became a part of me for ten whole years. Whenever it came up my wife renewed her petitions for me to get it seen to, but I claimed that, as I'd taken it this far, it was probably only days from resolving itself.

But here's the thing. One day, that verruca did resolve itself. One magical, blessed morning I checked the bottom of my foot and it had just disappeared. Probably the worst thing that can happen to an avoidant man like me is that I invent some logically dubious basis for postponement which gets proved correct, but only by good luck and the passing of time.

Since then, I've had other stuff which I left for ten years.

In 2010 I was told that I might need glasses. Ten short years later, I got my first pair of glasses and suffered multiple panic attacks when I realised I'd driven nearly half a million miles seeing life with all the visual clarity of old episodes of *The Simpsons* on Channel 4. I don't know what had stopped me from getting glasses. Did I think Specsavers were somehow lying to me? That they operated like cowboy mechanics, recommending a new cambelt I didn't need? Did I think my driving was so good I could basically get around Britain like a Jedi using the Force?

I currently have bunions on my feet. 'Get it checked out, Geoff,' my wife says.

Why? I've only had them four years. With such matters you need to give it at least another six before considering action. Anything less would seem hasty.

What can also be particularly maddening for women is that, in most areas, blokes generally aren't as fussed by their own physical discomfort. It simply doesn't register as highly on our personal Richter scale of things to give a shit about.

Sometimes I'll slump on the couch in a visibly piss-poor posture. My wife will cajole me to rearrange the pillows. 'Get up and sort yourself out, Geoff,' she'll say, 'you'll be more comfortable.'

Nonsense! I'll just ride out the lower back pain and grow as a person. Many women will watch men sitting or doing something in a cack-handed way and offer to help. We don't always want help. We don't know what we want, but we do know that we don't want fuss. Fuss is a pain, fuss is un-British, but most of all, fuss is un-blokey.

I'm not saying that all this is necessarily a good thing. As much as I'm amused by stoicism I recognise the need for change. Due to the way humans procreate, men are literally the place where evolution is – or should be – happening (maybe that's why I'm so freaked out by my balls – it's a lot of responsibility).

So we need to try to learn how to reach out for help.

But how do you pitch this to a meat-and-two-veg guy, steadfastly ignoring back pain or peculiar sensations in his chest?

Well, if making a fuss is the concern, a bloke dying needlessly young could be seen to be the epitome of fuss. Maybe that's the way to sell the idea of intervention to men with chronic white-coat syndrome. There would be a funeral to plan, people would have to take time off work (because for some bloody reason these things have to happen during office hours), there would be free food for relatives you're not fond of, and – worst of all – the bloody admin.

So maybe that's how you need to pitch a doctor's visit to the bloke in your life. Point out the potential lost earnings, the fact coffins are only single use (you're literally throwing money away, like when you drive a brand-new motor off the forecourt). Then hit him with the clincher, the worst of all these things: the criminal price of buffets.

He'll be down the quack's like a shot.

Aside: Since I wrote this chapter, my sister has clarified that my dad went ahead with the pedicure. Afterwards he was borderline euphoric, commenting that it was 'like walking on someone else's feet'. Not that he ever had one again, mind, which is classic blokery.

ARMCHAIR GENERALS

'I hated Hitler growing up but as I've got older, I realised without him I wouldn't have had as many good documentaries to watch.'

– Geoff Norcott Snr, 2013

There are some things which eventually come to all blokes over time. As a young man, you think that you'll be immune to the standard and clichéd interests of your forefathers, but in time these things call out to you like sirens of tedium: strong cheese, trains, peace and quiet, socks which don't make your feet too hot.

And, above all these, stands the enduring appeal of the Second World War.

For a certain generation of dads, the History Channel (or the 'Hitler Channel' as it affectionately became known) launched at exactly the right time. A lot of fellas from that era were retiring and the standard daytime televisual fare of talking women and gameshows didn't hold much interest. But the History Channel? Suddenly they could spend whole days immersed in the twentieth century's most re-tellable tale.

Before Channel 5 got lost in making the same royal documentary with a thousand different titles, the History Channel was doing the same with Hitler. *Hunting Hitler, The Rise of Adolf Hitler, Hitler's Legacy of Death, Hitler and the Order of the Phoenix* (I may have made the last one up). I used to mock my dad for how long he'd spend glued to these shows. It seemed like he was watching a replay of the same event from a million different angles (which, given modern sports coverage, is not entirely outside the blokey frame of interest).

At school, I'd had that first wave of interest in the Second World War that most boys experience. At that age, the appeal is obvious: primarily that England won (sorry, Britain won . . . Sorry, Britain and America . . . Sorry. Britain and *how many* countries?). I was aware of the big moments, the key figures and, on a basic level, the evils perpetrated by the Nazis, but as I became an adult man, like most blokes, I filed all that away for a while.

My, how things have changed lately. I don't know when I realised I'd become a Second World War guy. It might've been when I started listening to numerous podcasts on the subject and it became the only new information I had to relay to my wife. Over the course of a twenty-year marriage, I'd used up all my decent anecdotes, but what I could now do was regale her with exciting trivia about the war. Like, did she know that, during the war, Himmler once turned up in Britain unannounced? Was she aware how much Hitler detested smoking? And did she know that the name of the bomber which dropped the first H-bomb was 'Enola Gay'?

You're right. She *is* a lucky girl. It's the kind of thing any woman in a long marriage wants to hear on a rare date night.

'Would you like to see the vegetarian menu, Geoff?'

'No . . . but I'll tell you who else was a vegetarian.'

What's peculiar about Second World War history is that the more I aged the more it started to seem recent. I was born in 1976, only thirty years after the end of the war. My mum used to take me to the Imperial War Museum in London when I was small, but back then it all seemed like ancient history. When you're ten, forty years ago is four times your lifetime. By the time you're forty, something that happened eighty years ago is down to only double the time you've been alive.

Something else that happens as you age is that the concept of time is something you start bending to your will. To stop yourself feeling too old, the mind reflexively recalibrates your view of all history as less distant. Thatcher? Left office recently, didn't she? Second World War? It is closer to my birth year than we are now to the TV debut of *Mr Bean*. The pyramids? Surely they were built shortly before work was completed on the Elizabeth line.

Thinking of the Second World War as more recent also helps make it feel more real. It becomes less heroic and more a human endeavour that you have to try to get your head around.

The move from it seeming like something mythic to a real-life event made me go back over the inane questions I once asked my grandfather (who served in North Africa). As a boy, I asked him things I now regret, like did he drive a tank? Did he ever meet Churchill? And whether or not he shot anyone. If he was still alive today he'd probably shoot himself, such would be the wealth of info I'd be mining him for.

When I asked my grandfather those questions I had a simplistic sense of goodies versus baddies. As you age, you realise that few things can be delineated so comfortably. Most historical conflicts have two complicated sides. You even rewatch *Star Wars* thinking, 'Well, I don't like the way they went about it, but the Galactic Empire weren't entirely wrong about streamlining the clunking bureaucracy of the Old Republic.'

The Second World War, on the other hand – with some small caveats – does fall more easily into a classic sense of 'Jedi versus Sith'. You can talk with nuance about the effect of the Treaty of

Versailles in provoking the conflict, and the degree of culpability of the German people, but the Nazi high command were demonstrably evil. The things carried out in their name mean that no reasonable person could wish for anything other than an Allied victory.

The degree to which you celebrate or own this moral victory can be the tricky thing. In recent times, there's been a legitimate criticism of the boomer generation for constantly invoking a war they never actually fought in. Triumphalism is intrinsic to sport so there's always a risk that blokes can start connecting those same emotions to the war.

However, I suspect that when British blokes look back to the war, the defining part of the national story isn't drawn from heroism. Sure there's the Dam Busters, but is that about the mission itself or a cracking theme tune? There's the Battle of Britain, but all that aerial combat stuff is so elegant that it seems completely removed from the gritty reality of boots-on-the-ground combat. The things that really stick in the mind are the narrow escapes. Dunkirk is a far more meaningful analogy. As any football fan knows, winning 5–0 is so euphoric it feels almost otherworldly, but scraping a last-minute equaliser is where the true exhilaration lies. As a cricket fan, my most cherished memory isn't beating the Aussies at home 3–0, or bigger still winning down under, it's from 2009 when our two worst batters somehow survived twenty overs to bat out for an unlikely draw.

Stubbornness is often associated with blokes and what could be more downright bloody-minded than withstanding the Blitz? Those years were rarely about obvious acts of courage; it was men and women exhibiting bravery of a different kind. The bravery of just getting on with it and not giving in. Far from

British exceptionalism, these obdurate tales are the narratives which actually form our national character. The average bloke absolutely loves this stuff.

My son is already aware of the basic tenets of the war, but I wonder if the passage of time might ultimately mean his interest will exist on a much lower level than mine. It seems logical that it would. Mine might be the last generation to get so lost in the fact and mythology of the Second World War.

And there's a material reason so many of my contemporaries are still hooked: because so many men fought in the war, there remains a palpable link in its effect on the relationships between fathers and sons. My granddad came back from the war still a lovely human being, but troubled. My dad spent the first few years of his life without a father figure present and, when granddad was about, he had a lot on his mind. Consequently, the bond between them took a long time to recover. It affected how my dad would one day parent me.

All of which is a heavily convoluted way of saying I'm probably going to consume Second World War stuff until I die – and also that my dad never took me fishing and it's all Hitler's fault.

SPORTING HOLY TRINITY #2: CRICKET

It's hard to make an argument that Test cricket is quintessentially blokey when the numbers don't back up the sport's broad appeal. Once when I was appearing on *Pointless Celebrities*, the host asked us which young celebrities we thought the public would've heard of. On the board were people like Maya Jama, some chirpy bloke off *I'm a Celebrity*, and England captain Ben Stokes. I concluded that – given his lion heart and gargantuan achievements out in the middle – pretty much everyone would've heard of Ben Stokes, so I tried to get a low score by picking some funky dude from Radio 1.

It turned out that only 13 per cent of the general public asked knew who Ben Stokes was. Thirteen per cent? The Hero of Headingley? The Lion of Lords? Less famous than Maya Jama? (No shade on Maya but I don't remember her more or less single-handedly winning the ODI World Cup). So the purpose of this chapter is to convince the majority of blokes that they're missing out on a sport which is perfect for them. I'm taking a liberty with its inclusion, so let's see if I can win anyone over.

Not only do most people not like cricket, they seem to savour their antipathy, even though that's the majority position (similar to people who seem to want credit for telling you they don't like U2 or have never watched *Star Wars*). I can understand the superficial reasons so many blokes tend towards football rather than Test cricket. It doesn't make me angry – I just feel sorry for them. I'm not certain of many things in this life, but I am sure that Test cricket is one of mankind's greatest achievements.

I came to the sport at the best time possible, at England's absolute nadir. We were spending yet another summer getting beaten up by the all-conquering Aussies, to the point where even small achievements felt like big wins. One of our tail-enders, John Embury, scored a quick-fire fifty in a losing cause and was heralded like he'd found a cure for cancer.

Cricket is unique in that people who aren't in the team for batting still have to bat. In football, if a goalkeeper goes up for a last-minute corner it's normally out of desperation. If a striker goes in goal it might be because the keeper headbutted someone and got a red card. In cricket, however, this 'Freaky Friday' role changing isn't just an occasional one-off – it's woven into the fabric of the sport. The scope this creates for blokey banter is huge. A tail-ender who can't bat for toffee facing a world-class bowler at 90mph will pull people from the bars. He's either going to get hit in the balls or launch the other fella into the stands.

There couldn't be a more unlikely hero than someone like Jack Leach, a slow bowler who stood at the other end while Ben Stokes was performing his 2019 heroics. Leach faced seventeen balls for his solitary run, but the way he held up one end for the guy with the talent was the epitome of solid blokery. He even managed to throw in a comedy run-out chance when a kamikaze attempt for a single had him scrambling back to the other end.

Ben Stokes couldn't even watch when Leach was facing, and

spent almost all of his team-mate's seventeen balls on his haunches with his eyes covered.

When Jack did eventually score his solitary run it was with near comical nonchalance. Having ducked and dived the previous sixteen, Leach casually tucked the ball off his hip to tie the Test match. Like going on a stag-do and your weediest mate throwing the most powerful right hook on the arcade punch machine.

Another charge made against cricket's masculine credentials is that it's not very manly. It's an accusation often made by football fans, who, let's not forget, routinely watch multi-millionaires get taken out by a random gust of wind. And yet, in cricket, a rock-hard ball is propelled at your head at speeds which would attract six points on your licence. Admittedly, cricket can seem a bit limp at times as they do stop for a nice lunch . . . and afternoon tea . . . and yes, they do sometimes stop playing because it's a bit dark or drizzly, but when the real action gets down to business it's as replete with physical jeopardy as anything Formula 1 has to offer.

As a sport, cricket also boasts many features blokes tend to be drawn towards. It's got stats (I could quickly rattle off the batting averages of several players who retired when John Major was still in charge). There's also duration. If some of sport's appeal to blokes is about switching off, note that football is only ninety minutes; Test cricket is five. Whole. Days.

That's why me and my mates have made it an annual trip for so many years now. It's just more time watching sport.

In 2022, I went to see England versus New Zealand at Headingly. I arrived at ten in the morning and didn't leave until

6pm. That's just good value, plus we were well oiled and sporting a decent tan (we even applied sun cream that day).

However, this was post pandemic and I hadn't accounted for how much older we'd got in the intervening two years. Something terrible happened on our first post-Covid cricket day.

One of our mates had a little snooze during the afternoon session.

It was that nightmare image I'd seen for years, the one when, during a lull in play, the cameras would drift to an old duffer catching forty winks under the cover of a wide-brimmed hat. I'd always pitied those guys. Nothing makes a bloke look quite so old and worn out as falling asleep during the day, especially when so many recreational activities are within arm's reach. Imagine being so old that though there is the option of playing crowd beach ball or watching cricket, you instead elect to have a little sleep. There was a beer snake going on not twenty yards away.

If you don't know what a 'beer snake' is, I believe it represents the high watermark of blokey bollocks. As people drink beer throughout a day of cricket, an ocean of plastic pint glasses builds up in the seating area. Eventually – and I've never caught sight of the visionary who starts this process – some bloke will start collecting all the cups and stacking them one on top of another. I don't know if he starts out with genuine good intentions – maybe he's into recycling or helping the ground staff control the litter – but it starts to grow in length and becomes 'the snake'. Blokes from far and wide start running towards the snake to add to it. There's a weird shamanic chant which starts up, where people repeat the entreaty to *'Feed the snake, Feed the snake'*.

The snake quickly becomes more important than the cricket

and the need for its perpetual growth becomes an all-consuming focus. My wife rang me once to talk about important plans for the weekend, but I cut the call short, saying, 'Babe, can I call back? We're feeding the snake!'

She sent me a follow-up text, asking, 'What the fuck is the snake?' It was a fair question, particularly as it sounded like a euphemism for something sexual.

When I got home the following day I explained to her what the snake was and that our one had got so big that Sky had covered it between deliveries. No less than Michael Vaughan had expressed his admiration.

I think that explanation was worse than any of the potential answers she'd come up with in the meantime.

Test cricket gets its name for a reason: it goes on so long it can test the psyche. A 6–0 defeat in football or a hammering in rugby is at least over quickly. Defeat in a five-Test series is a soul-sapping examination of character. The duration also provides the sport with a depth which others struggle to match. The rivalries across a five-match series spanning several months can be epic. Consequently, some of the insults – or 'sledges' – have been so rich they've gone into folklore.

Jimmy Ormond was playing for England against an Australia team which contained the Waugh brothers: Mark and the more highly rated Steve. Mark Waugh commented that Jimmy wasn't good enough to play for England, to which Ormond replied, 'Maybe not, but at least I'm the best player in my family.'

Football is great, but the birthplace for such linguistic highlights as 'over the moon' isn't known for such withering put-downs.

Even the on-tour high jinx operate on a different level.

Football scandals are often a bit route one and sometimes very unsavoury. I don't know if a footballer has ever done anything as eccentric as borrowing a biplane to fly over the field his teammates were playing on while the game happened (doffs cap to David Gower), or as comically goofy as Freddie Flintoff nicking a pedalo to try to join a party on a yacht. Cricket anecdotes often go down in folklore, while football ones can end up in court.

Amid an increasingly rapid digestion of entertainment and sport, Test cricket is a stay against confusion. Is the duration such a problem? At a time when people routinely devour six series boxsets perhaps it still has a place.

And if all that hasn't sold you, let me say this: Test cricket is a place where you can have a beer in your hand before 11am and literally no one thinks it's weird.

You're welcome.

MAN FLU

'Man flu is a pejorative phrase which refers to the idea that men, when they have a common cold, experience and self-report symptoms of greater severity, akin to those experienced during the flu. However, there is evidence to suggest that viral infections affect men more than women.'

– *Wikipedia*

OK, so there it is. Wikipedia says that man flu is real so I guess we can finally stop arguing about it?

Perhaps not . . .

When it comes to illness, let's be honest and say that the average bloke's relationship with illness has changed over the years. If your great-granddad caught rickets or got winged by a stray shot from a musket, he'd still insist on doing his duty and going to work – even if he had to crawl on his calcium-deficient knees to get there. Bed was a place where he slept at night and procreated twice in a lifetime, not somewhere to spend time during the day under any circumstances.

Even worse, if he were to admit that he felt a bit under the weather it would lead to the ultimate nightmare scenario: women making a fuss.

Even if blokes have become less resilient over time, man flu is a contentious idea because it brings into play two strong and opposing forces: women, who, on the whole, don't really like hearing men moan about stuff, versus men, who claim to not like moaning but moan a lot when ill.

Whether there are sound biological reasons why man flu is a real thing or not, whining is never a good look for a bloke. We act like big kids often enough as it is.

But why do blokes become so moany when ill? When men have an infection or virus, testosterone levels decrease as the body redeploys energy to fight off the bug. This might be a reason why ill blokes whinge so much – because there's been a temporary reduction in the flow of that weapons-grade hormone which allows us to thrust and fight (or at the very least make a bold move for the last parking space). Not only are we ill, we feel biologically and emotionally weaker. The science is all there.

During the pandemic, men were 61 per cent more likely to die from Covid-19, but even this wasn't enough to spotlight the idea that men might suffer more acutely.

If that had been reversed and women had been more likely to die, I've no doubt there'd have been a UN commission on the subject and Emma Watson would've been wearing a tasteful ribbon bearing the numbers '61' – but, in the event, the disparity in Covid deaths warranted relatively little in the way of column inches.

Without sounding flippant, the pandemic gave the average bloke a new card to play. His Mrs may have been suspicious of the man-flu claims, but the idea it might be Covid had to be taken seriously. It was a risky move, however, because eventually he'd have to take the test – then try to sound convincing when claiming that he 'must have shaken it off already'. (Not that I was any good at taking those tests. It took me about five attempts before I even reached where my tonsils used to be. My wife said it was worse than giving tablets to the dog.)

At a time when we've become suspicious of toxic traits like victim-blaming, the idea of 'man flu' sails very close to the idea of 'gaslighting'. You tell someone something's wrong and they tell you it's all in your mind.

There's something minimising about putting the word 'man' in front of an ailment in order to undermine it. We're one step away from hearing things like, 'Oh, you've got man-kidney stones have you? I'm sure they're *very* man-painful.' On the one hand, men are being exhorted that they need to ;talk more' and learn to be comfortable with seeming vulnerable. On the other, domestically, many are still being told to 'stop moaning'. So essentially, it seems like we need to speak up, but quietly, and definitely not when we're ill.

My advice for blokes dealing with this quandary is itself very blokey: deal with it. Suck it up. Women will always be a little bit suspicious of the idea that you contracted the exact same cold as them but that, somehow the moment it got in your body it became a vicious brand of flu. It's like sitting next to someone on the very same mobile network with the identical phone yet declaring you have worse signal. And that's before you throw in the fact that the very concept of pain is a bone of contention in any marriage, especially one which has produced children. You may have a paper cut on your finger that stings like a bastard or a blister from wearing new shoes that has made your heel feel like it's on fire, but if you ask your wife for sympathy you are asking the wrong question. If you do want sympathy put that poorly finger in a sling and hobble your aching foot down to the pub where other men will feel your pain and show their empathy by cutting up your peanuts for you and gently trickling lager down your throat. And they will do all that for the simple reason that they've never given birth.

If you want the women around you to take your illness seriously, it's worth doing a bit of soldiering on. Let it get to a point where they independently realise you're more ill than you're letting on. That way, you'll finally get a bit of sympathy which is turbo-charged by their guilt for not taking you at face value in the first place (this can be a risky tactic – 'soldiering on' should never include 'missing chemo').

But you need to do something because it will never come down to simply how ill you *say* you are. Women are far more shrewd and tuned in to your usual behaviours than you are to theirs. They need to see concrete evidence on top of your own verbal reports (which may be a painfully transparent attempt to get out of attending their mum's sixtieth).

Blokes don't clock minor deviations in their other half's behaviour in quite the same way. It doesn't only happen with physical health; women can log a wide range of changes in behaviour (or they've simply mastered the magical art of 'paying attention'). They're making decisions based on a more rounded understanding of who we are. Consequently, a bloke exhibiting small behavioural changes can indeed make them take notice.

For example, I like my food. In forty-six years of life, I've had my full complement of three daily meals on every single day bar two. I like food so much that I try to eat lunch as late as possible, so I have more of the day with lunch still to look forward to. After dinner, I'll often leave pudding a good ninety minutes, so I have fewer waking hours where food isn't a prospect. So if I ever leave food on the plate, or even turn down an extra helping of mashed potato, my wife will often shoot me the same kind of worried look a zoo keeper gives a penguin who's off his fish.

So what can we conclude? That I have an odd relationship with food which stems from being breastfed for too long? Probably. However, more importantly, if I'm under the weather, me not eating is a more convincing sign of illness than whatever whiny claims I make. Women are great at playing the long game. Sometimes we should too.

And given that blokes seem to have done OK in the 'biological burden' tally chart, perhaps we just need to accept the irony that testosterone – as well as often being hostile to everything else – is also destructive to men's immune system. It can make us crash economies and start wars, but might also cause our immune system to occasionally annexe itself. But as we don't have to give birth or go through the menopause, maybe we can take this one for the team (if anything, our female partner's ability to grow additional hair in late middle age is something we might end up feeling jealous of).

Conversely, oestrogen can be friendly to the immune system. Surprise, surprise, the hormone most associated with being biologically female has the power to co-operate. I suspect oestrogen also remembers to send adrenaline a card on its birthday.

And if you, as a bloke, feel really ill and you want to go super-radical to get your wife or girlfriend's attention, you could take truly radical action, like, I dunno, booking a doctor's appointment.

IT'S JUST A BLUR ON A SCREEN

*The average age at which British men become
a father is 33.7.*

From conception to delivery, it's sobering to consider the pitiful
scale of blokes' involvement in pregnancy.

The average man at any given point carries enough sperm in
his testicles to impregnate if not the whole of Europe, then at least
halfway from Britain to Bulgaria.

An average woman, however, hits puberty with just enough
eggs to populate a decent-sized British city.

Like many aspects of maleness, that statistical potential is not
something blokes generally deliver on. If you take an average
British bloke who sires two kids in his life and reduce the equation
to the amount of times he had sex (5,778 for British men . . . I'm
thinking that graph skews heavily between the ages of 18 and 30)
then he has ejaculated the potential for many times the earth's
population. After all that semen, two kids is a fairly meagre
return. Most blokes like to think they're Harry Kane, but in the
fertility stakes, we're barely Emile Heskey.

Nature constantly hints that life and creation revolves
around women. All the most important things are round: eggs,
planets, suns, orbits . . . boobs. It's why men are so obsessed
with curves, because we know that without them the universe
simply doesn't work.

If we take the average duration of British sex (nineteen minutes in total, with nine of those for actual sex . . . again, I'm seeing another graph spiking heavily between ages 18 and 30) and compare that to the number of minutes pregnancy lasts across nine months, we find that the physical male investment in pregnancy and gestation is 0.00000000025 per cent of the woman's.

The real miracle about fatherhood – given that we don't carry the child or have any kind of tactile relationship throughout pregnancy – is how so many men are actively engaged in the first months after the child is born. Up until that point, the whole process might have felt a bit theoretical.

The physical burden of pregnancy falls exclusively on the woman, but the state of pregnancy is at least a tangible reality, with changes in her body and mood – plus she'll probably feel the baby move regularly. The man will be told about all of these things and in the case of mood, may see evidence of them as another plant pot goes flying past his head. But still, the whole project remains fairly abstract throughout gestation.

Even the first scan shows a human form which looks nothing like a human, via an ultrasound method that seems better suited to detecting submarines. You hold your wife's hand meaningfully and do your best simpering look, but the logical part of your brain is bugged by the poor picture and feels like you should check that the HDMI cable is in properly.

After that first scan, there's a long stretch when there's little else in the way of new evidence that this miracle is actually happening.

The second trimester passes and, for a lot of couples, things are pretty benevolent. She has a bump which seems to be a size and shape she's happy to show off. In many cases, her mood is good;

you see the glow you'd heard so much about, which is frequently just her feeling hot, but you take the wins where you can.

Then, right at the very end of this miraculous nine-month process, you see the first incontrovertible evidence of the process as your child is finally born. And it is a truly amazing moment. When my son emerged and took his first breath in the form of a cry the words 'oh God' slipped out of my mouth, in a moment of spontaneous spirituality.

Or maybe it was me thinking, 'Oh God, how am I going to feed and clothe this thing?' or 'Oh God, that's a *lot* of fluid.'

To this day, the sound of him crying always makes me smile because it remains the greatest sound I've ever heard. It was his first noise in the world, the first evidence he was OK, the first hurdle of being alive passed – the keenest gratitude I've ever known.

It must be weird for my son – every time he has a fall or grazes his shin, I'll be happily cleaning the cut to the music of his tears, letting him know it all 'Takes me back to the best day of my life.'

One of the least blokey things about me is how sentimental I am as a dad. Of my wife and I, it was me who had to work hardest to keep their shit together on my son's first day at school. I tear up in the big moments. Watching *Modern Family*, I'd always presumed I'd be the whisky-sipping patriarch Jay Pritchett but I'm much closer to the mollycoddling sap Phil Dunphy.

I still have my red lines, however. When my son was a baby I couldn't do the papoose thing. I tried, but have you ever put on a single item of clothing and felt like 40 per cent of your dignity instantly disappeared?

There's a certain bloke for whom wearing papooses does work: the hipster guy with his top-knot, long-sleeve white T-shirt and pastel-coloured long johns. I'm sure guys called 'Caleb' can strap on a papoose using the same evolved emotional state which allows them not to laugh at the words 'house husband'. But I generally wear polo shirts and jeans. To quote some social media feedback after an appearance on *The Mash Report*, 'Geoff looks like the kind of bloke who spends his weekend defending statues.' So if you saw me wearing a papoose you'd be far more likely to think I might have stolen that baby.

But, since I didn't want to miss out on the proximity with my boy, I decided to carry him everywhere. Carrying him all the time caused big problems with my wrists. To the point where I eventually needed surgery. I have a scar on my hand from the resultant operation. As I always tell my son, some people have tattoos to commemorate becoming a parent; I have a scar from carrying him everywhere because wearing a papoose made me feel like a lady.

Every generation of children grows up confused; I'm just finding my own unique things for my son to talk about during therapy.

One bit of good news for blokes is that we get loads of credit for doing simple acts of parenting. Be honest, when you see a dad loading two kids into a car and strapping them in you smile, right? Look at that hero! (Doing things which actually represent a legal obligation.)

When I took my son to Costa when he was a toddler, I'd notice that as I put him in the highchair and gave the surface a wipe down, there would be several middle-aged mums looking at me like they were witnessing something halfway between parenting and domestic porn. I'd get a different look off the older women, though, no doubt because their experience of raising a child saw much less in the way of male help. They'd look bewildered, almost angry, as they stared at me – like they'd witnessed a chimpanzee using hair straighteners.

I'm not saying that all modern men contribute fully but many more get stuck in than they used to. Fatherhood has evolved a lot within the space of a single generation. Even when I was growing up in the eighties, many men didn't expect to play a particularly active role in their children's lives. For some, the overwhelming responsibility of fatherhood was enough to make them abscond altogether. Dads 'doing a runner' was a familiar development.

'Heard about Terry? He's done a runner.'

'Done a runner' could mean a lot of things. It often meant moving to a different bit of Britain. Without mobiles or social media, men who were terrified by the responsibility of being a dad could piss off and live a lonely but quiet life in Norfolk. Today, women talk about being ghosted by men they've dated, but back then some men would ghost whole families. One day, many years later, their kids might be on holiday in Yarmouth, watching telly in their hotel room, then spy a familiar face behind a news reporter – 'Mum, is that *Dad* on Anglia News?'

Recently, I saw a viral TikTok of a male cat being brought into contact with one of its offspring, a small, mewling tabby kitten. The very presence of this kitten immediately activates the cat's gag reflex. The animal may have boaked for reasons other than the crushing pressure of fatherhood, but this cat retching at the mere idea of having a kid was held up as an analogy for how men react to becoming fathers. We go on to see the next stages of the cat's relationship with this kitten. It moves from that initial sickened response to a state of passive indifference, to finally being a hands-on dad (which in the cat world means occasionally licking the thing's head).

I'd like to think the success of that clip lies in the acknowledgement that, for many men, the idea of fatherhood doesn't come easy. I'm not saying it's simple for women either, but they have a head start on the tactile relationship between parent and offspring. Blokes are visual creatures and the first time we truly know we have a child to care for is when we see it right in front of us.

So, as well as being hot on the heels of bad and absent fathers, let's stop and reflect on all the blokes who – despite their flaws, limited role in childbirth and general sense of bemusement at the whole affair – stick around and try their best. Though many men initially retch like a distressed tomcat, in the end, the vast majority of us slowly but surely adjust to the role, even learning to enjoy the odd spot of paternal head-licking.

THE NEWS AT MEN

Long ago – and by 'long ago', I mean roughly 2008 – before news was something you could consume more or less constantly via the highly reliable filter of social media, there was a curious ritual men would engage in on the first day of a holiday.

On the first morning of a standard package break in the Med you'd see a familiar scene unfold. The wife would settle in for a decent shift of sunbathing, doing that mad thing you're supposed to do on holiday: relaxing. The bloke, however, would immediately look bored and twitchy. Eventually, after twenty minutes of fidgeting like a fed-up teenager who'd been coerced into that painful last holiday with his folks, he'd put his flip-flops back on and set off on a mission.

About forty-five minutes later, you'd see him return to the poolside looking pleased with himself, as he had a tabloid newspaper tucked neatly under his arm, exhibiting the pride and satisfaction once exhibited by hunters who'd caught prey.

He was happy. He'd found news. In an age when most things were freely available, news was the one thing he still had to hunt for. The 'kill' might not contain any sustenance, but he would be able to devour the results from last night's League Cup quarter-finals.

I was like this. Faced with the prospect of seven days away, I couldn't fully relax until I knew there was a reliable newspaper vendor nearby. It's an odd compulsion, as one of the purposes of a holiday is to escape from the depressing features of your normal life. Yet there I was on a beach in Malta looking at crystal blue water, azure skies and a sun unimpeded by clouds, but all I could think about was whether I could get a copy of the *Sun*. When I first started going on package holidays, before technology improved and overseas printing facilities made papers more freely available, the newspapers I did buy were often at least a day behind the ones back home. The news I was reading wasn't even new, but that didn't matter. I felt like some old emissary of the British Empire being kept abreast of developments in far-flung corners of the world by despatch riders who'd taken days to reach me.

'Your grace, Gazza has been found paraletic in another dodgy nightclub. And Debbie from Romford is still 36-24-36.'

As my holidays improved, and I went on more business trips, my overseas news consumption evolved because I could now watch it on the telly. The decent hotels often had Sky News and if they didn't, I'd watch CNN. The news didn't even have to be *my* news, just *some* news in a language I could understand. Even if I couldn't understand everything, I'd still give French news a go, which was fine, so long as the anchors were telling me their name, age and whether or not they enjoyed playing football dans le park avec their amis.

As far as I can tell, this news obsession does seem to be more of a blokey thing. That's not to say my female associates aren't interested in current affairs; they're just less interested and less often – certainly not when there's a pool nearby. They tend to devote their energy for detail to things much more immediate. That's why they're the first to notice that your child has pissed in the shallow end.

The news addiction gets worse for blokes as we stumble into middle age. As well as keeping up with the headlines, I've also developed an odd portfolio of global markets I check in on each and every day.

One is the price of crude oil (you're right, I *am* great fun on holidays). It all started after the credit crunch. As a club comic at the time, doing around 50,000 miles a year (sorry, Greta), the cost of petrol was my single biggest overhead. One unexpected consequence of all these banks going up the spout was that the price of crude oil collapsed. Then mortgages became a lot cheaper. So, in what was supposed to be the worst economic catastrophe for a generation, I was finally able to cut back on the supply teaching.

Just when I thought I could give up on checking the crude oil price, Russia invaded Ukraine. Once again, I'm checking those numbers twice a day, not to mention I've since added another habit into the mix: the gas futures index.

I also check the 'markets' continually. No idea why, it just feels like a grown-up, blokey thing to do (and a bit like I'm one of the sons in *Succession*).

This could be a problematic thing to say as it carries certain implications, but news does seem to skew blokey. Why is that? I guess knowing about worldly matters makes a bloke feel more important (superficial and easily forgotten though that information may be). It services the latter of those two key pillars of the blokey constitution: provide and protect.

We know that in the modern world the physical element of protection is rarely called upon, but that particular part of our mammal brain is still roughly the same size, so it draws other 'risks' into that space which often aren't worthy of the name. We might not be required to beat off a team of marauding scavengers, but we can engage that synapse by getting needlessly worried about a bloodless coup in Guatemala.

My dad, even in his last days, exhibited this exact trait. In the twilight of his life, despite being a trade union man, he opened a few share funds. He became quite obsessive about them, particularly after retirement, when there are several voids men need to fill.

He'd been very poorly for a while and the doctors warned us the end was nigh. One night, I was staying at his house keeping vigil. I was sleeping upstairs in my old bedroom in a bunk bed that was far too small (even for an average-sized UK male).

I heard a clatter downstairs and feared the worst. I sped down and went into the lounge, only to find my old man in his pants with his laptop open in front of him, staring at the screen.

I asked him, 'What are you doing?'

He looked at me like I was the mental one. 'I'm checking on my Prudential share fund is what I'm doing. There's been some ruckus in Bangladesh . . . what are YOU doing?'

I paused, because dads, in a moment of such madness, still get to act like the sensible ones.

He shrugged like I'd never really understood such things and said, 'Go to bed, Geoffrey, you prat.'

I trudged upstairs like the eight-year-old boy I was when I'd last lived in that house, knowing that, even in the last moments of his life, dad's word was final.

I'd also come to learn that one day I too would need to know what the hell was happening in far-off places for reasons I'd never be able to fully explain. I'm just glad my dad wasn't around when Twitter became a go-to place for news and world events. He'd have never left the house.

HEROES OF BLOKEDOM #3: BOB MORTIMER

There are some people who if you found out they were arseholes, you might just top yourself.

Into that category first I'd put Tom Hanks. If a video emerged of Tom harassing a junior assistant or drop-kicking a hamster I think humanity would be well justified in finally giving up. We might also consider throwing in the towel if it transpired that David Attenborough hated insects and 'only spoke all that nature bollocks for the wedge'. Or if it turned out that Martin Lewis doesn't in fact change his energy tariffs twice a month.

I think the same is true of Bob Mortimer.

Bob's journey towards national treasure status has been an unusual one. In his double act with Vic Reeves he was never the junior creative partner, but the fact that the first big TV show they did together was called *Vic Reeves' Big Night Out* insinuated that Bob was a sidekick when he was anything but. Anyone who watched Reeves and Mortimer shows throughout the nineties and noughties wouldn't have come away thinking that Bob was anything less than an equal partner in their act.

The thing that seemed to tip him into the category of national treasure was the moment he did stuff on his own. There were the now legendary appearances on *Would I Lie to You?*, where Bob's naturally tangential mind produced those rare moments where the 'cry laugh' emoji felt genuinely merited.

But if you need your top blokes to be not just a laugh, but also good humans, you should know that Bob did legal aid work as a lawyer and seems to be one of those people who gets on with being virtuous rather than tweeting about it.

I don't know Bob personally, but I know that everyone who's worked with him only has good things to say – but why is that so precious in showbiz?

Well, in entertainment, things aren't always as they seem. There are plenty of public figures whose main project on stage or screen is to make you think they're a good person. That's a tricky proposition when it comes to comedy. Personally, I'd much rather people think I might be a bit of a dick and if I come in anywhere under that threshold it feels like a win.

Open virtue and comedy are hard bedfellows to reconcile. As Shakespeare wrote in *Twelfth Night*, 'Dost thou think because thou art virtuous there should be no more cakes and ale?' Conversely, the comedians who take their negative characteristics on stage with them often turn out to be nice people. Do you think Jack Dee is really that grumpy in real life? And come on, deep down you already know how much Romesh loves his kids.

Luckily, there are a small handful of comedians who are exactly what they seem to be and Bob Mortimer would appear to be one of them. A nice man who is able to be extremely funny without being mean to anyone. There are no victims in his jokes.

Do you know how hard that is? It's literally like making an omelette without breaking any eggs.

He has a knack of making you laugh from places you don't expect, like with the following quote: 'At one point I was putting

17 sugars in my tea. I know it's unbelievable and I do wonder sometimes what my mum was thinking to allow it. The weirdest thing was that if I had 18 teaspoons it was too sweet.'

I don't know if that's true or false, or even meant to be a joke, but every time I read it I laugh again.

He'd already had plenty of success throughout his career, but what really tipped Bob into a strong contender for 'Britain's best bloke' was the fishing series he did with Paul Whitehouse. Not only did his usual fundamental decency shine through; we also had two men finding friendship as they recovered from big health scares. Male friendships are hard come by at the best of times, not least in older age, but here we had two of the nation's best-loved comics finding it without resorting to some of the cheaper tropes of an on-screen 'bromance'.

He showed resilience in that series, but Bob appears to have always been that way. His dad died when he was seven and Bob had been a promising footballer until early arthritis curtailed his career. He also supports Middlesbrough, which must have taken more out of him over the years than that triple bypass surgery he had in 2015.

So if it does turn out that Bob ever kicked a homeless person or sold arms to Russia then please keep it yourself. Britain isn't ready to hear it.

HIS BIG DAY

It's a well-worn cliché that from the moment a little girl knows what a wedding day is, she starts planning her own. We never really consider the bloke's version of this. Or if it even exists at all.

Men, ask yourself this question: when was the first time you considered your wedding day and what it might look like? Was it as a little boy? A young man? About five minutes before you were due to say 'I do'?

I always thought I'd get married to a kind and beautiful woman, have children, live in a nice house and enjoy the standard features of what would be deemed to be a happy life. But that was just because I was a general optimist; I never gave much thought to how I'd achieve all that, let alone what colour the place settings would be when the big day came around.

At the point when I (somewhat impulsively) proposed to my wife after just six months (apologies to any bloke whose girlfriend just read this and gave them an impatient glare) I was fully focused on the moment.

My mum, via a family thought process I can't recall the logic of, was the keeper of my nan's engagement ring, which, it had been decreed by the family womenfolk, I'd propose with when that day came. Looking back, I think there was more to it than mere tradition: the hidden agenda was that by being the keeper of the ring, my mum would be in a position to consider my state of mind and whether I was ready or not to make such a big life decision. When it came to it, Emma was so obviously me 'getting out at the top of my game' that my mum almost fumbled the ring as she tossed it to me like an over-zealous fly half.

What I – and many blokes – didn't understand is that a proposal can mean two fundamentally different things to men and women. In my mind, I was asking for her hand in marriage. In hers, it wasn't just that: I was also suggesting a wedding.

Many standard blokes have no idea about the giant process their simple proposal will unleash. They're bidding for the Olympics with no clue as to the kind of the work it will take to stage the event itself.

My family comes from a different socio-economic group to my wife. All I'd known on wedding days were registry offices, beige buffets and men standing around looking generally reluctant. I had no idea someone like me would need to do a tour of stately homes to pick a 'venue'. So I was a bit overwhelmed by it all and didn't play as much of a role as I should have. Emma often used to say, 'You'll turn up on the day and be surprised by your own wedding.' She was right.

On the big day, I was fairly nervous. Like all processes you spend a lot of time imagining yourself into, my wife was able to waltz through the day with great serenity and grace, whereas I – though I enjoyed it – was frequently uncertain as to what was happening next.

The vows were something I'd worried about. I was relieved when they went well, not least because I'd grown up watching *You've Been Framed* and seen far too many grooms pass out at the altar. Why *was* that happening? I'm guessing either nerves or because he and his mates had made the grown-up decision to polish off a bottle of sambuca the previous night.

My wife, having actually given some forethought to the day, looked incredible. I went with the default fashion of the era, which sadly hasn't stood the test of time quite so well. There had been a trend, led by Gazza, of blokes wearing ivory or cream blazers on their wedding day. I had so much gold and ivory on my top half that I looked like the lead in a Bollywood film. The blazer was also very hot, so, like many blokes not used to making a single concession of comfort in favour of fashion, I was frequently overheating – never more so than when my in-laws announced a big surprise.

They'd hired some doves for us to release. It was a lovely gesture but I was a bit rattled, so the handlers patiently showed us how to hold then release the birds. My wife's nestled calmly into her hands (she's always had a way with kids and animals – like Mary Poppins without the parlour tricks). Whereas my dove was a bit cranky from the off and started wriggling around a lot in my hands. The countdown for release was about to begin, so I alerted one of the handlers that I was having problems.

He said, 'Just hold it really tightly. Don't worry, the bird can take a fair bit of pressure.'

So I held the dove as I tight as I reasonably could and . . . it stopped moving. Then the countdown began and I was faced with the prospect that, at the moment we released these two beautiful animals as a transcendent symbol of our love, I was going to lob a dead bird of peace into the air.

As metaphors go, not great.

Luckily, just as the countdown got to one it finally started moving again, though its flight wasn't quite the elegant take-off that my wife's dove managed, and it only seemed to have one good working wing, so went round in manic circles for a while.

Sadly for me, everyone was arranged in a horseshoe around us, so there are photos from every single possible angle of me holding that dove with the face of a man with chronic constipation facing a firing squad.

When it comes to weddings, I might be the last of a generation. As society changes, men will change. A bloke's wedding day is already no longer something he begrudgingly agrees to attend. There may come a time when a young man, having secured that all important 'yes' to a proposal, immediately pulls out brochures from his favourite venues in the area.

Would the average woman want this? Possibly not. There's such a thing as over-correction and I don't care how much society changes – never steal thunder from the bride on her big day.

To prove this point, let me direct you to the TV show *Don't Tell the Bride*. Depending on how seriously you take weddings, this is either the funniest show on telly or a real-life horror film. The idea is that the groom is trusted with the budget and everything from venue selection to food and his bride's dress. I don't know why anyone would enter into this process, but I'm sure a free wedding and some sweet-talking TV producers have something to do with it.

'It'll be fine,' I'm sure they claim, 'We'll keep an eye on him.'

The problem is that if they kept an eye on him and he made sensible decisions, it wouldn't be good telly. So we get a knuckle-headed bloke running around making all sorts of awful decisions, from scrimping on the food to thinking he can get bridesmaids dresses at £15 a pop (why would you anger five women at once?). Some of their decisions cause genuine hurt, but some are bizarre and exemplify that essential boyishness so typical among blokes. One lad planned for the wedding to be at Muscle Beach, Miami. The bride was torn between genuine hurt that some of her family wouldn't be able to attend and the realisation that she was marrying a very strange guy. That wasn't the weirdest it got either. One guy picked the theme of an 'Alien Autopsy'. What kind of weirdo watches documentaries about Roswell and thinks, 'You know what this needs? A disco.'

The reason this nonsense happened is because when the guy popped the question, he wasn't thinking about the day, he was thinking about the union. When offered a central planning role, the bloke within took over and he thought the most important thing was that it was a good laugh.

Traditionally, the decision to propose has either been something blokes haven't given much thought to or have dragged their heels on.

But here's one final thing to consider: since 2010, in the West, the number of women proposing has more than tripled. I guess you could see that as yet another bastion of maleness being chipped away at. However, for many blokes, averse as they are to risk and fuss, taking the job off their hands might well be a blessed relief.

'This tummy is pure muscle.'

Daddy Pig, *Peppa Pig*

MAN-FRUMP

As a working comedian, I was chuffed to be asked on the TV show *Live at the Apollo* for a second time. For most high-profile TV appearances I check my clothing options with my wife, but this time I'd been working away from home and was shopping alone. Mindful of previous catastrophes that have occurred when I've had such scary levels of autonomy, she asked me to send a photo of my outfits hanging up.

The outfits were as follows:

Black polo shirt with white trim.

Black polo shirt with white and brown trim.

Blue polo shirt with yellow trim.

(I hoped that the blue shirt option proved I was willing to be a bit daring; for me, that was the equivalent of Lady Gaga stepping out in a meat dress.)

My wife replied in that enigmatic but loaded way smart women often do. 'I'm sure any of those would be fine, Geoff.'

Looking back, I think that was her subtle way of telling me there was literally no difference. What can I say? I'm good at reading women.

The phenomenon of wives or partners co-piloting their bloke's shopping trips is depressingly common. There are two main reasons for this.

One is that she probably has to attend to make sure the venture even happens in the first place. 'Shopping' is not usually fun for men in the same way it can be for women. It's just an unwelcome occasion where we're subjected to the rank indignity of not doing exactly what we want. There is a small list of exceptions to this – some shopping can be fun, like purchasing PlayStation games or sporting memorabilia – but anything else and I'm trudging around like an eight-year-old boy who got dragged away from a Minecraft party.

Despite my reluctance to undertake shopping trips, I know that on the rare occasions they do happen it's best if my wife is present. She needs to be there to stop me pretending that, yet again, the first shop I went into just happened to have everything I needed. Previously, I've bought trainers by entering a shop, walking in an unbroken line to the pair on the wall I want, then taking them to the counter, barely breaking stride. It's amazing how not fussed you can be when you want to get back to catch the second half. However, it turns out that you have to get granular on this stuff: try them on, walk about in them a bit – forensic stuff like that.

Jeans are another problem. It's taken me years to accept that it's really important to try jeans on, not only standing up but also sitting down. I'm already cursed with the problem of not having an arse, but I exacerbate that further by purchasing jeans where the seat rests somewhere behind my knees. It's a hard enough look to pull off as a rapper, let alone as a forty-six-year-old man getting out of a 2015 SEAT Ibiza.

Over the years, I've wasted enough money and seen enough images of me looking like a mess that even a man-frump like me has taken on board the need to actually try clothes on before buying them. But here's the thing: I'm not going to sacrifice that much leisure time so easily. Consequently, when I have walked around in trainers, sat down in jeans or reached upwards in a new T-shirt and decided I still want them, I look to bulk buy multiple items of the same thing.

I know I'm not alone in bulk buying: it's peak blokery. My whole wardrobe looks like it's set up for identical triplets. In my mind, I justify it by telling myself, 'Steve Jobs only had one outfit, and he invented the iPhone' – as if I'm buying the same Fred Perry shirt six times to free up the mental bandwidth to change global communications forever. It must be an exciting moment for any wife or partner to know exactly what their fella will be wearing for the next five years. You could argue that it loses a bit of excitement and spontaneity, but at least you know what you're getting image-wise. It's like locking in for a five-year fixed-term mortgage. What could be sexier than that?

This uniformity also extends to footwear. For a long time, I only had one pair of shoes and one pair of trainers. The shoes were for work, nights out and weddings, while the trainers took care of literally everything else. I'd describe my process for replacing the trainers as 'reactive'. The criteria usually being whether or not my socks were visible through the soles.

Don't worry, that was the old Geoff. Since then, I've come a long way with footwear. At last count, I had three useable pairs of trainers and two sets of shoes. God knows what would happen if one of my sitcom scripts ever got commissioned by Netflix. I might even consider more than thirty pounds for the next pair.

It's odd how blasé blokes are about their appearance, especially given how much it matters to women. It took me until my late twenties before I began to realise how much notice women took of shoes.

I finally had some sense knocked into me by a Mexican woman I was dating back in the early noughties. She was brilliantly blunt and told me my overall look was that of a *'bolsa de basura para caminar'* ('walking binbag'). She more or less forced me to spend the only bonus I've ever earned entirely on clothes. Her position was: 'I'm not your forever girl, I'm the one who's here to get you ready for when you meet the one who is.'

And she was right. On the night I met my wife, I was wearing some of the newest and most expensive clothes I'd ever bought. I'm not saying that was the only thing which got my wife's attention, but, importantly, my clothes weren't a reason for her to *not* speak to me. In some ways, I sold her a pup because before too long I'd reverted to type and every battle she's waged to improve my image since has been like trench warfare.

There has been perhaps only one occasion when I was on, if not ahead of, the latest fashion trend. In the early noughties, 'man-bags' became a thing. I don't know if it was the fact that blokey icon Joey Tribbiani had one on *Friends*, but I considered them both practical and acceptable. I'd seen my dad's generation stick with briefcases for too long. There was never so tragic a sight as a businessman sitting down on a park bench and pulling out a sad-looking ham sandwich. Briefcases should be for important documents, state secrets – not a flask of tea and some Quavers.

I never understood the resistance to the man-bag and the unspoken implication that it was somehow effeminate. It often came from the same kind of geezers who'd only allow you to drink orange juice in the pub if you were on antibiotics and had a note from the doctor. Even calling it a man-bag is a bit embarrassing. It implies it's full of red meat and bullets. Whereas in reality, it probably contains a Kindle and a set of keys which had started doing damage to your trouser lining.

Maybe the big difference between the average woman and your standard bloke is the fundamentally different ways we view the purpose of clothes – as costume or uniform. The joy many women take in dressing up suggests there are more who tend towards the former. For me, I want my clothes and character to reflect each other: everyday and dependable. The way I look should be an evolution not a revolution. I want the developments in what I wear to proceed at an almost glacial pace, so that, after thousands of years, you'll eventually see the appearance of an upstanding gentleman. Some ladies can wear incredible statement dresses. Some dandy men can look fantastic in a ruffled shirt and velvet suit. Me? I'm not that guy. The way I look is just like I am. It might not be that exciting, but it is something you can rely on.

TABLE FOR ONE

Whether it's Superman and his fortress of Solitude, the Batcave, or even Jesus getting his shit together in the desert, the idea of male solitude is corroborated in popular culture beyond mere stereotype (though I was never sure how realistic Superman's fortress was – if it really was his man cave where was the pool table and jumbo telly?).

During the third lockdown – the long, cold, awful one at the start of 2021 – as a working comic, I'd started to miss life on the road. At the time of the surprisingly benevolent first lockdown of 2020, I'd just come off a long and exhausting work schedule and didn't hanker after gigging as much as I would've thought. Sitting in the garden during that unusually warm spring, I confided to my wife, 'I don't even know if I'll want to go back to touring.'

I can tell you that from the frozen look of intense horror on her face I suddenly realised that the time I spend on the road gigging isn't just for me. It is the one way my wife can get some her-time before bed and watch *Bridgerton* in peace.

However, during that hard lockdown early the following year, I started to seriously miss my former working life. My wife, sensing that frustration, suggested I book into a crap hotel somewhere for a couple of nights to sort my head out. So I did.

Without so much as a reason to be there, I booked into a weird B&B in Newark.

The owners worked out who I was. It must've seemed odd to them that this touring comedian was doing the road bit without the stage bit. I didn't care. Having done this job for so long, I was clearly institutionalised and needed to make tea in a tiny kettle. Even the moment I found myself back on the motorway I started to feel better. Stopping at a roadside Greggs was therapeutic and just being alone in that weird B&B felt restorative. Superman had his giant dome of ice. My fortress of solitude had a dated trouser press.

One of the reasons blokes don't mind a lot of driving is because they recognise the value of that kind of solitude. Modern technology has made being in the car more agreeable, but back in the mid-noughties I'd still happily undertake a long drive armed with nothing more than medium-wave radio. I'd go all the way to Bude and back on a wet Wednesday with no podcasts or audiobooks and only Radio 5 Live for company. I couldn't relate to humans very well but could always tell you the travel news and whether a Labour minister had just resigned. Now, with a whole portfolio of history podcasts to catch up on, driving can be an actual pleasure. I don't know as much about the weather for the week ahead but I do have some excellent trivia on Joseph Stalin.

Personally, I don't mind being alone. Often, I quite like it. I take a perverse joy from staying in budget hotels. There's a Premier Inn in Aberdeen housed in one of the greyest-looking buildings I've ever seen. I think it used to be the head offices for the British School of Motoring. The bleakness seems to compliment and tease out the complex flavours of solitude. I never sleep well in expensive hotels but there's something about the musk of sad businessmen which sets me right at ease.

Is this blokey tendency to seek fortresses, sheds or bleak hotels in the north of Scotland a vestige of our primitive past? I wonder if this is just another remnant of hunting trips. Or the power of those adverts with Lenny Henry.

From time to time, these trips have offered me respite. They have also, sadly, led me to some of the most pathetic moments of my adult life.

I was doing a tour show on the Wirral in the spring of 2022. I was hungover from the previous night in Belfast. I'd had a bit of a 'trains, planes and automobiles' kind of day, so when I finally retired to the suitably plain Travelodge I was thinking only of a snack then sleep.

The vending machine had been vandalised (no doubt when someone realised a Kit Kat cost more than their room). There was nothing else open, so I trudged to my cell knowing that I struggle to sleep when hungry. It was then that I noticed one of the cleaner's carts left in the corridor. Without giving it much thought, I grabbed about sixteen small cartons of UHT milk. My reasoning was that those tiny pots could be enough for a mug of milk before bed. Once in the room – and I can think of no other word for this – I 'decanted' all sixteen of them into the mug, thinking that a milky drink might fill the hole until morning.

You might think that I'd have stopped at four pots and asked what had become of my life, but I kept going.

The moment of clarity came when I went to drink the milk but caught a reflection of myself in the hotel window. There I was, a man in his forties, in a Travelodge on the Wirral drinking a cup of pretend milk he'd patiently decanted. I should've at least done them like vodka shots, to feel like I'd had a night out.

The truth was that life on the road had blurred my perspective on what is normal. Occasional solitude can be good. Too much of it, however, can tempt a man into acts of tragic eccentricity.

And yet, for most blokes I know, the pull of getting away remains. How else do you explain why so many men get into cycling in older age? Fellas who spend all week commuting suddenly start spending their Sundays doing the same, but for fun. They get obsessed with it. It must be weird for their partners when, once again, they appear in the kitchen asking if they're allowed to go out on their bike.

Then there are the runners. I'd imagine one motivation for the middle-aged marathon guys is trying to kid themselves they're still in their 'prime', but a run is also a great time to be alone (though there might be something worrying in how many of these hobbies seem to involve men seeming to flee the place they live).

And what about going for a pint on your own? Is there literally anything more blokey than a man who has decided to do something as sociable as going to a pub, but elected to do it alone? I've done this plenty of times, but now – in another collision of old-world bloke meets new world – I've found that earbuds mean you can even listen to your own music! It's like a portable jukebox in your head.

Let's take it further still. Astronauts are almost exclusively male. Now, more modern, progressive thinkers will tell you that this is down to structural sexism (and it probably is) but I think it's also that some blokes have a deep desire to get as far away from other people as possible. Even if that means going into orbit.

And how about explorers? Christopher Columbus, Sir Francis Drake, Vasco da Gama; people assume they were motivated by the wonder of finding new worlds. Not a chance. They were just looking for some peace and quiet. Sailing to the Americas on the *Santa Maria* was the fifteenth-century of equivalent of 'going down the allotment'.

It's hard to understand the bloke's propensity for solitude. Sure, there's an aspect of retreating from the complications of life, of engineering a situation that is as simple as possible. There's an obvious appeal there. But I also think it could be genetic. Perhaps we're just convinced that we're all splendid chaps and feel honoured to get precious time alone with the best bloke we know – ourselves. Or maybe some of it comes back to some all-important mummy issues . . .

MUMMY ISSUES

'Mums and their sons.' It's a sentence which many girlfriends, wives and sisters will have said ruefully. It's a curious relationship, sometimes oddly close, sometimes damaged and sometimes damaging. Consequently, the relationship between a mother and the principal woman who comes into her son's life can be a delicate thing.

My mum's relationship with my wife started off on a very good footing.

Mum always had a mystical maternal ability to pre-empt things and – in a bizarre moment which I still haven't fully made sense of – I cosmically ordered my wife through her a few months before we actually met in person. Which sounds weird, but let me explain.

In my twenties, I'd been dating for a while and possibly enjoying the bachelor life a bit too much. My mum, sensing my aimlessness, asked me what kind of woman it would take in order for me to settle down.

I described a woman who would turn out to be exactly like my wife.

There were the preferred physical qualities (which you could argue might've been fairly predictable, and favoured by many blokes) – pretty, curvy, etc; however, some were fairly specific:

dark hair, blue eyes and ruby red lips. The personality stuff was where I got really granular, right down to someone who did a bit of charity work in her spare time.

When I met Emma it was like my mum had been involved in some kind of mystical mail-order bride racket.

The first time she met my mum was a key moment. Mum had heard the good reports and was glad my new relationship was going well, but we still needed the royal seal of approval.

It was my sister's wedding day and the house was fizzing with the organised chaos of women doing hair and make-up. Into this stepped Emma. We'd been dating for three months. It was 'serious', so her meeting the family on such an important day was a big deal on top of an already big deal.

Emma said a quick hello, surveyed the military hair and make-up operation going on around her and said, 'Shall I make tea?'

This was just about the best thing you could've said to my mum. She loved tea. I'd say, at a liberal estimate, Mum drank between ten and twelve cups a day. It might explain her energy and focus (or why she had to keep getting up in the night). However, there was one bump in the road ahead. Mum had an odd moral aversion to people having sugar in tea. I have no idea why (it was completely hypocritical as she always had two spoonfuls in coffee). Nevertheless, it was something everyone knew about Jan, so when my wife said, 'Where do you keep the sugar?' there was a moment where time seemed to stand still (imagine the saloon doors swinging, but with blowdryers being turned off and hair straighteners snapping shut).

My mum eventually smiled tightly and said, 'In the cupboard, dear.'

In that moment was a calculation where Mum must've

realised that her son was doing exceptionally well for himself, so she'd have to drop her ideological opposition to sugared tea. However, I'd rarely heard her call women 'dear' before, so this may have been the careful vehicle by which she allowed her irritation to register.

Once we got engaged, my mum – unlike some mums who try to hoard the emotional relationship between mother and son – started disclosing little 'tricks of the trade' to my now fiancée.

'Geoffrey likes a bacon sandwich on a Saturday morning . . . Geoffrey likes having sliced cucumber in the fridge so he can make himself sandwiches.'

I'm sure my soon-to-be wife was inwardly thinking 'Geoffrey can do all those things his fucking self' but she recognised the degree of trust this denoted and duly gestured that she was taking it all in, like shadowing somebody for a day at work.

I was lucky my wife and mother got on. There was a lot of mutual trust and respect (plus my mum was all too aware of some of the utter nightmares I'd dated previously). Even when the mother-wife relationship is going well it can be a tricky one, similar to dads and daughters but with an added layer of intensity.

Societally things have changed a bit, but my mum was not far downstream from a generation that saw sons as a family's best bet to go forth and make big things happen. Maybe they'd make a name for themselves or, in time, once the dad had passed on, be the one who'd step up, and provide for and protect the old dear. That idea had the power to skew the level of investment families would put into boys, not least their mothers.

Consequently, the 'Mummy's little soldier' phenomenon is a

minefield many women around my generation still had to negotiate. There's a lot of upbringing to unpack.

When I was a small boy, the way my mum used to look at me gave a sense of what it must've been like to be born into a dictatorship of succession. My every move was celebrated, my emotions mirrored. I felt like Kim Jong Il, who reportedly had an entourage of sycophants who'd burst into tears whenever he cried.

I was convinced of my own specialness, so you can imagine my dismay when I started attending primary school only to find out that there were *other little soldiers*. Hundreds of them. In fact, the whole world consisted of boys who'd been reared to think they were destined for great things. There couldn't be room for all of us.

There's also a point in the early life of a boy when your mum seems to be a living angel, this loving creature who cares about everything you care about and instinctively seems to know what you need. I'm a fairly hands-on dad, certainly by general historical standards, and my wife isn't excessively mumsy, but if my son falls or cuts himself there's only one person he wants to apply the plaster (and it definitely isn't the one who can't butter toast without ripping the bread to shreds).

In my childhood, many mums still dominated the emotional life of the house, a world in which a boy can almost get swamped by the sphere of a mother's influence. I remember occasional moments when I resented that power.

One of my earliest memories is of being in a shop, and I was cross with Mum for the babyish way she'd spoken about me in company. She asked if I wanted a toy. It was a small, bendable version of the Incredible Hulk. It was a good toy and I really did want it but curtly said, 'No'.

In my mind, I was teaching her some sort of lesson for a grievance I wasn't exactly sure about, but she shrugged, said, 'Fair enough', and put it back on the shelf.

When we got home I went straight to my room, shut the door, lay on the bed and cried my eyes out. I guess it was my first act of true rebellion against the sometimes suffocating regime of maternal love, but sadly it was a very shit form of rebellion as all that happened was I missed out on a really cool toy.

We speak a lot about male power in the public domain, but I've often thought about how the female power which often presides in the home and private sphere can be equally compelling on a day-to-day basis. Mums can control a child's narrative, certainly if they're with them all day and if Daddy doesn't come home from work until early evening. They can fashion their sons to hold almost any opinion with anything from light suggestion to full-on politburo-style propaganda.

There's a point in the early part of any small child's life where the mother and child are so intuitively connected that they almost become a separate unit in the house. I remember when my son was young and I was particularly busy I'd experience this. My wife and son had developed little catchphrases about my behaviour. 'Silly daddy!' my wife might say and he'd echo back 'Silly daddy!', and I'd be thinking, 'Hang about. Have I become a sitcom character in my own life?'

I felt compelled to justify my place in the hierarchy of the house.

'Silly daddy, is it? Who a few years back got us on a different mortgage which allowed us to ride out the chaotic reign of Kwasi

Kwarteng without having to worry. I'm VAT-registered mate, what have you ever done? Plus, I've been on *Mock the Week* . . . No, they didn't ask me back . . . touché my friend, *touché*.'

Why wouldn't a boy be in thrall to his mother during early life? She's loving, kind and responds to any new knowledge he's acquired like he might be in contention for a Nobel Prize.

I love my son more than life itself. Also, as a fellow boy, he makes sense to me. He looks very similar to me, has similar personality traits, he even shapes some of his handwriting the same way I do and has the exact same competence when it comes to looking for something in a cupboard (none). Genetically, it feels like a linear progression.

But, however close I am to my son, or fathers are to their daughters, we didn't carry them. Mothers of sons not only have the tactile legacy of having carried them but also the curious reality that, out of their female body, they produced a male. They now have a chance to make a man, to sculpt him, direct him and improve on some of the useless gits they've had to endure.

Many blokes from my generation were among the last to be indulged by their mothers on such a fundamental level and when I visit parks with my son today, I see how much things have changed. Mothers coax their daughters to be braver on the apparatus, bolder with their bodies and with risk. Why wouldn't they? They've seen Katniss Everdeen kick arse in the *Hunger Games*; they've seen Rey fly the *Millennium Falcon* in *Star Wars* and Liz Truss run the country (maybe scratch that last one).

However, there are still fundamentals involved in raising a

boy which change how you relate to them. Young boys on average use fewer words on a less frequent basis than their female counterparts. Whatever feminist beliefs a mother takes into parenting a boy, they'll be confronted by the reality that – certainly between the ages of three and six – he will just seem a bit less *capable* than females of the same age. Consequently, the mum might give him a bit more support, a bit more praise, a bit more encouragement, and lo, during the boy's most formative period, what he remembers is getting a lot of credit for doing the bare minimum (medal, anyone?).

I wonder if this helps explain the roots of mansplaining. When a small boy has successfully taken on information and relayed it to his mother she can act delighted, so his takeaway might be that all women need simple things explained to them.

I saw this phenomenon recently at a mate's house. The kid came back from preschool and said, 'Mummy, once upon a time there were dinosaurs!'

Delighted that he'd finally retained a single piece of information from his day, the boy's mother trilled, '*Dinosaurs*?? Tell me more about these dinosaurs!'

I wonder if the kid was then thinking, 'Hang about, love . . . you're a fully grown woman, shouldn't you know about that kind of stuff?'

Meanwhile, my mate, his dad, was looking over and competitively announced, 'A lot of people think the T-Rex was around during the Jurassic era but it didn't actually emerge until the Cretaceous.' He then smugly went back to staring at the telly.

In the space of a minute, the young boy's mum had thrown a ticker-tape parade for fuck all and his dad had reminded him who the true household expert was. Put that same boy in the boardroom forty years later and there might be a part of him trying to shout louder than the other males and expecting acclaim for repeating a woman's idea back to her.

It creates a challenge for the rest of the bloke's life that his first experience of a female loving him is complete and unconditional. Because in the real world, attracting and retaining a woman's love is highly conditional: it must be cultivated and earned on a daily basis. As it should be. If, like me, you married well and at the end of each week she's still willing to let you sleep in the same bedroom, you're doing alright.

Another challenge for blokes is how you evolve your relationship with your mother as you age; how does someone who was so physically and emotionally bound to you in your infancy become a friend in adult life? I've known many men who hit a point where they suddenly found their devoted mums, the level of their attention, the vivid scrutiny of their love, becoming oppressive.

One of the successful things my mum did, once she clocked that I was starting to file her away into the 'mumsy' role, was to change the relationship. She started debating with me about politics and challenging my reasoning. As a result, I wasn't able to pigeonhole her quite so easily. However, one thing she could never stop doing was – on the occasions I'd visit – sitting and watching me eat. Even when I was a man in my early thirties, she loved to watch me stuff my face. I found it odd. Eating isn't a performing art. But I indulged it as best I could because I understood that it was different for her.

When your body once fed a little thing within it, sharing all the same nutrients and energy that you were taking in, and when that creature spent the early bit of its life seeming like a hopeless little ball of chaos, it must be hard later on to maintain anything like a normal relationship.

BLOKEY FILM REVISIONS #3:
DIRTY DANCING

I don't mind admitting I was bang into this film as a kid. My sister watched it once a day every day for a whole summer. I had the luxury of grumbling performatively, but only for the benefit of the other lads present. I was totally caught up not just in the story and music, but in the classy-looking world of America in 1963.

Luckily for me, my wife is also a *Dirty Dancing* devotee. A few years ago, Secret Cinema put on a *Dirty Dancing* experience. Once again, I was able to play the reluctant male, being dragged along to something I had no interest in. Full disclosure: I was carrying watermelons with the best of them (apologies to any true blokes who do not get this reference . . . or at least pretend not to).

The premise of the film is fairly straightforward, sitting as it does somewhere between *Lady Chatterley's Lover* and *Romeo and Juliet.* The cosseted middle-class girl is swept off her feet by a diamond in the rough (in this case a dancer called Johnny) who is going to show her 'another' side of live (in these kind of stories, 'another side of life' often means 'powerful orgasms').

The dad starts off from a different place to Mr Banks in Mary Poppins. His daughter is the apple of his eye and says 'daddy' in that way in which American girls evolved their speech patterns to absolutely ensure they get a pony. But over the course of the film, as 'Baby' starts delving into the steamy underworld of the dancers working at the Catskills resort, a wedge is placed between father and daughter. Bit by bit, the upstanding Dr Jake Houseman is fibbed to by Baby and the whole thing comes crashing down when he has to patch up a potentially lethal backstreet abortion on Johnny's ex-squeeze, Penny. Baby had been LYING to her daddy (hand that pony back immediately). Dr Houseman is furious with his daughter. We, the manipulated audience, dutifully sit there thinking, 'Don't be so harsh, let Baby be free to live her life . . .!'

But you know what? As I sat in the Secret Cinema field re-watching this film with an army of women, once again completely buying into it, I started to think, 'Hang on just a *minute*. This is America in the early sixties. This hard-working father has taken his family on holiday in the Catskills resort. He knows it won't be long before she's a full-grown woman who buggers off to join the Peace Corps or whatever costly endeavour middle-class kids wasted their time with back then. He simply wants to spend some quality time with his daughter.'

What father wouldn't have issues with this 'Johnny Castle' prick? The flashy name alone should strike fear into the heart of any self-respecting patriarch. Tell me a conscientious dad who wouldn't be struck with terror by his daughter fooling around with some leather-jacket-wearing prima donna called 'Johnny Castle'. Or Johnny anything for that matter. Now, he may not have been the one who got Penny pregnant, but in early 1960s America, the combination of the name 'Johnny' and that much Brylcreem was likely to get a girl knocked up at a distance of fifty feet.

And let's not completely exonerate Baby from all this. She lies to her dad and gets needlessly drawn into other people's dramas. Whether or not the dad does go into a massive man-sulk, he saves a young woman's life (let's give credit to the film for indirectly making a pro-choice point without ramming it down anybody's throat).

By the end of the film, however, we've become transfixed by other things.

'He did the lift! Johnny did the lift!'

But what about the character who literally stopped a young woman dying? How can we be so manipulated that we rank 'the lift' above the preservation of life (though I concede it was an *amazing* lift)? But no, poor old Dr Jake Houseman is the grumpy old coot who needs to shape up, get with the times and let his daughter do whatever the hell she wants.

Despite my blokey re-reading, the emotional climax of the film still retains a fair bit of power.

It's the final dance and a glum-faced Baby is sitting with her parents. Old Johnny 'snake hips' Castle comes bowling over to the old man and utters the immortal line, 'Nobody puts Baby in a corner.'

The women at the Secret Cinema showing all cheered at this line, but I wondered how many of them had kids now. And of the ones who did, I wondered how many would be left with any respect for their husband if some flash git strode over and mugged him off in front of his wife and daughter.

At that point I wished Dr Jake Houseman had stood up and said, '*You know what, mate? Maybe Baby is getting older and maybe it is no longer my right to tell her exactly what to do with her life, but I have raised her. No doubt old muggins here will be paying for her personal growth when she's pissing about in the Peace Corps.*

'*So what's YOUR plan, Johnny Castle? Everyone knows dancing isn't exactly a young man's game. What are you gonna do when you've paso dobled so hard your hips blow out at the age of thirty-six?*

'*I did not work my arse off in medical school to put my daughter through college just so she could bank-roll some chancer – who, let's not forget, five minutes ago was turning tricks for bored housewives.*

'*So maybe nobody should "put" Baby in a corner, but I'd argue given the years and money I've invested in my daughter, if anyone should even consider putting Baby in a corner, it'd probably be me ... or my wife. Sorry, dear.*'

Of course I didn't say any of this, and I was up at the end having a dance to 'Time of My Life' with the girls.

But if we're imagining realistic sequels for these films, we all know that Baby would've hit her late twenties and suddenly developed a taste for men with qualifications and pensions. And in that film, Johnny Castle is a lot of things, but he's not your average bloke. For that look no further than the calm and dependable Dr Jake Houseman.

I'D RATHER DIE THAN GO ON A SPA DAY

'Pampering' is a common leisure pursuit for women. The simple act of being a lady is so iconic that it sometimes necessitates paid minions to file away at their nails or give those eyebrows a little massage. Just mention the words 'spa day' and see the mystical quality of those two words play out on the face of the woman you're with, in the same way blokes react when you suggest a 'Leo Sayer' (all-dayer).

Most blokes don't have spa day at the top of their list of leisure pursuits. We do reward ourselves, but those rewards rarely result in feeling and looking better. For example, one of my favourite things to do is spend a whole day at the cricket. If you caught me staggering back to the Premier Inn around 11pm after a day at the Test match you wouldn't see someone looking rejuvenated. The only 'face peel' I'd be sporting is my own skin because I'd reverted to not wearing sun cream.

For me, pampering has never felt enjoyable, to the point my wife has stopped suggesting spa days. She's able to submit to the full cucumber on the eyes indulgence of the affair, whereas I would dread the experience from the moment it was booked.

Right from arrival I'm expected to do things I find highly unnatural. First, you get given the biggest dressing gown you've ever seen, roughly three stories high as it's handed, folded, across the reception desk. Then you get the complimentary slippers. I think this is all part of the ritual; the ridiculously springy towelling of the robe represents a transition from people's scratchy everyday reality. And when else do you wear freshly laundered slippers, or taste water with so much mint and lemon?

On my first visit to a spa day, I presumed I'd get changed and head straight to the treatment room.

No. I was expected to come back and sit in reception, dressed in this ridiculous manner. In public, with the draught dancing around my partially exposed balls, my chest hair on show and the gown occasionally flapping open (because, being a cack-handed man, I couldn't tie it properly).

You do, however, see the occasional experienced male spa user who knows what he's doing. He sits in reception reading a broadsheet newspaper with breathtaking conviction. You try to follow his lead, maybe sip a glass of the weird water, but feel like you're impersonating a millionaire waiting for an X-ray.

Men from the continent seem a lot more at ease with the whole spa day experience. Massages instinctively feel a bit more European. Plus it's an extra challenge for British blokes to relax in fluffy slippers, given that those slippers rarely come with socks.

Then there's the issue of how bloody long the thing lasts. Even thirty minutes for a massage is a long time to be lying face down with your face through that weird hole. It feels like you're in a submission position. What kind of psycho can take an hour of that? What kind of vestiges of former imperial privilege reside that you can casually allow a stranger to attend to your comfort for that long? I reckon they're the kind of people who'd think nothing of being fanned by a giant palm leaf.

Maybe women can do it because they've had altitude training

in the form of long hairdressing appointments. I've had wrist surgery concluded more promptly than it takes my wife to have a cut and colour.

I'm not saying all women enjoy their hair appointments taking longer than a Test match; they don't. My wife has to psyche herself up for one, whereas, for me, going to get my haircut is often a snap decision, the by-product of happening to see a barbers while out and noticing that my hair is starting to create the silhouette of a motorcycle helmet.

Massages also carry the angsty concern over whether or not you get an erection. Being more overtly sexually driven creatures, a lot of men will worry that they might embarrass themselves by getting a boner. It's very difficult to dissociate from the fact that massage is something you normally do during sexy times with your partner.

Nervous erections are a real phenomenon and especially galling once you hit middle age, when such shows of potency are generally harder to come by, but here they are showing up like family dropping by without prior notice. Thankfully, I've never had this situation occur, but the risk of it keeps me on my toes and makes it very hard to fully submit to the experience.

When the masseuse says, 'How's the pressure?' I'm half tempted to say, 'Well, I nearly had a panic attack a minute ago but I think I'm finally starting to chill out.'

My wife and I will often reunite having had simultaneous treatments. She's in a dreamy state and ready to go back to the hotel room for a blissful nap on those high-thread-count sheets. I, meanwhile, head to the bar for a pint to steady the nerves.

In the same way pubs and bookies have made those environments more inviting to women over the last twenty years, my proposal is that we should look at making spa days more enticing to blokes. For us, it's all about distractions. I'm not saying massage rooms should automatically have sport on, but it should at least be an option. Also, if I'm right and spa days do make most blokes nervous, how about offering a relaxing beer beforehand? Next to the mint and lemon water they could have a discreet tap dispensing Moretti.

And we need to stop with the giant fluffy robes. We should be allowed to enter the spa in our own shorts and T-shirts – and yes, I recognise that replica football shirts should not be allowed. This is a classy establishment after all.

I'm not an animal.

DADDY'S SPECIAL SPAG BOL

Eight per cent of UK men only cook from
scratch once a month.

Recently, my wife and son were away for the night, so I was keen to take advantage of having the house to myself. The clichéd idea of how blokes respond to such freedom would run along the lines of walking around naked and drinking whisky on the treadmill. In reality, it's never really like that when you're the adult version of home alone.

The main thing to exploit is the novelty of being in your own house with the freedom to decide what's for dinner (and watch cricket without a collective groan). So I decided to cook myself a nice meal. Steak with thick-cut chips. Not only that, I preceded it with a crude but enjoyable prawn cocktail starter. I'd also been to the Co-op to get a nice bottle of red wine. At this point, it occurred to me: I was essentially on a date with myself. My wife, given a night at home on her own would never do the same. I was acting like a bloke in the first six months of a new relationship with a woman. Yet here I was, forty-six years into a love affair with myself and clearly that love was burning brighter than ever (plus, I was pretty sure I was going to get lucky that night).

Canvassing the opinion of other blokes, it seems my response to being home alone is fairly common, but I can't think of a single woman in a long-term relationship who would do the same. Indeed, before we had kids, when I was on the road most nights doing gigs, I'd implore my wife to make herself a decent evening meal but would usually return home to find yet another bowl and solitary spoon by the sink. Instead of wowing herself in the kitchen, she'd had Weetabix for dinner.

If you throw in the fact that men seem to be happier with their own solitude, you might start to wonder whether blokes are just more *into* themselves (I can already feel the female readers going 'Duh?').

It wouldn't be out of character – you are, after all, talking to mummy's little soldier here. If I'm honest, the little boy in me still believes I should be allowed to do what I want most of the time. I can be bang in the middle of bringing the shopping into the house and my wife will find me sitting looking at my phone. The more evolved part of my brain recognises that this isn't a reasonable whim, but from time to time, that part of me absents itself while the other bit looks up retro clips of nineties football despite the fact that there are still Co-op bags sitting outside the front door.

Cooking seems to sit differently in the minds of most women I know. My mum, wife and sister (the holy trinity of my female universe) all reported that making dinner itself could be a chore but that having to *think* of what the meal should be was the most draining part. Because blokes generally cook less often, our contributions can acquire the short-term razzamatazz of a showbiz cameo. We're very good at talking up our stint in the kitchen. When have you heard a woman burst into a front room and proudly announce: 'Hey everybody! Tonight I'm doing my special spag bol!' and stand there with arms outstretched like they just bought everyone in the pub a drink (and btw – 'special spag bol' just means we'll use stock and basil).

The truth is we've changed a lot and many modern blokes love cooking. Or rather, modern blokes love *cheffing*. My little boy learned from an early age that if he fancied something quick and simple he'd ask his mum to knock him up eggs on toast, but if he wanted something fancy she had to step aside while dad went into full-on Gordon Ramsay mode.

I live for when my wife asks if I fancy cooking this weekend. If it was the other way round she would simply have a quick look in the fridge, sniff a couple of things to check whether they were edible then turn out a lovely pasta dish ten minutes later. But that's too easy. I prefer the two-hour browse of the internet to find something needlessly exotic.

In this situation, most blokes will then proceed to make a lot of mess as they strive for the showstopper of the family's weekly diet. Often the things we cook won't even be suitable for the kids we're supposed to be feeding, then we'll sit sulking as, for some bloody reason, the four-year-old didn't want to try our spicy Thai noodles.

My own noodle recipe, like so many of the meals blokes tend to favour cooking, can all be done in one dish. I have mates who are excellent amateur chefs, but they still favour one-pot solutions. There's a gender divide not just in what we cook but in how we cook it. I don't know many men who are good at doing roast dinners. Roasts seem to require that mystical female skill of multitasking and an even bigger multitude of pots and pans. The difficulties men have doing roasts could even be seen to reflect our issues in and around foreplay. A roast requires forethought; you have to get the oven warm before you start and even then, to do the thing *properly*, it'll probably take a minimum of an hour. This is why many blokes favour the wok. Get it hot really quickly, chuck in the meat and it's all done in seven minutes. Sound familiar?

If roasts skew female, the barbecue has become almost comically aligned with blokery. There's something primal about cooking outside (granted, cavemen probably didn't make a herb-infused marinade and slice up halloumi, but still). Searing meat outside also calls to the ancient hunter-gatherer brain. The fact that I 'gathered' the meat from Sainsbury's doesn't matter. Some women think blokes like barbecuing for the love of food. But, like most things, it's just another excuse to be alone for a bit. You also know that any men who do talk to you will have to talk exclusively about meat, which is generally safe territory.

If you don't have time to destroy the kitchen or smoke out half the neighbourhood, the act of ordering takeaway is also replete with blokey rituals. When I was single, ordering a takeaway was a simple affair. Whatever the menu, I simply chose the dishes with the most chilli symbols next to them, asked for extra chilli sauce and added some rice. That took two minutes, the phone call was thirty seconds, and half an hour later I was burning my tongue in front of the football. Simple.

Once you're in a relationship, you have a very specific job when it comes to takeaways. Namely, that you have to order it, because for some reason when it comes to calling an Indian restaurant, your wife will suddenly turn into a 1950s housewife who's incapable of speaking to another person without your guiding hand.

If you're an elite bloke, you'll also drive to the restaurant to get that crucial 10 per cent discount. And once there, you have to make small talk and agree to buy a beer at the bar that costs the same amount as the 10 per cent discount.

In a way, it's odd that food ever strayed outside the realms of the blokey jurisdiction. When it comes to 'protect and provide', no one said you couldn't 'provide' a lovely meal (even if it does have way too much salt, chilli and you may never get the smell out of the kitchen).

YOU'VE GOT A SISTER?

Forty-one per cent of British men say they have friends
they 'like but don't bother to see'

One broad criticism of blokes is that the scale and quality of our friendships diminishes as we age. In our late teens and early twenties, we exist in literal tribes of man pals, but that rapidly falls off a cliff somewhere around the age of twenty-six and by the end you're down to a couple of legacy mates and that husband of the woman your wife recently befriended (who you have nothing in common with and who talks too much about Formula 1). It's all the more galling when women still seem to be recruiting friends at this time in life: friends from NCT, mums from school, someone they spoke to once at Morrisons . . . Whereas your friendship portfolio is like print media: in a constant state of managed decline.

The lazy blame for this phenomenon is often put down to a long-term partnership with a woman. She will – apparently – survey your friendship group like an incoming football manager and conduct a selective cull where many muckers end up on the transfer list. Despite being a cliché, this does happen a fair bit. Indeed, her assessment that some of your friends are 'wrong 'uns' is often proved to be objectively true (sometimes in a court of law). More often than not, however, the dwindling number of mates is entirely the bloke's fault.

Blokes should invoke one of their own core values and take

some bloody responsibility for this sad state of decline. Most men don't make the effort. We don't ask what's really going on in each other's lives. We don't remember each other's birthdays. In fact, to do so might create suspicion and resentment within the group, as you're just creating work for everyone else.

Like all things which seem inexplicable, there's a solid reason why most men act like this, however unsatisfactory it may be. The more you know about people the more you care and worry about them. The blokey psyche can drive a lifelong attempt to divest itself of such complicated responsibilities wherever possible. There's a liberating element in not having too many attachments. It's lonely, but, on the plus side, Christmas shopping can all be done in a lunch break.

The British bloke has a further barrier in that we're not so hot on tactility with each other. I've noticed the difference when I go abroad. In many Mediterranean countries, the man-hugs are full frontal. In the Middle East, men will often give each other a friendly kiss with no trace of self-consciousness. Meanwhile, in Britain, we rely on the handshake, which allows our torso to be as far away from the other man's as possible at the point of contact. There are hugs, but these often manifest in the form of two forearms sort of locked in front of each other and a manly slap on the back, which could be seen as camaraderie but usually means 'OK, I think that's more than enough!'

There's a brilliant film called *Up in the Air* starring George Clooney, which engages with this theme of men favouring a simple life. The main character is a travelling corporate trouble-shooter who goes into struggling companies and fires staff on the management's behalf. His USP – and the thing he's paid to do motivational talks for – is that he keeps everything in one rucksack. He has no partner and no children, he just roams from one place to the next, has meaningless hook-ups and a swim in the hotel pool, and then moves on to the next corporate cull. Eventually he desires connections but I'd be lying if I didn't admit that during the first act of the film I was thinking, 'This guy's got it made!'

His life is grey and limited, but it's peaceful. Plus he seems to be having a laugh.

I think a lot of women occasionally wonder if blokes' lives are generally more of a laugh. On a surface level, I think they might be. I used to have a comedy routine which I'd end by saying, 'Then I leave for work; two miles down the road, I've forgotten I've got a family.'

Obviously that's not true but there's a noticeable difference in mine and my wife's capacity to just 'switch off' from family stuff.

This detachment from the details of life can have a downside. You could be twenty-six years into a friendship with one of your best pals and find yourself saying something like, 'You've got a sister?' Blokes simply don't spend enough time asking each other what's going on in their lives.

Why is that? Maybe there's a desire not to seem impertinent or – worse still – nosey. We also recognise that grown-up blokedom involves a lot of stress and responsibility, so the last thing you want to do on an all-dayer is get deep and meaningful. You want to talk bollocks, not have Big Steve tilt his head sympathetically and say something like, 'But Geoff, how did losing at darts make you feel? Like, *really* feel.'

Talking bollocks can be dismissed as completely meaningless but it's not – there's a code there, if you wish to decipher it.

The bloke telling you he can't watch the Premiership any more because of all the diving is telling you he doesn't like change.

The guy who thinks the Bond franchise has lost its way is . . . also telling you he doesn't like change (look, once you reach a certain age, a lot of it is about the fear of change).

I also wonder if that mate in your friendship group who's started constantly wanging on about social justice issues just wants it acknowledged that he's a nice guy. We could save hundreds of minutes of virtue signalling if we just put an arm around him early doors and said, 'You, Jakey boy, are a quality human being. Now can we shut up about Greta and get back to talking bollocks?'

One thing which has been a game changer for bloke's friendships – and indeed all human interactions – is the advent of WhatsApp groups. Technology has finally found a way of keeping groups of men in regular touch with each other. These groups can be a laugh, a distraction and – sometimes – a comfort. They're so useful to male camaraderie that if we'd had them during the First World War I doubt any shots would've been fired or poetry written.

There are pranks too, lots of them. One of which came to public prominence in early 2023 when a group of blokes managed to get a stunt onto a live *Match of the Day*, with planning so intricate it was like *Ocean's Eleven* on a stag-do.

The sting was this: what initially seemed like an interesting viral video that most blokes would watch (like a honey badger fighting a lion) would, right at the last minute, ambush you with the high pitch soundtrack from a porn film of a woman reaching a noisy climax. The pranksters had somehow changed one of the crew's ringtone to that sound, and rang it repeatedly.

Gary Lineker reacted with reasonable good grace as the noise sounded off time after time in the *MOTD* commentary booth. Loads of blokes were laughing in recognition, but those watching with their other half might have quickly had to explain why a pornographic sound effect had them laughing in fond familiarity.

Bringing another bloke down a peg or two is an intrinsic part of who we are. Admittedly it's unfortunate that we don't communicate enough in the first place and that when we do it can be in the sound of humiliating sex noises. This does begin to change in middle age. There's something about the softening effect of fatherhood and losing your own parents that has tuned me and my mates into each other's real lives a bit more. We show more concern about the big life events. Thankfully, it seems that when actual life takes us down a peg or two we're there to raise each other back up. However, on a day-to-day basis we still don't delve too deeply into what's going on with one another. When blokes don't ask their mates the real questions it's often because they perceive it as 'bother' and they personally have a general desire not to be bothered.

Talking about the big things is an effort, but the problem is that over time, those minutes when you're not disclosing the real issues stack up. They become hours, days and months when you're not downloading your deepest fears and resentments to anyone. If you're not engaged in talking therapies either, this can eventually manifest in destructive behaviours.

It's hard for many blokes to be a good friend. My wife often has to coach me. She, like many women, is bewildered when I return from two days away with the lads without a single new piece of information about them or their families.

The exchange normally follows this pattern:

Her: So, how are the boys?
Me: Good.
<Beat>
Her: What's been happening?
Me: [worried] What have you heard?
Her: I mean in their lives. I know Austin's youngest has started college and hasn't Mandy got a new job?
Me: Er, I don't know about any of that.
Her: You didn't ask any of your friends about what is going on in their lives? That's a bit sad.
Me: Eh? That's what was great about it. We spent forty-eight hours together and barely scratched a millimetre beneath the surface. It's practically a superpower!

So we need to evolve a bit, but that's not to say that men suddenly have to transform themselves into full-on head-tilting empaths who, instead of talking about the upcoming Ashes series, are asking whether you've ever felt 'genuine intimacy' during sex. It's just a case of checking in and keeping up with the main developments in each other's lives. The last thing you want to do is to be comforting your mate over the breakdown of his third marriage when you're not even fully sure what happened to the second.

'ER INDOORS

- ▰ -

Women file for 62 per cent of all divorces in
England and Wales.

I realise that with a chapter heading like 'Er Indoors, I might be running the risk of losing a certain kind of reader (unlike 'the Mrs', ''Er Indoors' is very much a phrase that now sits squarely in the past). I guess what I really wanted was your attention because this chapter is actually about something painfully underdiscussed: men's difficulty in talking about the state of their relationship.

In my long career of observing the average bloke in his natural habitat, there seems to be a real issue with talking about such problems. I'm not saying I actively want to hear my pals complain about their wives or girlfriends, but it's peculiar how rarely I've heard any man make specific criticism of his other half in my company.

For context, it should be said that me and my friends have all done pretty well for ourselves, and a group of men so clearly punching above their weight will always be mindful of not rocking the boat. When we get together it looks like a reunion for a group of people who met on series three of *Love Is Blind*.

One reason that men complain less about their relationships – and marriage in particular – is there's plenty of evidence that married life provides men with more benefits than it does women. Life expectancy for women goes down a whole year when they are married (maybe the toilet seat being up really is an existential risk). And being divorced carries such an additional premium of male risk that the phrase 'happy wife, happy life' starts to sound like something your doctor should write on a prescription. After their female partner dies, men are in more danger of dying, and over a longer period, than a woman is, should the man be the first to go.

When blokes of my dad's generation lost their wives there was a clear gender difference in how they dealt with it, possibly exacerbated by the degree to which men of that era depended on their partners. If she did go first, the poor bastard wouldn't know what to do with himself. Within a week, he'd be eating dog food in the dark or trying to wash his Y-fronts in the shower. It's a bit different the other way around. If the bloke goes first the woman will of course be sad, but that's less likely to stop her going on a world cruise with her best mate.

However, this data doesn't let us know exactly how happy men are within those marriages. Any creature who eats and sleeps better will live longer, but that doesn't mean their relationship is necessarily happier or more romantically fulfilling. Remember, animals in captivity live longer (and if my wife is reading I'd like to be clear that I am no way comparing myself to one of the rhinos at Woburn).

Could it possibly be that women are simply better to be around? If I stop and think of the older couples I know, I don't see much of a difference in terms of general likeability. For every grumpy old git there's a battle-axe. For every inattentive man there's a woman who exits social gatherings early because she's 'got one of her headaches coming on'.

Blokes generally don't complain about their relationships as much as women, but they can sometimes act in a way which suggests they're angry about *something*. In that survey, which revealed that one of men's top gripes with women is that they rarely initiate sex, it emerges that another big bugbear is that women rarely say sorry when they're in the wrong. I wonder if this is a resentment which grows after couples have children. Partly because the bloke no longer feels comfortable seeking apologies, as his status in the house has irrevocably changed and he needs to 'fall back' a bit.

This is natural, as dropping down a level helps to provide a steady backdrop to prioritise the needs of an infant. Blokes don't generally mind, either; they're just grateful she seems to know how to keep this tiny thing alive. What this new household ranking does is encourage men to drop a lot of issues for a quiet life. In short, blokes start to lose a lot of arguments they could have won. This isn't necessarily a problem – more a strategic retreat, which can last several years. Or for the rest of their lives.

Some blokes allow this to breed resentment and end up acting out in destructive ways which ultimately hurt them too. They lost too many arguments, said sorry too many times when they thought they were in the right, and got rejected sexually so many times that their stupid penis found them in bed with Claire from accounts (I've no idea why these examples always include someone from 'accounts' – particularly odd given that people working in this department have rarely struck me as sexual titans).

It's a dumb kind of self-destructive retribution that blokes seem to specialise in, an elevated version of punching the wall to show they're angry, then spending the next twelve hours in A&E.

The problem is, a lot of us don't really know how we expected a marriage to feel, in the same way we never think about our wedding day when proposing marriage. Blokes never had romantic fairy tales to dream about as small boys. The TV and films we watch rarely contain specific ideas on how women should act in relation to us once we're in a relationship.

Our culture may heavily implant in us ideas of how woman should look, but even then the average bloke remains fairly easily pleased. Similar to their views on body shape, most blokes are fairly open-minded about behaviour too. Women aren't expected to be gallant or romantic or funny, just . . . nice.

If men do have gripes about women's behaviour, it'll normally come down to general issues with mood across a longer period of time. Even then it'll take a while before he'll feel able to mention the atmosphere at home to any of his friends, and it still might take the form of a classic piece of understatement like 'she had a face on'.

The more progressive reader might baulk at old-fashioned language like that, but not all the old phrases are without merit – if someone says their Mrs 'had a face on' it can be understood to have been one of those days when she was on the warpath and the little annoying things he did which usually got a free pass would face the scrutiny of the Chilcot Inquiry.

I've also got no doubt that the stereotypical bloke has his own equivalent of 'waking up with a face on' – such as if his first three answers of the day are delivered in the form of a grunt. Or if his solution to a problem sounds suspiciously like the exact same one his wife suggested several minutes ago when he wasn't listening.

In the event that men are profoundly unhappy at how their relationships are going, the language and opportunity for them to express this dissatisfaction is limited. Compare this to the discourse on a show like *Loose Women*. The whole concept of this highly successful programme is that it's socially acceptable – encouraged, even – for women to get together and bond through sharing, which can include criticism of either how rubbish their bloke is or blokes are in general. The show works because it's a phenomenon we recognise, plus we understand it to be a legitimate form of female bonding. This is in serious contrast to how most blokes operate when it comes to criticising their partner.

Moaning about your wife – certainly in the male friendship groups I've been part of – would seem a bit off at best and, at worst, a bit treacherous. Not only that, you're also burdening your mates with information they'll have to pretend they don't know about next time they see her. If anything, the men I know tend to eulogise about their wives to the group: 'She's great with the kids', 'I don't know where she finds the energy', 'I think she only married me for a bet' – that sort of thing. It's a far cry from older generations of men who would happily cast their wives as screeching harridans whose only goal in life was to piss on their joy.

Women, on the other hand, seem to have little problem sharing intimate details about their bloke, even if it undermines him in the eyes of their female friends.

My wife is fairly respectful in this regard, but I've no doubt that during past relationships I've shared a meal with women who've previously had intimate details about me relayed to them over a glass of wine. I'm pretty sure I've spoken to women who've seen a detailed impression of my 'sex face'.

Maybe blokes don't do the same because moaning about our

situation threatens the crucial idea that we've done well for ourselves, that we married above our level and are 'punching'. The man who does routinely moan about his wife is viewed with deep suspicion by the group. What does he want us to say in return? To *collude*? To criticise *his* wife? There's always the risk that he's just having an off day and the next time you see him you're now the guy who criticised the love of his life.

And how the hell are you supposed to make eye contact with his Mrs next time you see her once you're in possession of private information? Like how you know she got drunk on their only romantic date night of the year and passed out in an empty bath.

It may sound old-fashioned, but a lot of blokes feel that stuff like that is better remaining between couples. Possibly because we know full well that in the grand scheme of embarrassing behaviours which could be shared we'd probably come out worse. It's a form of wishful thinking, that if we adopt some kind of mafia-style 'omerta' it may be honoured in return – and the fact that we left the family's passports on the Heathrow Express might get brushed under the carpet.

There is, consequently, a bit of a gulf in the capacity blokes have to communicate the overall health of their relationship. This can lead to men not being able to pull the trigger on situations they haven't been happy in for a long time, as a lack of general discussion about what's going on in their love life can allow them to live in a state of denial. All of which leaves blokes at a significant disadvantage in terms of how they process the way their love lives are going.

I'm not saying that women don't stay in bad marriages – or indeed feel that they literally can't leave – but rather that duty can be a disproportionately high reason men don't feel like they *should* leave and why they remain in loveless situations even when this doesn't benefit them, their wife or their kids.

Women seem to be significantly better at valuing their own happiness, eventually. And men who do pursue happiness are often mistaking that for a younger woman who gives them the kind of erections they haven't had since the late nineties.

So the simple answer would seem to be this: let's talk more. Let's moan more. Let's gossip more. Let's do those unflattering impressions of our other halves which makes our friends squeal with laughter during whatever the male equivalent is of a bottomless brunch.

However, there's still a problem.

There's a very good reason no TV exec has ever commissioned a regular male equivalent of *Loose Women*. It's because *Loose Men* would be awful. We've got thousands of podcasts for men to moan at the state of the world, but literally no one would want to hear one where they moaned about their wives. For all the Joe Rogans and Jordan Petersons of this world, tackling the difficulty that society has in accommodating typically masculine thinking, have you once heard them say, 'My partner hasn't been very nice to me recently'? And thus blokes are left a bit impotent in their facility to articulate what their love life is missing.

So let's talk about our marriages a bit more, but not too much. Let's compromise and discuss our relationships, but using the cryptic devices often deployed by politicians.

Instead of saying 'She's bleeding useless', like one of the Loose Women might happily say of their hapless fella, let's settle for a diplomatic, 'Lately things have been sub-optimal.' Other blokes will know what that understatement means without you sounding like a scab crossing the marital picket line. And let's not go back to the old 'ball and chain' analogies of previous generations either.

I had an uncle who whenever he saw his new wife's name appear on his mobile would blow his cheeks out and say, 'Uh-oh, the Fuhrer calls.'

Was it politically correct? No.

Was it funny? Sort of, but there has to be a middle ground between moaning about 'er indoors constantly and never moaning at all.

HEROES OF BLOKEDOM #4: PETER CROUCH

Reporter: What do you think you'd have been if you weren't a
   footballer?
Peter Crouch: A virgin.

I don't know if there's ever been any other quote that has so
quickly identified someone as a good bloke. It has everything.
Not only does Peter Crouch's answer turn the exchange into a
proper joke, with the rhythm of set-up and punch, but more
importantly, it's underlined by a rare level of self-awareness. In
an era when young footballers spend as much time being media
drilled as they do completing shuttle runs, in two words, Crouch
identifies himself as an actual person. As a normal bloke, and a
self-deprecating one at that.

Since he went into a post-football career of presenting and
punditry, we've forgotten the charm that opened up those career
possibilities for Peter in the first place. The famous 'virgin' quote
wasn't his only zinger either.

In a reference to his looming six-foot-seven frame, Peter once
claimed he was 'five foot nine at birth'. Answering a question as
to why he hadn't joined the trend of footballers getting tattoos,
he explained it was because 'none of my limbs are wide enough
to support a visible image'.

All of these sound like the kind of retort you learn through the crucible of dressing-room banter. The best kind of defence mechanism is always to pre-empt criticism and get ahead of it. Peter was doing the football equivalent of Eminem's character at the end of *Eight Mile* when he takes on his detractors by listing every single one of his perceived weaknesses. Crouch was effectively rapping, 'I *am* really tall, I *do* have skinny limbs, my wife probably wouldn't have liked me if I'd been working on the bins.'

Crouch was also famous for the ironic 'robotics' goal celebration, which spawned a thousand substandard stag-do imitations. Such was his ability to land memorable moments in the public psyche that many people think it was Crouch's usual response to scoring. In fact, he only did it twice: once in 2006 playing for England against Jamaica and then a second and final time when he netted his hundredth Premier League goal. If you watch that moment back, the cheer when he reprises the robot is up there with the noise for the goal itself. The fans lucky enough to be present were smart enough to realise that they were seeing something special, the football equivalent of Springsteen getting back with the E Street Band.

All this self-awareness must have been something the young Peter Crouch had to master pretty quickly in the world of football because his size and frame would've marked him out for attention. In his early career, the terrace catcalls tended to either compare him to Rodney from *Only Fools and Horses* or – worse still – he had to endure thousands of grown men chanting 'freeeeak'. It's unfortunate, but that's football; any perceived weaknesses will duly have vinegar rubbed into that paper cut. And not only by the opposition fans.

In the late 1980s, my team, Wimbledon, had a player called Alan Cork who'd gone prematurely bald in his late twenties. We used to chant, 'Alan Cork, Alan Cork, Alan Alan Cork, he's got no hair but we don't care, Alan Alan Cork.'

Why were we playing mind games against one of our own players? We brought up his baldness but quickly countered that we were fine with it. If we were fine with it then why bring it up in the first place? We sounded like a wife subtly trying to initiate a dialogue about her husband getting hair replacement therapy.

Above all, Peter Crouch's humour showed intelligence, which was both everyday yet uncommon. Conscious footballers are all the rage now but back then, answering questions with more than one syllable could get you a reputation as a maverick.

Before Crouch, winger Pat Nevin had been seen as an oddity at Chelsea, not just because he looked like the guitarist in a New Romantic band but also because he'd been rumoured to read the odd broadsheet. A few years later, Graeme Le Saux, also of Chelsea, was subject to awful homophobic provocation by Robbie Fowler in a game against Liverpool. Piers Morgan speculated that no one really cared if he was gay (he isn't), the bigger problem was that he'd been known to read the *Guardian*. I'm not sure about that, but letting his smarts be known certainly didn't help.

Somehow, Peter Crouch managed to pull off wearing his intelligence on his sleeve without being persecuted for it, like his predecessors. Quite a feat.

When the Lad Lads Lads nineties morphed into the Wag Wags Wags excesses of the noughties, it sometimes felt like Crouch was the one guy in the England team who didn't take himself seriously – even if he had pulled a tabloid-approved 'stunner' in Abbey Clancy.

If anything, a thoughtful figure like Peter Crouch might be more at home playing right now, at a time when footballers are just as likely to be on the phone to Unicef as they are to their bookies, and the only girls invited back to Marcus Rashford's hotel room would be to balance the gender diversity in his and Kieran Trippier's book club.

The tribal nature of football can often bring out the worst in fans and players alike. Where fans tend to shout abuse, sometimes a modern player's first thought when celebrating a goal is to run the length of the field to do that awful 'shushing' thing. The joy on Peter Crouch's face when he scored, however, always seemed a lot closer to any normal bloke having a kickabout down the park with his mates. His success seemed as much of a pleasant surprise to him as it did to everyone else.

Peter Crouch had great gifts but they were delivered in an unlikely lanky package.

Blokeiness can demand a degree of conformity but, equally, nothing wins the respect of the group quicker than resolutely being yourself.

He had the good grace to acknowledge he was unusual and in the face of relentless banter and abuse, he stood tall.

Very, very tall.

THE BIG ONE (OR THE AVERAGE ONE, FOR MOST OF US)

The average erect penis in the UK is 5.17 inches.

So here it is. In many ways THE subject. The big one. Or the small one. Or the average one, depending how nature treated you.

Penis size.

An ex-girlfriend once said to me, 'You're a lot more interested in penises than I am.'

As a heterosexual man, it was an odd thing to hear, but undeniably true. Bluntly put, men know a lot more about willies than women ever will.

We own one. We have, through the process of sport and shared locker rooms, seen more penises than the average woman. We know more about their sizes and shapes but admittedly a lot less about how they look up-close and erect (unless you were *very* close team-mates).

For a long time, women's inferior knowledge wasn't helped by the lack of willies in films and television shows. The balance has been redressed somewhat by the Channel 4 show *Naked Attraction* (which, let's be honest, could've been called 'Who wants to look at some dicks?'). Though that programme hasn't exactly enhanced the brand of the male genitalia. The penis wasn't particularly aesthetically pleasing in the first place, let alone when stood exposed in a neon Perspex box, teased by a prior peak at some bloke's hairy shins.

No matter how many dicks have been available in popular culture, for all blokes, there will have been a point where they'll have considered their own penis and wondered, 'What's mine like? How does it compare?'

Are you a grower or a shower? Have you been cursed by the gods or gifted? Or are you, like almost every single bloke on the planet, making your way in the middle lane of member mediocrity?

I'm not sure exactly when I first became conscious of the existence of very large penises. I do, however, remember sitting with my then girlfriend one night watching *The Word* on Channel 4 in the mid-nineties. The programme showed an interview with the porn star Jeff Stryker. He was wearing cycling shorts and his manhood seemed to be resting somewhere just above his knee (what is it with Channel 4 and knobs? Was showing some one of the public service remits when the channel first acquired its licence?). I looked at my girlfriend, tried to gauge how she was responding, and sensibly concluded she could only be thinking that mine was now completely unsatisfactory and her only realistic option was to leave me, head to Vegas and set up a new life with this Stryker fellow.

It might've been a slight over-reaction on my part but the experience did speak to something I hadn't realised I'd internally concluded: women are drawn to men with larger penises.

Cards on the table: I have, like most blokes, measured my own penis and everything comes in around the average. I could add euphemistically that I've 'never had any complaints', but it would be a particularly cruel woman who would finish having sex then hop straight onto DickAdvisor to administer a withering two-star review.

Most blokes are aware that consistent majorities of women claim that size makes no difference to sexual fulfilment. But what if the majority of women are simply being nice? *Maybe* the third of women in a survey with Dating Advice who said a longer than average penis does improve sex are the honest ones? Or maybe they have larger vaginas? And why are these studies always about length rather than girth? It's like talking about a car's top speed without considering miles per gallon.

While women are judged more overtly and frequently about how they look, penis size is the one anxiety many blokes carry around with them, however irrational it may be.

I've spoken with blokes my age to try to work out where this self-doubt comes from (conversations which, as you might guess, prompted them to assume I was hung like a strawberry on a bird's nest). One thing that did come up was a glut of 'dick-shaming' in the nineties. Several of us could recall that gesture women would often use to emasculate a guy – the one where they'd hold up their little finger derisively.

There was also a song around that time called 'Short Dick Man' by 20 Fingers, which somehow got radio play. The song includes some charming lyrics, including asking if the imaginary man needed tweezers to put that thing away and inviting him to 'put his pants back on' and depart (the polite translation). Harsh enough, but there's also public record on YouTube of that song being performed on kids' TV. I don't know what happened to the boys who were in that studio audience, but I'm guessing some of them break into a cold sweat at the sight of tweezers.

Women might counter that boob size is an equivalent point of concern, but while fun, breasts aren't directly involved in the experience of penetrative sex. And if women are really anxious about cup size, they have, finances allowing, the option of doing something about it. Despite all the advances in surgery, there are no reliable procedures to enhances penises. The ones that exist all seem to leave it looking a cauliflower which got run over by a tractor. So for now, penis size is another bodily feature, like height, which men can do nothing about. Believe me, if there was an exercise which blokes could do to increase their size we'd be down that gym day and night.

Big penises also have mystical cultural power, so much so that we all know about the well-hung men of history, like Errol Flynn, Milton Burrell and Rasputin.

Rasputin's large member was so feted that some refused to believe it had died with him and came up with a lurid tale whereby it was kept in a box and handed around women in Russian high society (though the thing they were passing around was most likely to be a dried-up sea cucumber – which itself sounds like an unflattering euphemism).

The penis is seen as a vestige of your masculinity; it's even called your 'manhood'. Additionally, we now have a new name for the inner confidence of the well-hung man: 'BDE', meaning 'big dick energy'. That quiet self-belief which emanates from knowing at least one part of your body could elicit gasps from a crowd.

All of this speaks to the idea that our virility and reputation as a lover is bound up with the proportions of our genitals. Perhaps that's why some women choose to mock and humiliate, because, for all men's perceived power, the penis acts like nature's Achilles' heel.

The words around penis size seem to imply the idea of quasi-religious interventions. 'Well-hung' implies a gift from the gods. 'Blessed', 'well endowed', 'first in the queue' all make it sound like Mother Nature did you a solid.

A large schlong can, however, be a mixed blessing. Some particularly well-hung men suffer issues sustaining erections and others report dizzy spells while aroused. To my unevolved bloke brain, though, that still sounds like boasting. 'Lads, it's so big that if I get a boner I have to have a sit down.' It could be classed as a nice problem to have, like complaining about how much it costs to heat your swimming pool.

If you're in the absolute top tier of willies, it must be an interesting life. According to *Everyday Health*, only 16 per cent of men have a penis longer than six inches. Anything significantly above that and your gift is so statistically rare that it must feel like a kind of superpower. You're a Marvel hero who can only strap on his cape during the rare occasions you're having sex.

In my experience, most blokes in this elite category will find a way of letting you know they're well-hung. Sometimes they'll just straight out tell you. Or they'll get drunk and produce it on a stag-do. And who can blame them? If it was me, I might like everyone to know I was Superman rather than plain old Clark Kent.

Forty-five per cent of men were dissatisfied with the size of their penis, despite only 16 per cent being shorter than the average range – which means the vast majority of men's anxiety is entirely irrational. However, all the things said to reassure men about the size of their manhood sound suspect at best and patronising at worst.

'It's not the size of the ship, it's the motion of the ocean'.

That sounds suspiciously like something your nan would tell you, up there with your mum assuring you that when you get older there'll be girls 'queuing around the block'.

You can't help but wonder: 'What if your ocean had great motion AND a massive ship?'

Early in their lives, blokes are wired to think that big is good. Big planes, big trucks, big rockets – consequently, it's very difficult to imagine that not being able to do a proper 'windmill' is somehow an advantage. But as blokes age, we reconcile ourselves to our place in the scheme of life generally, not least where we fit into the global dick index.

And if you're still harbouring a lifelong grievance that you weren't one of the penile 1 per cent a further consolation is that once you get into late middle age you realise the former legends of the locker room aren't able to give their hardware a run-out as often as they used to. By that point, with tiredness and reduced libido bearing down on their sex lives, it must be like having an expensive sports car they can't take out for a spin due to the rising price of fuel.

* With heavy irony, this chapter is almost the exact average length when compared to the others in the book.

WHY BLOKES KNOW BETTER THAN SAT NAV

Up and down Britain, on the motorways and B roads, many blokes are locked in an ongoing and bitter dispute. It's not with their wives, partners or even their kids. It's with the technology they're using to get where they need to be: the sat nav. It might be generational – young men may have evolved to accept technology's judgement more willingly – but there's something about the mindset of many blokes which leads them to think that the sat nav is some kind of malevolent sleeper cell trying to destroy their life.

It's not just the conviction that I know better; as a bloke, I believe the sat nav is actively out to thwart me.

A few years ago, I was on the A14 (solid road) heading from west to east when the device told me to come off at a junction and take the third exit on the roundabout and join the dual carriageway . . . which brought me straight back onto the A14.

OK, that might not be the most exciting line you've read in a book this year, but it was one of these tedious travel developments that, while no one else gives a toss about it, when it happens to you, you deem it worthy of a phone call to your wife to relay this latest outrage.

Have you had this feeling you're being tooled with by technology? Or are you still evaluating my assessment of the A14 as a 'solid road'? That's because your proper bloke will always have an opinion on the big travel infrastructure.

On my last tour, I posed a regular question to some of the boomer generation men in the audience. I asked them what their biggest childhood fear was. Most replied 'nothing', 'I don't know' or something weird like 'wild dogs'. However, when I followed up by asking them their favourite motorway service station every single one of them answered in a heartbeat (a lot of love for Tebay service in Cumbria, if you're interested; personally I'm more of a Beaconsfield man myself). I do love a service station. The modern versions have evolved and many now contain pubs, a Pizza Express and, in some cases, a Nando's. They're practically resorts (though I might stop short of suggesting to my wife that we spend next Easter at Leigh Delamere). The fact I feel so at home in places designed for people between places is probably another one for the counsellor.

Going back to sat nav – my aversion to it isn't just my own misplaced male pride. As previously discussed, I often find driving to be a pleasure, so the idea of spending every single journey constantly waiting for a disembodied female voice to alert me to the next junction is another example of drawing too keenly on the teat of technology. It plays into my fear that while masculinity is evolving rapidly, some of the good things about being a bloke are being washed away with the bath water. It might be a ball-ache to work out a route before you set off, but at least you can get your head up and actually take in where you're going.

I've got a mate who's been working at a call centre since Covid and he follows the sat nav's directions every single day. Maybe it's a form of quasi-meditation, where being told 'in 200 yards, take the next left' is a way of realigning his chakras, but he's a disgrace and is lucky I still talk to him.

Being a stand-up comedian and always on the road, I know how to get to most major towns and cities in the UK without even consulting a map (yes, another medal is probably in order). Not only that, I can tell you which services have a KFC, which have Burger King and all the ones that have those weird vending machines which dispense disposable toothbrushes. My hope is that by the time my son becomes an adult, my extraordinary directional sense will rank me somewhere between Bear Grylls and a sorcerer.

It all comes from a belief that I shouldn't need help with directions. In my childhood, before the advent of sat nav, I wasn't the only one who heard his mum implore his dad to just 'pull over and ask for directions'. This never felt like a great option, not least because the chances of the locals knowing anything about where they live tended to be pretty low. Not only do you undergo the emasculation of being lost you have to endure someone else going through their own personal shame when – despite having lived in a place for thirty years – they can't tell you how to get from the train station to the leisure centre. Or they know their town too well and think they can impart that wisdom by plotting a route using landmarks only a lifelong local would know – 'Turn left by the growers farm, carrying on past the bombed-out bus shelter then pull up by Dave the tramp.'

Since the arrival of Uber and a generally more professional brand of taxi driver, a further dimension of directional arrogance has emerged as the driver will often ask if you have a 'preferred route'. My wife cringes at this as she knows I'll launch into my pet subject of why the M25 is actually a better bet late at night, providing there are no roadworks. Still, it's better that they ask rather than blithely accept what sat nav offers up, leaving me scowling on the backseat, asking loaded rhetorical questions like, 'You sure the A1 is the best option? Nope, *you're the professional* . . . all I'm saying is that crossroads around Fiveways corner can get *pretty* congested around this time of night.'

Navigation is something I expect to form part of my narrow repertoire of blokey skills. It's an important USP for men, as there aren't many areas in which we demonstrably outperform females. In aptitude tests, there's almost no area where young boys exceed their female counterparts, apart from the ability to mentally rotate images. This suggests that males may have a slight edge on working out how to get places (or why we were better at Tetris).

The unfortunate flipside, however, is that now most smartphones have effective map applications, once we get universal 5G, men may become completely obsolete.

'*A man who doesn't spend time with his family can never be a real man.*'

Don Corleone,
The Godfather

SPORTING HOLY TRINITY #3: DARTS

'Stand up if you love the darts.'
(Most common chant at darts events.)

I do, indeed, 'love the darts'.

If you're a rugby fan reading this, please don't be offended that your sport didn't make the cut for the holy trinity of sports. I accept that, nationally, the three premier sports in Britain would generally be perceived to be cricket, football and rugby. I respect rugby but I can't shake off the sense that it's a load of emotionally repressed men finding an excuse to hug for eighty minutes. And I know no one actually says 'rugger' any more but I also can't shake off the peculiar class-based hives that word brings me out in. Even if rugby is played extensively in Wales and Hull, I can't quite escape the idea that everyone on the pitch knows which knife to use for fish. I was also never sold on the idea that all of rugby's violence is completely excused by the fact that they call the referee 'sir'. It's like trying to avoid getting a prison sentence for armed robbery because you were polite to the arresting officer.

Darts, on the other hand, is the most supreme of blokeish pursuits. Most sports aren't things you could do in your house. Snooker and pool tables are not things the majority of people have the space for. But if you have a dartboard and the length of an oche available, you're playing exactly the same sport as the true greats of the game. A 180 scored at the Lakeside requires the same technical proficiency as one scored in the garage of a two-bed semi (though you might have slightly fewer blokes in Super Mario fancy dress singing in the background).

My mum used to love watching darts, back in the eighties, a time of huge viewing figures and household names like 'Crafty Cockney' Eric Bristow and 'Jocky' Wilson. Apart from wrestling, this was the only sport in Britain where the 'athletes' had nicknames. Or where the athletes looked nothing like athletes. The sight of men drinking and smoking their way through high-level competitions made the game look like a world I was used to. The wood panelling, the burgundy carpets – all of the big tournaments seemed to take place in venues which looked like my dad's local.

By the time I first went to the darts in the mid-noughties, things had changed. The first thing you need to understand is that I went to '*the* darts', the proper one, the BDO at Lakeside, not the glitzy PDC version at Ally Pally, which you might have seen on Sky Sports. It had barely evolved from the sport I watched on telly as a child. The venue was now smoke-free but in its place was the thick smell of stodgy fried food. The grub was so heavy that if you'd had five pints plus their pie and mash it would take its toll. During the mid-evening session, you'd see hundreds of blokes asleep in the background like they'd been shot with an elephant dart.

The Lakeside venue itself reminded me of an eighties caravan park. The walls were adorned with various big showbiz names who'd performed there in the past. I'm talking big hitters. Carolgees, Norman Wisdom, Duncan Norvelle and Sinitta. The whole place was stuck in a comforting time warp. Though they'd made one or two concessions to modernity. Now all of the players had nicknames rather than just a select few. Some were more organic than others. I never really understood the point of Ted

'The Count' Hankey, other than that he was a bit creepy and threw out some toy bats on his way to the oche.

Over the years, the BDO standard didn't keep up with its more illustrious and financially backed glitzy rival (the breakaway PDC), but, in a way, that was part of the charm. You'd see a guy called something like Steve 'Sizemic' Southern appear from the dressing room amid a sea of lasers and dry ice. As Steve 'Sizemic' bopped out to the strains of 'Cotton-Eyed Joe', you'd realise that the nickname was more a comment on his BMI than on his darts ability. Nonetheless, it was great to see an ordinary bloke who looked like he drove a van get his moment in the sun.

The quality of the darts was helpful but not essential. Darts is a brilliant game because it's always moving forwards, and even if two cloggers eventually end up chasing a double one for half an hour you can take refuge in gallows humour.

Rather than supporting one or other player, people who go to darts tend to support 'the darts'. If you watch highlights of great matches on YouTube you'll see fans cheering a 180 by one bloke then cheering even more if the next bloke does the same. It's all about the love of the game, arguably more so than cricket. The competitors might come second but the supporters never do. You might support Neil 'Duffman' Duff but if he lost to Thibault 'The French Touch' Tricole you'd still come away happy if it had been a good match. You can't lose as a darts spectator; it's like an each-way bet on the boat race.

Hence one of the most popular chants is 'stand up if you love the darts'. No one watching their favourite football team getting a hiding has ever tried to get their fans doing a conga for the sheer love of the game.

I have dabbled with the more glamorous PDC at Ally Pally. It was fun, but with all the razzmatazz I got the sense that the actual darts was more of a sideshow.

I attended with the comics Seann Walsh and Romesh Ranganathan. The fans, always on the scout for new and interesting banter, spotted the infinitely better-known Romesh and Seann and started having some fun. First they chanted 'Seann Walsh down a pint', which he did. Then they moved on to imploring Romesh to down a pint.

They must have spotted me looking left out and, somewhat charitably, followed up by singing, 'Comedian's mate, down a pint.'

It's that humour I love.

Despite that one flirtation with the big time, the BDO, with its darts purism and general sense of chintz, was always going to be my natural home.

However, in 2020, the BDO lost their minds and moved away from their spiritual home of the Lakeside and tried to set up at the snazzy Indigo at London's O2. They'd tried to keep up with the Joneses and it was a massive mistake. Crowds plummeted and the eventual winner ended up on less than a quarter of the tournament's usual prize pot. In the subsequent inquest as to how this had happened, many blamed not consulting with the players. I think they should've consulted with the fans. So much of life now occurs in these ubiquitous grey monoliths like the O2, with the usual array of Five Guys and Pizza Express, that a yearly trip to the Lakeside represented a stay against changing times. What could be more blokey than that?

The Lakeside still being the Lakeside was something you could rely on.

Pizza Express? That's something you do with the wife, but the

Lakeside had beer, crap food, bad decor, banter and – crucially – it all felt like something you could have a go at, given half the chance.

Despite large crowds of pissed-up working-class blokes, you rarely get any crowd trouble at the darts because everyone's supporting the same thing: having a laugh.

The only time there's a chance it might genuinely kick off is if the bar shuts early.

DEVIL WOMAN

The British public's obsession with Harry and Meghan is a curious and much remarked upon thing. Most debates on the couple will eventually alight on the question of 'why do we care so much in the first place?'.

It's pretty simple. The change in Harry's personality is something we recognise from similar relationships involving men we know. We saw Harry as a good bloke, then he got married, started to change and seem like less of a laugh, so many of us concluded that it was all Meghan's fault.

But was it?

In any bloke's lifetime there will be several fellas who after meeting the love of their life, seem to shed their original skin, seemingly overnight. Often, that kind of bloke – let's call him 'Duncan' – has picked someone who doesn't easily fit in with the group. Consequently, there's chatter within the family unit, possibly even a breakaway WhatsApp group, raising the very real risk someone gets their groups wrong and accidentally posts something meant for the 'we hate Alison' chat to the main group.

It all kicks off. The family's very own John and Yoko stop showing up for get-togethers.

Duncan then becomes outspoken on issues he previously didn't care about.

One of my most voracious meat-eating mates suddenly became a vegan two months after moving to Scotland with his new Mrs, who just happened to be vegan. There were numerous sightings of him at late-night drive-thru KFCs, but he became very defensive when those meat-free credentials were questioned in front of his new lady (even if he had just been for a random drive and was clearly fighting the meat sweats).

But does this analysis of the manipulated man fall into well-worn clichés around female manipulation, stretching right back to Adam and Eve? If your view about the male–female dynamic is traditional you could credit that theory, especially when you factor in the beauty of the bloke's new partner.

Meghan is a good example in this respect, as she's very good-looking and – superficial or not – this matters. Let's put a number on it: she's a nine and Harry is a six. Don't feel bad for Harry; historically speaking, those are pretty strong numbers for a ginger (sorry, I'm a stand-up, had to do a ginger slam – union rules). When you factor in Harry's general princelyness that could drag his average up at least another half point.

Despite the dream of every bloke to be punching above his weight, if you punch too far you could end up with a skewed power dynamic which takes the relationship to strange places. Taking the fighting/punching analogy further, Meghan is MMA while Harry's playing thumby wars. We've all seen this dynamic up close.

Growing up, everyone had that pal who liked a beer, played the field and was squarely one of the lads. A Duncan.

Then one fateful night he meets Alison.

You can tell from the first minute that Alison has changed him. Even when she comes over to say hello to his mates she is already suggesting that 'maybe he should have a soft drink this round'. This guy always used to be on the dancefloor singing all the words to 'Jump Around' but now he's looking on like a teacher monitoring the sixth-form disco.

Over the next few weeks and months, you don't see much of your mate Duncan. When you do see him something's clearly changed. He's a bit on the serious side these days. He's backtracked on the lads' holiday and is now saving up for a trip with Alison, which involves some sinister activity called 'sightseeing'. On the odd occasion he does come out, Alison has developed the ability to control him merely using her eyes. Simple movements left to right or up and down can get him to do things, as they indicate which activities he shouldn't take part in.

Then you finally get Duncan out for a lads-only night. He arrives to the pub late (the group have already speculated that she's deployed some last-minute psych-ops to get him to cancel). It's clear on entrance that he's been comprehensively restyled. He's wearing white chinos, a black turtleneck and stinks of Issey Miyake (it's the nineties in this story, but that's context rather than a legitimate excuse).

The black turtleneck is a big giveaway. I don't know any bloke who has willingly put on that garment unless he was relaunching himself as a philosopher or tech wizard. Duncan is also sporting a new hairdo which is, frankly, a bit on the busy side. You can see as he shuffles his way across to you that, deep within, he knows he's let himself – and the entire bloke brotherhood – down.

It's quiet as he sits. Everyone is trying to work out what they can say to this poor fella who seems to have come to a fancy dress party dressed as a knob. Ultimately, the group opts for the simplest line of attack: the black turtleneck. There are several variations on the Milk Tray theme (remember, this is pre-Steve Jobs).

Eventually, Duncan flips: 'You know what? Fuck you lot. You're so immature [bear in mind he's twenty at this point and was doing bunny hops just the other week]. I'm going round Alison's; we've got an early start tomorrow.'

Everyone nods and goes quiet. We can only hope that the early start isn't for a spa day.

OK. There's a chance that those experiences were underscored by sexist presumptions. Duncan might have actually *wanted* early nights and giant dressing gowns. The turtleneck could also have been his idea (doubt it, but we can't rule it out). And so, too, we have to concede that Harry might not simply be under some sort of trance-like spell from the 'evil' Meghan.

The idea of a man re-evaluating a family culture which involves briefing to the press after Christmas dinner isn't that much of a long walk, especially when you factor in what happened to Harry's mother. In fact, taking into account his conviction that the British tabloid press indirectly killed his mum, if a story broke that someone had stolen an Apache helicopter and shot up the majority of British newspaper headquarters it would certainly be worth asking Harry where he was that afternoon.

It's hard, though. Just like with Duncan, we were all quite invested in Harry as a bloke. Who couldn't be after what happened to him at such a young age? No one who watched that poor lad trail behind his mother's coffin with his head bowed low could ever forget the consequences of what he was born into.

We followed his early 'jack-the-lad' romantic entanglements with interest. Many were sort of proud that he went on active service for the armed forces (rather than the cosmetic surface kind favoured by some of his relatives and ancestors). Most of us were eventually forgiving when we saw photos of him playing strip billiards in Vegas (it turns out that what happens in Vegas doesn't stay in Vegas if you're second in line to the throne).

The fundamental change in Harry's character speaks to what we know about certain blokes when they fall head over heels in love. They pick women who seem to want to de-bloke them. Women who drive them towards less time for hobbies, less time with the lads, and more time mooching around farmer's markets.

The impulse to change a man is hard for blokes to understand. Getting into a relationship with a woman is a much more linear thing. Blokes meet a woman, think 'I like her' and if they like her a lot they'll want to spend more and more time together. The process of whittling them down or improving them isn't something that generally occurs to most men. When it does, it seems to be the preserve of an extreme, controlling, small band of genuinely toxic pricks.

Conversely, we joke openly about women seeing men as a 'project'. I've got no issue with that, so long as it's a drive towards evolution rather than revolution. Not just because I want my mates to still come to the darts with me each year, but because I don't understand why a woman would settle down with a bloke she had so many issues with in the first place. If his grunting, drinking and watching sports bother you so much maybe he's not the guy.

None of this, however, changes the fact that it's ultimately the bloke's responsibility to either not couple up with a woman who wants to change him or admit to everybody that he knows which side his bread's buttered and is happy to go along with it for a quiet life. There are plenty of blokes who weigh up the domestic comforts afforded by being in a stable relationship and conclude that there's less to lose by becoming more distant from family and friends.

So let's stop blaming everything on the Meghans and Yokos (even the Alisons), and keep some space for the idea of holding men accountable for how they become separate from the people who've always loved them. This kind of dislocation happens because the bloke allows it. Even if the woman *is* on 'manoeuvres', they're grown men.

And if it really is a bad relationship, in the long run it will inevitably implode. The job of everybody else is to keep close enough to pick up the pieces if and when it does go tits up.

WHO NEEDS ABS ANYWAY?

Women can have visible abs with 14 to 20 per cent body
fat, while men's needs to be as low as 6 to 13 per cent.

There comes a time in the life of most blokes when – like deciding you're going to learn a language, master the art of playing poker or brew your own beer – you decide you're going to develop abs.

You're going to get 'ripped'.

Even the language of getting fit is different for men and women. Women get in 'shape'; they 'tone up' or 'slim down'. Meanwhile, men get 'ripped' or 'shredded'. They 'monster their guns' and 'beast their pecs'. The feeling also persists that whatever issues exist in your life, whether they be mental, physical, career or relationship, they might all be solved by having washboard abs.

When I was young – certainly before the discussion about men's health and grooming evolved to where it is now – the belief lingered that abs were achievable through doing a few sit-ups every now and then. If a bloke did a hundred sit-ups a day for, say, I dunno, a week and a half, they'd be walking around looking like one of the Hemsworth brothers. One hundred sit-ups a day wouldn't have done anyone any harm, but most people came to understand that having abs is a bit more complicated than that.

Men might need to have as little as 6 per cent body fat for abs to even be visible. Imagine having just 6 per cent body fat and still not showing. It must feel like an oil exec knowing the volume of fossil fuels stashed beneath those pesky glaciers.

It's one of biology's few cruel tricks on men that women, who feel less societal compulsion to have visible abdominal muscles, can achieve them much more easily (however, given childbirth, menstruation and all the other stuff, maybe we can let that one go).

The bottom line is this: it's really *hard* to have a six-pack. So hard that when you think about movie action heroes or actors who spend their working day in capes, it's surprising how little they bitch about that requirement for the job. We hear a lot from actresses about the pressure for them to have a good body and look young, which is fair enough, but I can't recall a single interview where Robert Downey Jr sat and whinged about the need to still have groin cleavage well into his fifties. I don't recall a tearful Jason Statham chat where he detailed doing a savage bicep workout on two boiled eggs and a handful of chia seeds.

It's not just about being slim enough to have abs; most of these lads need to devote a daily couple of hours in the gym so they'll look like they'd have the upper-body strength to gut punch Thanos. The guns have to be spectacular, the chest like Kevlar, and the abs need to look sharp enough to grate cheese on.

If anyone in Hollywood should be moaning about oppressive ideas of physical perfection it should be the male cast of Marvel. But they don't because the broad idea that men are inherently privileged means we don't want to hear the rich Batman guy complaining about having to do squat thrusts or the mighty Superman whinging about a shoulder injury he sustained doing Tough Mudder.

It's not just superheroes either. A lot of people (me included) remember the shape Daniel Craig was in as he emerged from the sea in *Casino Royale* in *those* trunks. He was in such eye-catching physical condition that it was the first time I'd heard a bloke described as wearing 'those' anything. Finally, we had a male equivalent to Liz Hurley in 'that' dress. It's tempting to think Daniel Craig is just a naturally well-built fella, but his Bond-bod wasn't just a consequence of cutting back on the carbs or having slimline tonic with his Martini. Looking like that is a full-time job, one where you'd need to hit the gym most days in order to sculpt a physical ideal.

The multimillionaire gods of Hollywood may never moan about their lot, but just know that I see you, lads. I hope you feel seen. My wife has certainly seen you a lot and she likes what she sees.

Another aversion blokes have to abs arises from sheer pragmatism: once you know what it takes to have them, the ownership of a solid keg is an external acknowledgement of your vanity and need for approval. Other blokes will know it's not just dietary control and a bit of exercise: you've sacrificed large chunks of your life so that your stomach looks like an irrigated field in a dry country.

My suspicion of a strict fitness regime is that I've always been wary of any activity you literally *have* to adhere to. There's no room for vegging out or giving it a miss to watch golf all day. Some blokes watch sport in the gym but that's ruining a thing of beauty, like putting ketchup on curry.

The whole culture of the gym operates in a male sphere where I've never felt comfortable. The glossary of terms make me flinch in the same way 'rugger' does. 'Spotting', 'benching', 'power lifting'. It doesn't fit too well with the blokey drive towards not taking anything too seriously.

Also, gyms are like playing the one-armed bandit – you don't have to hang around one too long before someone starts giving you unsolicited advice. The most common one is that 'cardio isn't great for weight loss, dude, you should be pushing weights'. But I don't *like* pushing weights. I can just about tolerate a few bicep curls between the running and rowing machines. I do the cardio stuff because I like it and, afterwards, feel a bit better. I'd rather have to be winched out of my house for weight reasons than ever deadlift while keeping full eye contact with myself in the mirror. So you can be in terrific shape, but you might have to hand your bloke card back in. At least temporarily, like an MP declaring a conflict of interest.

The other issue with suddenly taking your image too seriously is that, if you're middle-aged and in a reasonably long marriage, the development of abs could – just like the flowers from the petrol station – be a cause for suspicion. Unless you've got a third audition for the *Avengers* reboot you might have to reassure your wife that you're not trying to impress some twenty-year-old in the office.

I've been between thirteen and thirteen and a half stone for about ten years now. I am overweight but, crucially (I tell myself), it's stable. Just like with my clothes, my wife knows what she's getting and throughout our relationship she's been in better shape than me. If I were to suddenly get ripped this may produce undue pressure on her to match me pound for pound. That's why I don't do weights – this kind of development at our time in life would be, frankly, ungentlemanly.

So when it comes to blokes getting abs, particularly middle-aged blokes, the advice is to go quietly into the night. Abs are a young man's game. Older blokes were lucky enough to be raised at a time when there was no such expectation for the vast majority of men. During an era when so much male privilege is being reassessed, that's a win you can take to the bank.

Instead of striving for something so hard, do personal work on how you see your belly. A slight paunch, rather than suggesting laziness or complacency, actually represents the acceptance of the passage of time. It's philosophically sound reasoning. Buddha had a little gut on him – and if it was good enough for Buddha it should be good enough for you.

WHAT GOES ON TOUR STRAYS ON TOUR

The average British man gets married at thirty-two.

Stag-dos are the gala dinner of being a bloke. Oddly, given their centrality to the male experience – and high billing on the rites of passage list – they tend to start happening relatively late in life.

Thankfully, things have moved on from the reckless former incarnation of stag-dos, which took place the night before the wedding. Some things which seem odd in retrospect might have made sense at the time (caning, smoking in cinemas, your doctor having a bottle of brandy under his desk) but I cannot fathom why getting monumentally hammered the night before your wedding was ever seen as a smart move. Perhaps, given that marriage was often spoken of in negative terms back then, with the implication that most marital unions were happening under duress, the pre-wedding drink-up may have felt akin to a condemned man being granted permission to drink himself to oblivion the night before facing the gallows.

The way men talk about marriage has changed a lot in a short space of time. I can still remember even into the early noughties crafty shouts of 'Don't do it!' in the church while waiting for the bride. Today's more emotionally in tune young men might shout 'don't do it' but only in relation to a poorly thought through shirt and tie combo.

There tends to be a glut of stag-dos around a bloke's early thirties. Most of the disposal income around this time gets gobbled up by raucous and expensive three-day jaunts. Men of this age know they should probably be saving up for a deposit on a house but instead find themselves throwing hundreds of pounds at easyJet and adult go-karts.

Like all aspects of the blokeosphere, your experience of stag-dos can vary wildly. Each stag-do has its own tone and I don't want to sound snobbish, but I'm glad I haven't yet been on one which involved the wearing of novelty T-shirts. You don't need a printed nickname to let strangers know who you are. If you are 'Shagmonster' or 'Gassy Gavin' all of that should become apparent soon enough. Though, in their defence, themed T-shirts might be a good way of keeping a large group visible and together, plus serve as reassurance for anxious partners back home that you look like such dickheads the only women who'll show an interest in you will be muggers.

Another interesting feature of a stag-do is you get to find out who your mate's other friends are. Luckily, with blokes, the jeopardy of crossing the friendship streams isn't quite as fraught as it can be for women, but it's still new territory. You can come to learn whether your friendship category is 'legacy' or 'aspirational'. It can be revealing too, as if you're a mate from way back, you see a different side of your pal around his new muckers and whether he's putting on airs and graces or this is just who he is now.

You can be surprised to find out that you're not even the most blokey group of friends he has. I have mates who most people would class as fairly route one, but on a stag-do a few years ago we felt like ladies-in-waiting compared to the other animals the stag had brought along. There will also be a level above the animals – the 'wrong 'un' mates. The group of legacy friends who aptly demonstrate why he moved to a different city.

British stag-dos seemed to reach a zenith just before the credit crunch. Jacked up on cheap borrowing, a strong pound and never-to-be-repeated budget flights, they went from a one-night trip to the local curry house, to Blackpool, then Prague, until finally you had mates pitching up in Vegas for a month. I don't have a verifiable number, but I'd imagine those epic overseas adventures resulted in a lot of postponed weddings, either by misadventure or the bloke deciding he wasn't ready for commitment and preferred to get a job working the door for Siegfried & Roy.

Whatever kind of stag you're on, a lot can be gleaned from that first stupid o'clock mustering at the airport. There are early acts of bravado which can set the tone.

I'll risk losing blokey points here but, despite my love of lager, I'm not into the early-morning pint with a fry-up. I'm all for drinking at unusual times, but I'm resolutely of the belief that the flavour of lager simply doesn't go that well with fried eggs and meat. There's going to be so much drinking you really don't need to douse a good breakfast with the taste of Carling. (You'd actually probably be better off with a sparkling wine – however, crazy talk like that could go down badly and you don't want to spend the next three days being called 'Patsy' in a hilarious reference to *Ab Fab*.)

There is a kind of man for whom the stag-do is the only time he fully comes alive. He's the same bloke who always turned up for Saturday-morning football still stinking of snakebite and boasting of the previous evening's sexual conquest. He'll arrive with his head bobbing back and forward like a hyperactive pigeon of manly fun, already talking loudly and calling anyone who doesn't want to do shots outside the airport Starbucks 'ladies'. You'd think this guy would be intolerable, but he serves a talismanic purpose in the early knockings and is often proved to be a massive lightweight when push comes to actual shove. The same guy who was downing pints at the airport Wetherspoons is usually missing the first dinner to nip back to the hotel to get his head straight.

Conversely, there will often be one guy on a stag-do who pretty much no one else knows. A friend of the groom's Mrs's sister's fella. This quiet mouse of the early capers will often be the session monster you have to bail out of the police station on Las Ramblas. A suburban Frank the Tank. Plus, he's lost his phone, so you have to go full Interpol while someone tries to work out how to contact and reassure his wife.

The activities on the stag often veer between those childish things you wouldn't be able to do in any other circumstance and a cartoon version of manliness you feel you have to adhere to. Where else could you take part in go-karting without children present and not get stared at like you're a weirdo?

On my stag-do, we booked a five-a-side pitch in Liverpool for the Saturday morning. It was one of the worst decisions I've ever made. Some of the lads hadn't got to bed until 6am but here we were running around with faces so red it looked like we'd been doing poppers.

Some activities can be more 'grown-up' and the kind of thing you'd only get to do in the context of a weekend away. Clay pigeon shooting has become popular in recent years. It's not my bag but it helps form the narrative of the trip. You'll have the guy you expected to do well but does badly, then the guy you thought would be crap but suddenly seems like he's ex-special forces.

Paintballing is also fairly popular. I've seen that game do weird things to men. It gives you a brief glimpse into what could happen if society crumbled and it turns out that some men are never happier than when safely ensconced in a foxhole trying to shoot their best mate in the balls.

If social media is anything to go by, British blokes do seem to be somewhere near the top of the league when it comes to going nuts on a stag-do. The Americans whoop a lot, but don't seem to last the pace when it comes to drinking. You'd think the concept of a stag-do might be a bit beneath the French, but if anything the language they use suggests they take it even more seriously. It's called *'l'enterrement de vie de garçon'*, which roughly translates as the 'burial of the life of the boy' (alright lads, let's keep it light, eh?). However, that idea does tally with the principles of the first-known examples of stag-dos, which occurred in Sparta, where military comrades would feast and toast one another the night before their wedding. The groom would say farewell to the freedom of his bachelor life but swear continued allegiance to his comrades.

I'm not sure whether, for an increasingly childish adult population, anyone does suddenly grow up in the manner the Spartan stag-dos imply. You only have to look at the increasing number of men who have a games room and the growing popularity of 'adult daytime raves'.

Perhaps the enduring appeal of the stag-do is that most blokes never really grow up, we just pretend to. The stag-do is a place where, just for a couple of days, a bloke can stop pretending.

WE SHOULD TRY TO GET AHEAD OF THE TRAFFIC

One bona fide indisputable benefit of being a bloke is the capacity to wrap up any social interaction promptly without having to explain yourself. Whether it's a phone call with another bloke, a text exchange or even a friend's wedding, you can – when it's obvious the main business has been concluded – simply say, 'OK, bye now.'

The fade has many names, which often allude to nationality. The Irish exit. The French exit. We could just as easily call it 'the Bloke's exit'. Or 'Bloxit', except, instead of holding a referendum, you leave a boring Christening without uttering a word.

This capacity to call time on interactions has often perplexed and infuriated the women around me. They just don't get it and I wonder if they're a little envious at how uncomplicated our social lives can be. Their equivalent – a sudden goodbye to a female friend or leaving a hen-do without hugging every single person – can be taken as rudeness and fire the starting gun on several months of conflict.

One of the most perilous spheres of female communication is the WhatsApp group for a hen-do. I've heard of all manner of thermonuclear eruptions in this context, as competing whims can be subject to the most forensic misreadings.

Stag-do planning tends to come from the opposite place, more like a benevolent dictatorship where it's widely accepted that one bloke is totally in charge. We all accept that being in control of such a thing is a massive ball-ache none of us really wanted so we will – to the best of our ability – simply consent to whatever plans are put in front of us (providing they're not illegal . . . in the country we're doing them, anyway). Any attempt to create fuss in the planning process will likely trigger a group roasting where you may be compared to notable divas from the world of showbiz. Even people being slightly late with their replies, or slow in transferring their monetary contribution to paintballing, can result in some fairly direct rebukes: 'You lazy pricks ANSWER THE FUCKING MESSAGES' or 'SORRY, HAVE I GOT TO REMORTGAGE JUST SO YOU TWATS CAN GO PAINTBALLING?'

I can't speak for all – or indeed any – female WhatsApp groups, but I do have a hunch that any message which started 'Where's my money you lazy bitches?' would spawn several breakout chats.

Anyway. When we go and visit friends, my wife's approach to calling time on the visit is completely different from mine.

I'll have often spent twenty minutes thinking, 'Well, this feels like it's done', but, having previous offences on my charge-sheet for prematurely thinking things are 'done', I hold off for as long as I can.

Eventually, my wife will give me 'the eyes', which indicates that, despite her greater sociability and social decency, she too thinks it's 'done' and departure is imminent (either that or she just can't be arsed with me moaning because we've hit the worst traffic on the westbound stretch of the M25). She'll exchange those coded signals which all parties recognise to be a sign that things are drawing to close, such as 'What are you guys up to tomorrow?' which can often mean 'When can we fuck off today?'

Then she'll sigh expansively and say, 'Annnnyway, we'd best be going.'

At this point, I make my first mistake by standing up far too quickly and saying, 'Yes!' Sensing I might have appeared too keen, I qualify that with, 'I mean, yes, in the sense of getting ahead of the traffic.'

I'll barely disguise my glee as I go on to talk warmly about the value of avoiding the traffic on the westbound stretch at this time. Then I stop talking. Then something odd happens.

Nothing happens.

Both the women remain seated. Perhaps embarrassed by the clunking unsubtlety of my desire to do one, my wife might start another conversational thread – 'Did you hear back about Danielle's situation with the school?'

At this point, I'm in trouble because I've already stood. I've played my hand. I can't sit down again because I'd be seen to endorse anything up to a further forty-five minutes of chat. However, I can't risk being even ruder than I've already been by tapping my watch and saying, 'Babe, I thought you said we were going?'

So, after a couple of minutes standing in the middle of someone else's lounge like human furniture, I say, 'I'll grab the coats!' I even throw in a toilet pit stop on the way just to give them even more time to wrap up the chat.

I get back into the lounge, with the coats under my arm like the maître d' at a fancy restaurant. But they're still seated. At this point, I drift into an odd twilight zone. I've gone all in and have no cards left to play so I stand there like a tool.

You start wondering whether they hatched some plan while you were getting the coats: 'Let's see how long we can make this idiot stand there, to teach him a lesson.'

Even as you're finally waving goodbye at the door, another conversation crops up.

You try to understand. They're more invested while in each other's company so perhaps it just takes longer to unravel that process. But you're anxious too as you sense that your standing holding coats, sighing like a bored eight-year-old, may not have gone unnoticed and could be a topic of 'discussion' on the way home.

But none of it matters. You take the punishment, she eventually sighs and you move towards the car door. Everyone now thinks you're a dick, and not without justification, but more importantly, you have beaten the worst of the traffic.

'He's just a man . . . be more man than him.'

Apollo Creed, *Rocky III*

HERO DAYDREAMS

Ten per cent of British men think they could beat a chimpanzee in a fight with their bare hands.

There's long been a stat doing the rounds which claims that men think about sex once every seven seconds. I've always been a bit doubtful about this. It doesn't allow nearly enough other time for all the other silly bollocks blokes routinely contemplate.

One mental preoccupation I've never seen much written about is our tendency for hero daydreams.

A recent poll by YouGov suggested that 34 per cent of British men felt they could land an aeroplane with no training, but with the qualifier that they'd have some support from air traffic control (the figure for women was half that).

I like the caveat about air traffic control, which seems to suggest: 'Hey, we're not saying we wouldn't need *any* support. It's not like we're *deluded*.'

For some reason, there's a part of the blokey psyche which needs to believe that when the shit hits the fan and the hero's call to action sounds we will undoubtedly rise to the moment (probably in slow motion, with really cool music playing in the background, barely flinching at a large explosion behind us).

Landing planes isn't the only high-pressure situation where many blokes back themselves. Just under 10 per cent of British blokes think they could win a fight with a chimpanzee. Get real, fellas. We've all been to the zoo. Having seen the upper-body strength of those lads as they swing effortlessly from tyre to tree, there's no doubt in my mind that – in the event of a man vs chimp conflict – my swaying dad bod wouldn't give the alpha male too many sleepless nights.

It's not just the contrast in general physical condition – animals fight differently. They don't run their actions through a rational prism, wondering if they'll get arrested or thinking, 'Will this inflame my carpal tunnel?' In the world of fight or flight, they don't leave anything on the table. Forget chimps, even a badger with nothing to lose could pose a formidable opponent.

Around 13 per cent of men think they could beat a large dog in a fight. I have some form in this matter. When my cockapoo, Lilly (you shuddup, it IS a manly breed), was about six months old I was out walking her when I spotted coming towards me a man who seemed like he might be a little bit drunk, which at midday on a Tuesday wasn't a promising sign. Another red flag was the fact that he had a Staffordshire bull terrier by his side and the dog wasn't on a lead (I know there are many people who love Staffies and will defend them to their dying day, but the breed has 'form' – all dogs can have a bad day at the office, but when Staffies do it's backed up by three stone of muscle and teeth). The man suddenly put his arm out to the side and the dog promptly sat down, so I thought, 'Fair play, it's clearly a well-trained dog', and felt guilty about my prior 'breedism'.

Then the fella walked off and the dog didn't follow. *It wasn't his dog.* The hand gesture and the dog sitting was mere coincidence.

The Staffie was now looking at my diminutive Lilly like she was either an enemy or lunch. Suddenly, it started attacking her; at one point, it had Lilly's whole head in its mouth. I tried to intervene and ended up on the ground wrestling with the two of them. I eventually got the dog's jaw free and Lilly ran across the road into a neighbour's garden. I was left holding the Staffie around the neck when it slowly turned to look at me, but luckily it didn't have the taste for man flesh that day.

It broke free and chased Lilly into the garden. I followed in hot but reluctant pursuit. I spent several minutes trying to get between the Staffie and my precious Lilly. (I've tried to block it out now, but I think I was screaming my dog's name in a very high-pitched voice. I've often wondered what this must've looked like to passing drivers. The grass in the garden was high and they may well have only seen a deranged-looking man hopping about shouting the word 'Lilly!' like a mad horticulturalist.)

I was eventually able to scoop up my poor terrified pooch and started walking away. The Staffie was hectoring me in that manic way feral bullies do once they've tasted blood. I eventually walked past a car wash and told the staff what was happening and left the beast to them (God knows what I expected them to do with it). I strode off with Lilly in my arms. Even though I'd been screeching (and possibly crying a bit), my mind's eye had rendered me as Bruce Willis in *Die Hard*.

I got Lilly home and thought she might be traumatised so should probably see a vet. The vet checked her out and reassured me that she was fine. I had a few cuts and bruises, but, moreover, was wide-eyed and still shaking.

The vet smartly realised who really needed attention.

'Are you OK, Mr Norcott?'

'I'm fine,' I replied too quickly, 'I'm just worried about Lilly.'

She nodded, then asked me to sit down and went to make

tea – with several sugars in (a part of the story I'd never share with my mum).

I still proudly sport a scar on my left wrist from this encounter (sadly for the purposes of my hero delusions, it wasn't from hand-to-paw combat with the dog, but from contact with the pavement I launched my thirteen-stone frame onto).

The truth was, Bruce Willis was nowhere to be seen.

Maybe it's all the superhero films we watch growing up, but the idea of saving everybody is intoxicating. I remember when I was in Afghanistan entertaining the troops (I don't like to bring it up) (I won a medal) (five tours) (three of which were on forward bases) I was on a Chinook which was circling high above Helmand province, as there had been reports of hostile activity below.

My mind went to a very strange place.

During the time we were circling, I engaged in one of the most ridiculous daydreams I've ever had. I imagined the Chinook got hit and we went down in enemy territory. Not only would I survive, I'd somehow seize the rear gunner position and provide covering fire for the RAF mechanics as they tried to get the aircraft going.

This is deluded enough in itself (I might not even have had the upper-body strength to remove the safety catch) but the worst of the narcissism centred on what would happen after we were rescued. I'd nobly refuse to take any public credit for my act of heroism. I actually played out myself shunning the Dictaphones of assembled reporters at RAF Brize Norton upon my return, choosing instead to run towards my family.

My daydream was punctured when real-world Geoff was still in that Chinook and had become so dizzy with all the circling that he needed to be violently sick in a soldier's helmet.

The truth is, blokes never grow up, so hero daydreams are a natural legacy of our flights of fancy as small boys.

I remember watching the first *Superman* film: the costume, that theme tune, the modest way he'd never take any credit, the fact that even the bad girls loved him too. I'd secretly pull my shirt open the way Superman did. There was also something intoxicating about the Clark Kent/Superman dichotomy. It planted in young boys' minds that no matter how plain or nerdy you might seem, there was a lot more going on beneath.

Sadly, that was where the cultural parallels ended.

One implication of American cinematic dominance is that the superheroes we worship all tend to roll their Rs. There are barely any British superheroes (with the honourable exception of Bananaman). The closest we come are guys like James Bond and Sherlock Holmes. Which makes sense, as if there was such a thing as a British superpower it would almost certainly be sardonic wit. Plus, I'm not sure the Americans have ever heard of 'Mondeo Man'.

Recently, I got to be the hero and protector I've always hoped I would, should the moment arise. Maybe not enough to earn the Victoria Cross, but good enough for me.

I'd taken my son to watch AFC Wimbledon playing Colchester away on 27 December 2022. We were sitting behind the goal and the players were warming up. They were pinging the ball pretty hard and several shots had already seen fans diving for cover. I thought about a couple of viral clips I'd seen of dads at baseball matches who, when the ball was coming towards them, had selfishly got out of the way and allowed the ball to smash into their partner or child. What an awful thing to exhibit – to demonstrate to the world that, when it mattered, you abdicated one of your primary male functions to protect. I wondered how the women in the bloke's family felt about him after this and whether or not he was still allowed the honour of carving the turkey at Christmas . . .

. . . as I was thinking all this, a ball came hurtling towards me and my son. I don't know if it was the reflections I'd just had about public shame, but I was ready to act. I snapped out my forearm in front of my son's head and managed to angle it so that the ball not only *didn't* hit my son but went up, taking the pace off it, and didn't slam into the face of the old bloke behind me.

There was a genuine gasp from around us, not for my reflexes I suspect, but for the idea of what such a pacey shot would've done to a child of his size. So I don't want any credit. No, just doing my job, ma'am.

* Seriously, though, if anyone could source video of that moment I'll pay £1,000 for the footage. Genuine offer, that's why I included the game and date. Contact the publisher.

BLOKEY FILM REVISIONS #4:
STAR WARS

*All of the main male characters from the original
Star Wars trilogy grew up without a father.*

Even as an eight-year-old, I was conscious that the final moments
of *Return of the Jedi* had a particular effect on me, but I wouldn't
understand why until I became a fully grown man.

As the film reaches its climax, Luke Skywalker – (spoiler alert)
son of Darth Vader – is in the throne room of the evil Emperor
Palpatine. Luke had believed he could save his father and turn
him to the light side of the force, overthrow the emperor and
bring peace to the galaxy (a tad optimistic given that the first
and only previous meeting with his dad was a few weeks before
and Vader chopped off his hand).

Alas, what happens is that his new dad turns Luke over to his
boss, then father and son have another big fight. After Luke
eventually prevails in the lightsaber duel, the emperor realises the
son cannot be turned to the dark side, so tries to finish him off by
firing lightning bolts at the young Jedi. Darth Vader, bruised and
battered, famously 'more machine now than man', eventually
decides he's had enough and lobs the emperor into a giant
recycling bin. (This may be a slight oversimplification of the plot.)

When I first saw the film, that particular scene made my whole
body come out in goosebumps. Not just the moment of Anakin
Skywalker's (Vader's original name) redemption but the swell of

John Williams's incredible score (before George Lucas butchered it by adding in Vader shouting 'Nooooo', like a punter who'd lost money on the favourite at Cheltenham).

There were good reasons why that moment was more resonant for me than my contemporaries. At that time, my relationship with my own father was pretty strained. Not only that, Dad also had a prosthetic limb (though his was from a motorcycle crash rather than a lightsaber duel on a burning pit of lava). Like many dads at the time, my old man was also a bit lost in his work and consequently sometimes sombre around the house. I'm guessing Darth Vader was very much the kind of dad who – if you had friends staying over – would also shout 'don't make me come in there'. However, my dad was way less likely to force-choke someone through a wall.

It took me years to work out why that scene held such power for me. It must have been very odd for my then counsellor when I was talking daddy issues and suddenly blurted out my latest personal revelation – '*I'm* Luke!'

Having written that famous *Return of the Jedi* scene into my own central narrative, I was recently forced to revisit it. With a son of my own and seeing in his eyes the variety of things he needs from me on a daily basis, I started to wonder whether Darth Vader had really earned that redemption after all.

Let's be clear, it takes him quite a long time before he jumps in and saves his son. Luke had already been fairly fried and would probably need ECGs for the rest of his life. And we're not talking about a dilemma between one relative and another – this is between work and your own blood (though admittedly trying to run a galactic empire could count as a passion project). Not only that, but we're just a few short moments down the road from

243

Vader finding out that Luke has a twin, Princess Leia. His dad's response to learning he has a daughter is to repeat 'Sisssster', like the kind of uncle you wouldn't let babysit. But no, at the very last minute, like an intergalactic version of Jim Carrey in *Liar Liar*, Darth realises he's been going about everything the wrong way and so gets his hero's redemption and is allowed to be one of the cool blue ghosts just before the end credits.

Forget robots and lasers, the theme of fathers and sons is the true engine room of the *Star Wars* saga. Maybe that's the reason why so many blokes of my generation became obsessed with it.

George Lucas's dad was around in his youth but got lost in the day-to-day grind of running a convenience store. They eventually became estranged. So it's probably no coincidence that the three biggest characters in *Star Wars* – Anakin (the artist subsequently known as Darth Vader) Luke and Han Solo – all have daddy issues, though they react to them in very different ways.

It's less prominent in the franchise's extensive mythology, but Han Solo grew up as an orphan, which might be the reason why he has one or two issues with authority. It could also explain why the closest attachment he forms in his life is to a giant rug who makes dog noises.

They're all looking for something to fill that dad-shaped hole. The reason the young Anakin turns to the dark side in the first place is because the evil Chancellor Palpatine is smart enough to realise he's on the look-out for a father figure. He tees up the daddy thing so smartly that I'm surprised the trilogy didn't include a scene where the emperor took him fishing.

Luke is lucky to have a strong father figure around in his uncle

Owen, so is less drawn towards unsavoury types. And when he does put his faith in an older man, its kind old Obi Wan Kenobi, who is more interested in saving planets than blowing them up. Having had decent male role models, when Luke does eventually find out that Darth Vader is his real father (in an epic Jeremy Kyle DNA test in space reveal) he's a bit gutted (I'd imagine it's up there with finding out that your nan's side of the family were Hitlers). And then his hand is lopped off by Vader's lightsaber. Not only is Luke owed years of pocket money, he's also down a few digits.

But by the time the third film starts, Luke has gone all zen about it and just wants to redeem his dear old dad. Maybe he's able to be so evolved due to the positive influence of men like his uncle and Obi Wan (until Obi Wan informs Luke he has to kill his own dad to save the galaxy and is revealed to generally be a bit of a Billy Bullshitter).

I guess, on a subconscious level, my teenage self considered itself very much in the Luke mould. Though I'd had issues with my dad, I could see he'd had a tougher life than me and was doing his best. I understood that losing an arm at such a young age must have been a massive bolt from the blue, in the same way Luke realised that being chopped in half by your best mate might rankle a bit. So I put his emotional distance down to him adding layers of defence after each of the big tragedies which had befallen him. I wanted to get behind my dad's armour to check who was inside.

As part of this mission to rescue him, a couple of years before his death, I resumed hugging him. We'd gone several decades without any kind of tactility beyond a firm handshake and a nod. I'd always presumed that was his preference. However, in another counselling session last year (with my counsellor beginning to wonder if I could discuss any of my feelings without relating them to either *Star Wars* or cricket) my mind released a memory to me, in the same way the CIA sometimes declassify files when they think the public are ready to hear the complicated truths.

I was fourteen and my dad was dropping me back to my mum's house after another one of our stereotypical divorced father-and-son get-togethers at a nearby Burger King. My sister and I had always given Dad a kiss when he dropped us off home, but that night I'd decided something was going to change. We'd had a nice enough time but I told him I wouldn't be kissing him any more, what with me being fourteen and now a big man and all that, so I offered him a handshake instead.

I was too young to understand everything that must have been going on in his mind at that moment. As a dad now, I can speculate on the parental lump in the throat he must have felt on crossing one of those small but devastating thresholds that children pass through. You know they need to evolve, but it can still be crushing as they casually close the door on whole eras.

My emotional spider senses must've logged the atmospherics of the moment, but my hard drive had saved it in the back-up files until I was ready to remember.

I'd always thought my dad stopped hugging me, but it turned out to be the other way around.

I'm not saying we can excuse Darth Vader blowing up whole planets, but sometimes blokes disappear behind their armour because we let them. And for some men, a silly bunch of films about battles in space will do more in unlocking their understanding of themselves than a whole lifetime of counselling.

ME: BINS. YOU: EVERYTHING ELSE FOREVER

The UK public spent £1.7 billion on
cards in 2017

Something odd and unspoken happens when a man marries a woman. Yes, there is love, yes, there are the vows you make in the company of friends, family and God, but there's another commitment that never gets said out loud but is usually observed: the woman will take on the responsibility of buying and, probably, sending birthday cards for the bloke's relatives, friends and, in some cases, business associates.

Don't shoot the messenger. I'm not saying this is something the woman formally agrees to or that it's even OK, just that's how it tends to work in most couples. Not just the married or straight ones, either. In any kind of loving partnership, there will be a 'card buyer'. In the heterosexual ones it's almost always the woman.

The phenomenon of birthday calendar responsibility isn't formalised and rarely gets spoken about, it just somehow transpires that, bit by bit, the man will casually outsource this job over time. She will end up at a point where her own iCalendar is dotted with all his important dates, which will look every bit as incongruous as the one for the Battle of the Boyne.

The difference doesn't run along class or cultural lines either. When I rang another comic to speak to her about this idea, she was in the process of writing a card for the sister of her liberal and middle-class husband. It's non-binary, to coin a modern phrase.

And yet it's something which isn't biologically specific to one sex or the other. The ability of women to send birthday cards can't be put on a list alongside breastfeeding.

But why does the birthday card responsibility fall in this manner? Can we claim that holding onto important dates is somehow genetically harder for blokes?

It's a hard line to push, especially when I can tell you the exact date Wimbledon FC beat Liverpool in the FA Cup final. And that I'm more likely to remember Ben Stokes's birthday than my best mate's. We clearly have the power to retain this kind of information but only when it suits us.

Facebook has helped in this respect. Where, once upon a time, birthdays would get missed and the first you'd know of it was when a family member was scowling at you during a christening, Facebook at least affords the chance that, at some point that day, you'll register that several hundred people are making a fuss of someone you love.

But why is it all such hard work for us? Do we simply not care? In fairness, there's a degree of equality to how blokes treat important dates in that we don't make much fuss about our own. The number of people I expect to remember mine is fairly small: my wife, my son, my sister – preferably before 4pm but any time before midnight will do. And that's about it. If my birthday was forgotten my first thought wouldn't be that people didn't care about me, rather that they were busy. Furthermore, as we age, people often excuse the scarcity of the presents bought for blokes by claiming he's 'difficult to buy for'. What that can really mean is that they refuse to buy a man in his mid-forties a virtual reality headset.

The other reason for blokes' crapness in and around cards and gift giving is that we're allowed to get away with it. So perhaps the way to get the message across is for women to perform a bit of tough love. Let him spend a couple of years forgetting the birthdays of everyone close to him, then when his fiftieth birthday is just him standing alone next to some sausage rolls, your point will be made. Perhaps that's a bit extreme but I suspect any change can only come from women saying enough is enough (which I accept is outsourcing change to women to correct the original outsourcing of social responsibilities to women, but that's the way it happened in my house, and I suspect the only way it can happen more broadly, as blokes are inherently lazy if given half a chance).

A few years ago, my wife – given the fact my family is very small and she still has plenty of living relatives to worry about – said that I needed to take over all birthday and social duties for the small number of Norcotts left. I resisted at first and resorted to weak and desperate arguments (at one point stooping so low as to plead that her handwriting simply looked better on birthday cards), but I'm glad she stood her ground.

One of the founding pillars of masculinity is the idea of taking responsibility for your own shit. There's something profoundly babyish about a bloke who wants to hand all that stuff over to his Mrs . . . for *life*.

I'll admit, it's been a long road, with one or two bumps along the way. And yes, some cards have needed to be couriered because I've remembered so late. It's also true that possibly as many as 60 per cent of cards are opened with the price tag still on. And I have made liberal use of online card sellers, like Moonpig.

(Moonpig, by the way, is a great option for blokes but you need to be careful when using the card designs as they often have default settings. I still owe my sister an apology for when I left a proforma entry on and she received a birthday card for the mysterious 'Stephanie'. Though I was afforded far more latitude than any of my female family members would've received for making the same mistake.)

It doesn't just stop at birthday cards either: women will also keep a general overview of what's going on in the lives of the people around them. They'll remember the names of any new babies (I'm OK with the first two but if any couple are selfish enough to have a third I often refer to it as 'third baby').

While I've made great strides in card sending, I've still got a long way to go in terms of being across the information side of things. In a typical moment familiar to many married couples, we'll often park up to visit family or friends and the last ten steps from the car to the front door will resemble a weird presidential briefing, with my wife as the clued-up advisor trying to make sure her very own version of Joe Biden doesn't put his foot in it. She'll have a lot of information to relay in a short space of time, much of which will be things not to say, but as they are often things I wasn't aware of in the first place, an argument will ensue regarding whether it was foolish to let me in on such 'state secrets'. I'm pretty sure no American president has ever been in possession of the actual state secrets – you can't trust one bloke with something that important. In the same way, I can't be trusted with gossip about someone being a 'weekend lesbian'.

The social stuff might be harder to crack, but for everything else, the good news for blokes is that technology has made life significantly easier. Not just in terms of purchasing cards online or repeat reminders on the iCalendar, but the actual process of buying presents. You can nip on a website like Amazon and type in some fairly easy searches. All you need to remember is the sex of the person you're buying for and their age (OK, the second one might be tricky for some blokes, but shoot ballpark and you won't go far wrong).

You can even type in 'presents for middle-aged women'. My big tip here is never to go for the suggestions on the first page. Women are smart so you could at least put in some effort. I'd recommend starting with at least page four. The last thing you'd want them to think is that you're a bit lazy.

HEROES OF BLOKEDOM #5: MY MATE MICK

The last of my blokey heroes is another person I've had the pleasure of knowing, but he's an everyday hero rather than one in the public eye.

I first met Mick in the mid-eighties when my mum divorced my dad but decided to leave him with the house and move us to a council estate in Wimbledon (an interesting strategy which must have confused her solicitor). Most people wouldn't associate Wimbledon with the idea of council estates, but it's not all strawberries and small houses which cost more than a condo in Beverley Hills – back then it had its dodgy areas too. (If this gritty milieu is of interest to you, I heartily recommend my memoir, *Where Did I Go Right?*, available in all good bookshops.)

On the estate, I suffered the incongruity of everyone I met elsewhere thinking where I lived was 'posh', despite having both a football club and a greyhound stadium on my doorstep. These are two nailed-on horsemen of the 'shit area' apocalypse; the third is that you're living above a nail salon or a bookies.

There were some boisterous kids on this estate, so I quickly palled up with a much calmer proposition: Michael Edmonds. Mick. His character beamed out and – even as a kid – I recognised him as possessing the qualities you find in what most people would consider to be an excellent bloke.

Mick liked music, football and fast food. He liked a laugh and didn't take himself too seriously, plus he enjoyed occasionally going out on the smash. We were always going to get along. The eldest of six, he was a caring older brother who pitched in with raising his siblings. They loved and depended on him at a deeper level than just that of a brother. In the same way, I came to rely on him as so much more than just a friend.

Mick was calm, helpful, patient and, like all proper blokes, could actually build and fix stuff. One day, I got hammered and locked myself out of the flat we were living in. In my drunken state, I thought I could barge through the back door and get away with only damaging the small metal lock, which would be easy enough to fix once I'd sobered up. In the event, I took the whole door off, half the frame and a good chunk of the wall and plaster. Mick came back from a long day at work (actual manual work), surveyed the damage and got straight down to the repairs. He never once bollocked me or even took the piss.

The very least I deserved was a new door-based nickname.

Sadly, it is often the case that nice guys don't get the breaks they deserve. Mick died shortly before his fortieth birthday, survived by two fantastic sons and a loving wife.

A nice bloke, a calm bloke, dependable, handy and loyal – if you were ever looking for the definitive good bloke, look no further than my mate Mick.

HOLIDAYS

I have, in my line of work, done a lot of travelling, meaning I've spent a fair bit of time in airports. Sitting alone, you do more people-watching than usual. One of my guilty pleasures is clocking just how many blokes seem to be getting told off by their partners in departure lounges. It's the most basic kind of schadenfreude: I know what it feels like to be that guy and I'm glad that today it's not me.

Couples flying without kids row too, but the stresses of having children around makes a showdown outside WH Smith far more likely. And, as you'd expect, those tiffs are more pronounced when taking early flights. You can see it's been a bastard of a morning for all involved and we can reasonably presume the woman has done more to make the holiday happen. Yes, the dad might have done what he thinks of as the 'project management' end of the planning: heroically worked out how many Avios they had in the household account when booking the break and – without a thought for his own personal safety – checked the travel insurance covered Turks and Caicos, but even on the actual day of the holiday, the woman is likely to have been the busier of the two – wrangling children and supplies while the bloke stares at the 'live departures board' on his phone like that's an actual job. When you see a grown man getting a dressing-down from his wife outside

Boots, it's likely to be the culmination of a week where he didn't help packing then spent the morning of departue wandering around like a tit in a trance, hoping that the complex endeavour of getting a dog to kennels and three small children to another country would somehow magically occur.

I can't help but find the spectacle a bit funny. There's the bloke, his pleading arms outstretched, a dumb look on his face, like a man who ignored warnings of a gale now realising that it's a hurricane.

I saw one of these dressing-downs recently at Heathrow Terminal 5. The woman tore an absolute strip off her bloke, proper Sir Alex Ferguson stuff. I thought she might even sub him at halftime. This would have been a very different moment if the guy had been verbally laying into his Mrs. If he'd have raised his voice that loud for long enough, someone might have intervened. But the bloke took it. Why?

Firstly, he was smart enough to know that the well-being of his family unit in transit will be enhanced if he takes his medicine and lets her get it out of her system. He could pull the nuclear option and say, 'Fuck this, don't speak to me like that, I'm going to the Wetherspoons for a pint.' But sadly, it's not the seventies any more.

Sorry, I mean, happily, it's not the seventies any more.

The fact that the woman probably did the majority of packing won't have helped. I don't know many blokes – even among my most feminist mates – who pack for their own holiday. Equality is one thing but their other halves aren't yet at the point where they'll trust him to know the right clothes for ten days in Cape Verde. However, what seems like incompetence can just come down to different priorities. Left to his own devices, a bloke will often think of the stress of getting shitloads of heavy luggage from the house to the airport and beyond. Consequently, he may decide that two pairs of shorts for an entire holiday will suffice, imagining that he'll rinse and dry them in the hotel room, like a Poundland Ant Middleton.

The other reason blokes may not be asked to do something as important as packing is that they were allowed to once and made an absolute hash of it – which brings into play the murky area of 'constructive incompetence'. Constructive incompetence isn't so much doing things deliberately badly, it's more allowing our natural lack of common sense to do the work for us. I genuinely wonder whether Kwasi Kwarteng wasn't doing this during his time as chancellor. To me – a bloke well-versed in constructive incompetence – that definitely looked like the actions of a man who never wanted to run the economy again.

As with so many aspects of blokery, our crapness in some areas means we need to make up for them in the areas in which we are still relied upon. The 'pre-holiday admin' should be the bloke's domain. Not just the aforementioned booking of hotels, but the relevant visas, ESTAs and inoculations. (I realise most of these are things you can do on your phone while sitting on the couch with terrible posture, but it's a start.)

The holiday admin workload went up exponentially for anyone who dared to fly during the pandemic. I almost cocked this up and my wife and I ended up having to test twice in twenty-four hours, which made us look either paranoid or incompetent.

Then there's picking a restaurant in a foreign country, a process which sometimes means you have to compromise between your desire to have exactly what you want and the pragmatic demands of feeding a small person. You may want the place with the good reviews, but sometimes the child is screaming for the kind of calories which haven't appeared on any TripAdvisor top tens. In a situation like this, never be the guy who says, as I once did: 'But babe, that place is only a 3.5. Do you know how many twos a place would need to average 3.5? If we just walk another mile there's a cracking 4.2.'

My big tip for holidays is to arrange a surprise airport transfer. These days, it can be as cheap as booking an Uber when you get there. Whatever uselessness you may have exhibited in the build-up to departure, you can pull it all back if, after a long and stressful flight, you come out of arrivals to a bloke holding up an iPad with your name on it. A lot may be forgiven. And if you've just remembered you left your child's beloved iPad on the plane, all that can wait until you get to the hotel bar.

THE DEATH OF DIY

*Eighty-nine per cent of over fifty-fives can change a
lightbulb compared to just sixty-three per cent of
eighteen- to twenty-four-year-olds.*

Historians often chart the big changes in society via high-profile
tectonic geopolitical shifts. The abdication of a monarch, wars,
a new prime minister (though the gloss has recently come off this
particular phenomenon). For ordinary people, however, while
those kinds of changes do register, the things which really stick
in the collective memory and actually change life at ground level
can be more everyday – like pound notes going out of circulation,
mandatory seat belts, and the rapid disappearance of cash as a
legitimate form of payment.

I experienced that kind of small but seismic moment recently
when a friend who works in the car industry told me that most
new standard model cars no longer come with a spare wheel. I
asked him why and he explained that there are a number of
reasons, like cost and space, but high among them is the reality
that people whose tyres do have a puncture are now very unlikely
to set about the task of resolving the issue themselves.

I asked him if by 'people' he meant 'blokes'. He repeated the
word 'people' defensively because he's one of those successful
modern boardroom types who has risen to great prominence by
not always acknowledging the part that statistical likelihood
plays in the real world.

I took this dismal DIY news badly. I understood the disappearance of spare wheels from the boots of cars as an assault on all blokery. Basically, the car industry had taken one look at us and gone: 'Nah. Not for you boys, eh? Why don't you go sit on the grass verge and wait for a real man to come and sort it out. Maybe journal how this whole experience made you feel.'

I was concerned, but I am also a part of the reason a decision like that had been made. Because, while luckily I've never experienced a flat tyre while driving, if I am honest with myself, can I genuinely say I'd have gone through the process of setting my hazard sign fifty yards down the hard shoulder and got to work by the side of a busy road? Would I have known how to use the . . . I was going to write about the tools I'd have used but I don't even know what they're called.

It's shameful, really. My old man wasn't the handiest bloke in the world but if he couldn't have done something as simple as change a tyre, he'd have handed back his man card immediately. And he only had one arm.

Even if I somehow managed to fit a spare wheel, there would be a cold, silent drive home as neither my wife nor son would have any faith that I'd executed the task safely.

So alas, I have to admit, if I'd experienced a flat tyre at any time in the twenty-six years I've been driving I would have been on the phone to the AA just like the rest of them (except I'd have adopted a Terry Jones-style lady's voice to hide my shame and get a quicker call-out).

So what has gone on in the last few decades? Is the phenomenon of blokes becoming crap at DIY an unequivocal stain on my generation? Is there a general change of tide when it comes to building or fixing things?

Someone performing car surgery by the side of a busy road might in fact seem like something of an anachronism in this increasingly risk-averse age. In a world in which people have spent a couple of years wearing masks on public transport, can we handle the shock of seeing a bloke in a business suit under a Renault Picasso by the A40? It might register like one of those blithe two fingers to health and safety from a bygone age, such as seeing a pregnant woman smoking. While she changes a tyre.

The dissipation of DIY skills isn't without context. The last decade has also seen a rise in the number of people using dedicated builders of flat-pack furniture. Yes, flat-pack assembly, the angry epitome of blokeiness, is routinely being outsourced to men who come to your house and assemble furniture for you.

Where does it stop? Do we get stronger men in to carve the Christmas turkey? Will we start hiring professional barbecuers? (As I write this, I'm picturing women, tired of cremated chicken and food poisoning, weighing up the pros and cons.)

Before I seem too fusty and conservative, there's a practical reason why men should lament how this generation of blokes has drifted away from DIY. One area in which we definitely have the edge on women is physical strength. And when women are living more independent lives and enjoying ever greater earning power, men simply have to deliver in the few fields where we still hold a natural advantage.

This isn't to say that there aren't strong women who can put their own furniture together – more that, in terms of the statistical average, we have a little bit more torque strength when it comes to screwing and tightening bolts. Blokes, we have to own this USP because if we don't the market will decide.

There's an actual website called 'Hire a Hubby'. Currently, they limit themselves to household maintenance, but how long before women start making requests on other occasions when a bloke could come in useful? Like renting a man to be the plus-one at a wedding. Or getting a day lease on a fella for that bit at airports between getting the luggage out of the car and checking in.

On the whole, marriage provides significantly more benefits for men in terms of general well-being. Having a bloke can arguably be socially convenient for a woman, but there being someone around to kill spiders won't help her to live longer.

This is the cold, hard transactional reality of the male–female marriage dynamic. So it's imperative that if a tyre needs to be changed or a radiator has to be bled, in this small handful of circumstances, blokes provide a reminder that our presence still makes life a bit easier.

Simply put, if a bloke doesn't make himself useful on occasion, then his very existence is under threat.

Don't worry, the DIY doesn't have to be the high-level stuff. You're unlikely to be asked to build something as complex as a cupboard. It could just be the odd nod in the general direction of that duty.

Recently, and without prompting, I noticed that the door handle barrel (I had to google the name for it) was starting to come a bit loose. And so . . . I fixed it! Did I use a breadknife instead of finding the correct screwdriver? Perhaps, but the point is that I dealt with it.

I was on a roll then and so pulled out the WD-40 to manfully address a squeaky upstairs door. What happened next was magical – my wife brought me sandwiches like I was a returning Viking conqueror. I've now gone from avoiding DIY to actively looking for things to fix.

LET IT ALL OUT

Crying only once every few months was reported by 27 per cent of men, while 47 per cent of women said they cry once a month.

The capacity and willingness to cry changes a lot over the course of a bloke's life. When we're little boys we cry easily as much as girls, arguably more. Boys' peculiar tendency towards solipsism means there's the feeling that – along with all the standard things children blub over, like grazed knees or having to wash any part of their body, ever – every lost board game or inability to immediately master some new and complex skill is just cause to turn on the waterworks.

Little boys cry a lot but there comes a point when those boys start becoming men and these feelings are managed downwards to avoid looking weak.

I can hear the liberals trilling, 'But crying isn't weak, it's actually a sign of strength!' It can be, but as a bloke, you've got to be realistic about the frequency with which it can happen.

Women have more liberty when it comes to crying in public. During my time working in offices, the occasional crying woman was a common staple of working life. It would often happen on a Wednesday afternoon, for some reason. The day would be drifting aimlessly towards 5pm when you'd suddenly hear sniffling in the corner. The other women in the office – blessed with an ability to animatedly mouth things wordlessly across a room – would try to get the attention of the hitherto heedless blokes sitting closest to poor old Janine.

'Ja-nine is cry-ing in the cor-ner,' they'd carefully mouth.

The blokes, not recognising the attendant quiet protocols, would shout back, 'WHAT'S WRONG WITH JANINE?'

Some of the most emotionally retentive fellas sitting nearest to the stricken Janine would start to look agitated, turning around, trying to call in female air-support. 'Could some of the women DO something about this please?' their pleading eyes would say. 'I've asked her if she's alright, she said she was fine. I don't see what more *I can do at this juncture.*'

Female colleagues would duly support their fallen sister in the form of a team of first responders on the scene, who'd spirit Janine away for some chat and understanding while the blokes would breathe a huge sigh of relief.

One woman would always mysteriously return for her bag. I never found out what that bag contained, but always presumed it was tampons or Valium.

I probably sit in the middle ground in terms of my blokey capacity for empathy. In the workplace, I'd generally rather people kept their emotions in check, but if they do have an issue I won't pretend nothing's happening. Not all blokes are like this.

In the mid-nineties, I was working in an office with one other lad. Our line manager was an Antipodean girl called Kirsty, a nice girl and very mild-mannered.

One Wednesday afternoon (of course), Kirsty came into our small office and straight away I could tell she was ticking. My fundamental selfishness made me consider glossing over it, but I eventually checked, 'Are you OK?'

This question can be a catalyst when you're not OK, the glint of human empathy can tip you over the edge, and sure enough, it all came flooding out. She'd had a brutal board meeting where they'd torn a strip off her and she needed to have a bit of a cry.

I sat down next to her to talk about what had happened and do the sensible thing of agreeing that yes, they were all arseholes and *of course* she was awesome and they didn't know how *lucky* they were to have her (even if I broadly concurred with some of their criticisms of Kirsty's frankly flaky management style).

My colleague, Grant, asked if she wanted a cup of tea. Kirsty thanked him but said no. He asked again a couple of minutes later and she said no again. He asked a third time and I realised the tea wasn't really for Kirsty, Grant just wanted to get out of there, so I said, 'Actually, I'll have one mate . . . and can you get it from the café . . . by the Prince of Wales?'

For his own good, I sent him as far as I reasonably could to get that tea. He may still be waiting around the corner to see if the coast is clear.

Male emotions in public have a premium based on their scarcity, which is why when a male sports star cries after a major sporting event it can hold a lot of power. We understand that he's worked so hard for this moment that, with the task at hand successfully concluded, he has finally allowed the dam to break. Those tears aren't rolling down his cheek, they're *escaping* against his better judgement. This is allowable male crying – he's earned it.

That might sound harsh but imagine Rafa Nadal being interviewed after getting through the second round of

Wimbledon against a lowly ranked wildcard and suddenly bursting into tears. You'd be thinking, 'OK, bit weird, Rafa, but maybe you've had a tricky day.' If he proceeded to do that after every round, and sometimes during training, you'd start questioning whether Rafa needed some time away from hitting balls.

If you're a blokey bloke, go ahead and have the odd cry, but be aware that it's an act that – if you don't do it very often – you're not going to look especially comfortable doing. Just like our old coot near the beginning of the book cack-handedly applying suntan lotion to the awkward bit of his lower back, men who rarely cry finally having a blub can look, well, *ugly*. Because they don't do it often, when the tears do finally come it's a whole body experience. Rather than bleeding the radiators, they've opened the door on a walk-in bath filled to the brim.

When my wife has a little cry she can – somewhat incredibly – still multitask. She'll also be talking, wiping away tears and, on some occasions, continuing to fold clothes. When I was going through a sad period, however, my crying was visceral and primitive, like I wasn't just having a little blub but was engaged in the painful process of becoming the Hulk. My body contorted and convulsed; I looked to be in physical pain. It must have been an awful sight, so fair play to her for continuing to listen and not turning the hose on me.

Since my mum passed, I've become a late convert to crying. What the repressed me hadn't realised was that it isn't just for when you feel sad, it can be for other emotions too, like anxiety or frustration. So I love a good cry now. It's cathartic. Lads, we cannot let women walk around holding this strategic advantage.

The feeling after a good cry is incredible. I feel calmer, happier – the world even looks more colourful.

In fact, I've got so attached to that refreshing feeling that if I'm off out on a big day or setting off for an important work event, I'll often ask myself if I could crank out a quick cry beforehand – a bit like the emotional equivalent of a tactical chunder during a day on the piss.

So when we talk about blokes crying, let's not descend into platitudes and pretend that it's exactly the same rules as for women. I'm a firm believer in the restorative power of a good cry, but also think it's OK if the majority of that is done in private. You can have too much of a good thing.

My big fear for blokery throughout this book has been that, in trying to adapt and fit in with a fast-changing modern world, we lose some of the useful stuff. And the complicated truth about blokes crying in public is that it's good to do it sometimes, but take a hint from the tennis players and save it for the big games rather than the qualifying rounds.

'I've always said that if my son thinks of me as one of his idiot friends, I'll have succeeded as a dad.'

Phil Dunphy,
Modern Family

EPILOGUE

When I was writing the last chapter of this book, it occurred to me that, despite my own qualified support for blokes' right to have a good cry, my son might have reached the age of six and a half without having seen me shed a single tear.

So I asked him. 'Son, have you ever seen me cry?'

He looked up from his Lego. 'No. No, I don't think I have.' (This might seem wordy, but his sentences are often structured like those of the nice guy in a Jane Austen novel.)

'I do sometimes,' I said, 'I do cry . . . you know that, right?'

He nodded and seemed to be in an open mood, so I pushed the subject a little further. 'What do you think you'd do if you did see me cry?'

Very quickly he said, 'I'd tell you to get out!' and pointed to the door.

He must've registered the shock on my face because he immediately came over and sought to reassure me that it was just a joke.

Not only that, the phrase 'get out!' is one I often use when pretending to be angry with him for a comically minor transgression. He was just echoing it back to me for a laugh.

Like all novice pranksters, he was a bit alarmed that his joke had worked too well, and reassured me, 'Daddy, if you were really crying I would just ask you what was wrong.'

Beautiful, right?

A good kid, but also one who now clearly understood the principles of banter.

And not only that, but when to stop.

I don't know what the future is for blokes generally, but if they're anything like my brilliant son, that future will be in very safe hands.

SOURCES

Display quotations
Homer J Simpson, from the TV show *The Simpsons*, Season 5, Episode 18, 'Burns' Heir' (1994)
Forrest Gump, from the film *Forrest Gump* (The Tisch Company/ Paramount Pictures, dir. Robert Zemeckis, 1994)
Mrs Doubtfire, from the film *Mrs. Doubtfire* (20th Century Fox/ Blue Wolf Productions, dir. Chris Columbus, 1993)
Daddy Pig, from the TV show *Peppa Pig*, Season 4, Episode 3, 'Basketball' (2011)
Don Corleone, from the film *The Godfather* (Paramount Pictures/ Alfran Productions, dir. Francis Ford Coppola, 1972)
Apollo Creed, from the film *Rocky III* (United Artists/ Chartoff-Winkler Productions, dir. Sylvester Stallone, 1982)
Phil Dunphy, from the TV show *Modern Family*, Season 3, Episode 4, 'Door to Door' (2011)

Chapter openers
British men do approximately half the amount of housework of their female counterparts. 'It's official! Study shows women do 70 minutes more housework each day than men', by Victoria Allen, *MailOnline*, 10 March 2022. https://www.dailymail.co.uk/news/article-10596575/British-women-doing-70-minutes-household-chores-day-men.html
On holiday, 82 per cent of women wear sun cream, versus only 65 per cent of men . . . who are probably acting under strict instruction. 'Sunscreen/sun tan lotion usage in Great Britain 2017, by gender', published by Dominique Petruzzi, 2 February 2022. https://www.statista.com/statistics/750001/sun-tan-lotion-usage-by-gender-in-great-britain-uk/
More than half of British men gamble. 'New research shows almost

half of people in Britain gamble', Gambling Commission, 28 February 2017. https://www.gamblingcommission.gov.uk/news/article/new-research-shows-almost-half-of-people-in-britain-gamble

Supporting the football team your dad followed is the top reason people pick a side. 'Reasons why football fans choose who to support – from team's kit to family', by Sarah Lumley, Mirror.co.uk, 12 May 2022. https://www.mirror.co.uk/sport/football/reasons-football-fans-choose-who-26942614

The average age at which British men lose their virginity is 18.3 years old. 'At what age did Britons lose their virginity?', by Peter Raven, 1 March 2023. https://yougov.co.uk/topics/society/articles-reports/2023/03/01/what-age-did-britons-lose-their-virginity#:~:text=Men%20are%20slightly%20more%20likely,compared%20to%2017%20for%20women

Five foot nine is the average height for a UK male. 'Average Height by Country 2023', World Population Review. https://worldpopulationreview.com/country-rankings/average-height-by-country

What do you think you'd have been if you weren't a footballer? legendary Peter Crouch interview that has been acknowledged by him in numerous subsequent interviews.

Women make 50 per cent more visits to the doctors per year than men. 'Are men less likely to visit their GP than women?', by Dr Jen Tan, A. Vogel, 17 October 2018. https://www.avogel.co.uk/health/mens-health/are-men-less-likely-to-visit-their-gp-than-women/#:~:text=On%20average%2C%20men%20visit%20their,suffering%20from%20a%20serious%20problem

Man flu definition. 'Man Flu', Wikipedia, accessed 20 June 2023. https://en.wikipedia.org/wiki/Man_flu

The average age at which British men become a father is 33.7. 'Birth characteristics in England and Wales: 2021', Office for National Statistics, 19 January 2023. https://www.ons.gov.uk/peoplepopulationandcommunity/birthsdeathsandmarriages/livebirths/bulletins/birthcharacteristicsinenglandandwales/2021

Eight per cent of UK men only cook from scratch once a month. 'How often do you cook from scratch?', published by Nils-Gerrit Wunsch, Statistica.com, 30 November 2021. https://www.statista.com/statistics/1140395/frequency-of-cooking-from-scratch-by-gender-uk/

Forty-one per cent of British men say they have friends they 'like but don't bother to see' 'YouGov Big Friendship Survey', YouGov.co.uk, 16 December 2021. https://docs.cdn.yougov.com/byav0wzw4d/You-

Gov%20-%20The%20Big%20Friendship%20Survey.pdf
Women file for 62 per cent of all divorces in England and Wales.
'Divorces in England and Wales: 2021', Office for National Statistics,
2 November 2022. https://www.ons.gov.uk/peoplepopulationand-
community/birthsdeathsandmarriages/divorce/bulletins/divorcesinen
glandandwales/2021#:~:text=Among%20opposite%2Dsex%20cou-
ples%20in,and%2037.4%25%20with%20males%20petitioning
The average erect penis in the UK is 5.17 inches. 'The average penis
size for a male isn't as big as you think', by Annie Hayes, *Men's
Health*, 5 December 2022. https://www.menshealth.com/uk/sex/
a25932392/average-penis-size-uk/
*Women can have visible abs with 14 to 20 per cent body fat, while
men's needs to be as low as 6 to 13 per cent.* 'How long does it take
to get abs? And how to speed up the process', by Emmie Satrazemis,
Trifecta, 26 June 2021. https://www.trifectanutrition.com/blog/how-
long-does-it-take-to-get-abs
The average British man gets married at thirty-two. 'All you need
is love (and a marriage certificate): Marriage since 1900', *Olympic
Britain: Social and economic change since the 1908 and 1948
London Games*, 10 July 2012. https://www.parliament.uk/cont
entassets/004e41737ee74530af256372e5e6840b/olympicbritain.
pdf#page=37
*Ten per cent of British men think they could beat a chimpanzee in a
fight with their bare hands.* 'Which animals could Britons beat in a
fight?', by Matthew Smith, yougov.co.uk, 21 May 2021. https://you-
gov.co.uk/topics/society/articles-reports/2021/05/21/which-animals-
could-britons-beat-fight
*All of the main male characters from the original Star Wars trilogy
grew up without a father.*
The UK public spent £1.7 billion on cards in 2017. Greeting Card
Association's 2018 market report. www.gca.cards
*Eighty-nine per cent of over fifty-fives can change a lightbulb
compared to just 63 per cent of eighteen to twenty-four-year-olds.*
'The decline of the UK's DIY skills', *Insight DIY*, 3 October 2018.
https://www.insightdiy.co.uk/news/the-decline-of-the-uks-diy-
skills/6533.htm
*Crying only once every few months was reported by 27 per cent of
men, while 47 per cent of women said they cry once a month.* 'Cry
like a man: How women really want their men to show emotion', by
Dani-Elle Dubé, Global News, 22 February 2018. https://globalnews.
ca/news/4039294/cry-like-a-man-how-women-really-want-their-men-
to-show-emotion/

ABOUT THE AUTHOR

Writer and comedian Geoff Norcott is well known for his TV work on *Question Time, Live At The Apollo, Backstage With Katherine Ryan, Late Night Mash, Mock The Week* and *Have I Got News For You*. He has also fronted his own documentary, *How The Middle Class Ruined Britain*, for BBC2.

A regular on Radio 4, he's known for his comedy specials and won the 2019 BBC Radio & Music Award. Geoff often appears on Times Radio and is also the host of the popular podcast *What Most People Think*.

His first book *Where Did I Go Right? How The Left Lost Me* was published in May 2021 by Monoray.

The ULEZ Files

In the War on Motorists
Every Mile Could be a Lie

B. C. Guy

Copright @ 2023 by B. C. Guy

This book is a work of fiction. Names, characters, businesses, places, events, locales, and incidents are either the products of the author's imagination or used in a fictitious manner. Any resemblance to actual persons, living or dead, or actual events is purely coincidental.

For information about permission to reproduce selections from this book, write to the author at BrownCarGuy.com.

First Edition, 2023
London, United Kingdom

Published by BrownCarGuy

ISBN 9798871964200

Cover layout & typesetting
by Zahid Bashir

The moral rights of the author have been asserted.

Dedication

To all those affected by the London ULEZ expansion in 2023,

To the countless individuals whose daily lives were altered, to the businesses that struggled to adapt, and to the communities that felt the weight of its imposition,

To the tireless campaigners, protesters, advocates, politicians, political activists and ordinary citizens who stood up to highlight its injustice and illegitimacy, who raised their voices in defence of civil liberties and our freedom to own cars, as well as our right to freedom of movement,

To all of the car community including the enthusiasts, the owners, the collectors, the restorers, the racers, the builders, the designers, the customizers, the tinkerers, and those with an unwavering passion for all things automotive

This novel is dedicated to you all - your resilience, your courage, and your unwavering spirit.

May your efforts continue to inspire and bring about the change that truly benefits us all.

Let us drive into a better future together.

- B. C. Guy

CHAPTER 1

The rain-slicked streets of Central London gleamed under the glow of the streetlights, casting ephemeral reflections of hurried pedestrians trying to stay dry, but failing. Silent taxis splashed past. Max Turner stood alone, leaning against one of the huge plinths sat on top of which was one of Landseers' enormous bronze lions guarding Nelson's Column at Trafalgar Square.

His trademark brown leather jacket, its patina deepened by the soaking, hung open revealing a grey T-shirt above classic blue jeans. His grim face was a mosaic of a chequered past, the hard lines softened by the healing passage of time. His deep-set eyes peered into the night, searching for elusive answers to silent questions, while a lean unburdened posture suggested a man finally hoping to be at ease with himself.

The motoring journalist and content creator was on the cusp of his forties, still sporting a full head of dark hair, just about, his features more engaging than conventionally handsome.

The easy grin that had once been a staple of his 'Influencer' persona was now reserved, a reflection of a more introspective self.

His jaw, set with a blend of determination and vulnerability, spoke of a man who had faced his demons. His fading worry lines hinted at recent chapters of therapy and healing, of traumas acknowledged and the quiet hope that stirred in contemplating new horizons. He embraced the rain's cathartic properties, let it soak him through, hoping to be refreshed and renewed.

Yet, beneath this hopeful veneer, he braced for a final reckoning with the remnants of a not-so-distant, turbulent past; there was yet a painful echo of failed endeavours to still face.

His gaze returned to the illuminated screen of his smartphone. He pulled down on the display to refresh it again for the hundredth or so time, awaiting what he knew would be an inevitable headline. The story hadn't yet broken.

It was all a stark reminder of the public battles he had engaged in, the personal conflicts he had wrestled with, the freedom and rights he had championed, and the unexpected cost it had all had on him.

Why was he back here? Because ULEZ. The so-called Ultra Low Emission Zone. Trafalgar Square was the site where so many Anti-ULEZ Expansion protests had taken place. Protests that some had callously dismissed as fruitless and pointless wasted efforts. He disagreed. He'd been to most of them. The passion and emotion he'd witnessed, the painful stories he had heard, had had an impact. On him. On his audience. On the world at large.

Four years ago, ULEZ had expanded from Central and Inner London to the whole of the English capital city under the orders of the then Mayor of London, Khalid Siddique. From being neatly bound in by the North and South Circular Roads, it expanded to a jagged, ill-defined border, in some places reaching out as far as the M25, London's orbital motorway. Nearly six million additional people now found their cars were subject to strict emissions regulations as ULEZ expanded from 225 square miles to over 600 square miles, making London the biggest low emission zone on the planet.

A precedent? A moment of national pride? A chance to lead the world in striving for cleaner, healthier air for urban living? Maybe. That is if people had been given time to adapt, to find the funds to trade up to newer cleaner cars, to adjust to altered lifestyles, and to see an improved public transport network in outer London, where frankly it remained abysmal. But none of this had happened, and people had been left flailing close to financial disaster as their daily drivers transformed from essential everyday runabouts to redundant relics of past roving freedoms.

ULEZ had been enforced on a populace still reeling from a cost-of-living crisis, brought on by the economic upheaval inflicted on the UK by the twin hammer-blows of Brexit, and the unilateral pausing of the economy thanks to the COVID-19 Coronavirus pandemic.

The motor industry had been particularly hard hit, with production having slowed by factory shutdowns. When pent-up demand eventually exploded post-pandemic, the industry found it physically didn't have the bits it needed to build new cars fast enough. The resultant impact on new and used car prices and supplies meant that, even if well-meaning citizens wanted to change to new or newer cars, they literally could not.

Max closed his eyes and was instantly enveloped in the visceral tapestry of memories from the Summer of 2023. He could almost feel the warmth of the sun that bathed the tumultuous sea of protesters, their anxious faces etched with frustration and new-found zeal for dissent.

Vivid banners and handmade placards bobbed like boats on a choppy ocean, each emblazoned with vibrant hues and bold lettering, slogans calling out 'Stop ULEZ' in a show of unified defiance. A solidarity further manifested by a rhythmic chorus of chants, the collective voices of the crowd astonishingly drowning out the usual clamour of London's rush hour.

Traffic slowed, drivers honking not in the frustration that typically filled the city's arteries but in a symphony of support, a raucous salute to the cause. The protesters, a mosaic of society, ranged from suited office workers to seasoned activists, with weary workmen standing shoulder to shoulder with impassioned professors.

Many, he remembered, had confessed it was their first ever act of protest — ordinary individuals driven to extraordinary action. They were united not just by a common enemy in the form of the ULEZ expansion, but by the shared realisation of their power to demand change, a collective awakening that had sparked demonstrations in the capital's historic streets.

People were worried. They were anxious. Some said they were feeling suicidal. "No, please," Max would implore, "don't think like that, it's not worth it. We'll fight this, we'll win."

Empty promises? Spurious strength? Turned out he was the weakest of all. "Self-flagellating again?" he admonished himself. He quickly shook off such thoughts and opened his eyes. The rain had eased but the drizzle persisted. Wiping his phone on his jeans, he pulled down on the display again.

The dreaded notification finally flashed up across the screen. He'd been tipped off by a contact at a major broadcaster that it would be announced this evening. Everything had been leading to this anyway, despite the politicians' denials. Nonetheless, the words cut through the soggy night air like a hot laser, rekindling a fire of frustration that had never truly died out: "London Announces Pay-Per-Mile Road Charging in Shake-Up for the City's Streets."

It was the beginning of August, still relatively warm, but a chill fizzed through his drenched body. His fingers tightened around the iPhone; he would've involuntarily crushed it if he could've found the strength. He couldn't help but feel a sense of bitter irony, standing just below the landmark lion statues that symbolised the city's resilience. "Resilience against what?" he wondered.

Through the slowing patter of the drizzle, he thought he heard a sigh, from above him. Was it from the lion? Was its once proud roar, now just a wretched whimper?

For sure the crowds would be back here again, protesting against this latest imposition of restrictions on freedom, under the new guise of Road User Charging. The protesters would roar, even if the lions no longer did.

"I'm with you though, mate," he almost glanced up at the frozen beast, but the rain had picked up again. He would not be joining any more protests. He would not be covering this draconian oppression of the motorist, and of civil liberties. He would not be standing up for the right and freedom to travel when and where citizens chose; and how they chose. He would not, because he was done. He had to be.

He had poured so much time, effort, energy and expense into investigating the spurious claims made to justify the ULEZ expansion; covering protests; interviewing so many; creating credible content that indisputably rebutted pro-ULEZ contentions. And yet, despite it all, he had had to witness all those efforts come to nought as the expansion went ahead, as planned, on 29th August 2023.

The personal and mental toll had been great. Nearly three years of therapy had finally gone some way to healing the wounds Max had carried from the ULEZ ordeal. The depression that had engulfed him had ebbed away, replaced by a cautious optimism. Especially with the promise of a new future.

He reached into his inside jacket pocket and pulled out an envelope, not minding the raindrops hitting it, because he knew exactly what was in it. He'd read it dozens of times. Pulling out the letter from within, Max glanced down at it again. An offer letter, he hadn't had one of those in years. It was nice that some people still sent out physical letters in addition to emails. Classy touch that.

Yes, an actual offer letter. An offer. An offer to a

fresh start. An offer to a new life in new place. An offer to get back to doing what Max loved doing the most, creating car content. An offer to head up a new automotive outlet in Dubai, United Arab Emirates. More crucially then, an offer to move to a place that was still very much in love with the car. And did not just outright hate the automobile and motorists, particularly enthusiastic motorists. As London evidently now did. And potentially, sadly, not just London either.

Stamped on the missive in his hand was his beacon of hope, a chance to leave behind the turmoil that had so pummelled his mental health. So why was he here? At Trafalgar Square? The same square where he had once stood defiantly against the tide of ULEZ restrictions.

Admiral Lord Nelson towered above, anchored by his column to this iconic place. But unlike Nelson, Max felt adrift in a city that was veering off course, its priorities askew, its values compromised. "Trafalgar" is derived from the Arabic "Taraf Al-Ghar" or Cape of the Cave. He imagined standing on that cape; finally, having stepped out of the cave and eagerly staring out to sea. To new horizons. To new adventures.

Perhaps he'd come here for closure. But it was time to move on. As Max strengthened his resolve to let go, the rain intensified, as if the very sky shared his inner frustrations and conflicts. The raindrops ran down his face echoing the tears shed when the Mayor's triumph mocked the multitude that railed against the restrictions.

The people would be back, but he'd be gone. With any luck, before Road Charging arrived, Max would be sitting behind the wheel of a V8 muscle car, off the leash and ready to ravage a desert road, revelling in unfettered and rampant combustion power. Max could almost hear the hot engine roar and smell its tyres smoking.

Just as he peeled his soaking back off the plinth, his phone lit up again. An anonymous WhatsApp Message: "Stop Max Turner! Stay where you are and accept the following Air Drop."

What the...?! Before he could even fully react, the AirDrop message appeared – the "Accept" button awaiting his thumb. His thumb, however, hovered over the 'Decline' button, the instinctually correct thing to do with any unsolicited messages.

But he was hesitating. The message addressed him by name. It appeared to know where he was, and that he was about to leave. The sender had to be close by to use AirDrop. Max looked around but couldn't see anyone who might be responsible. Another WhatsApp message appeared: "Hurry up! I haven't got much time, he's nearly here, and you need to see this!"

Journalistic curiosity kicked in at that point.

Hitting "Accept" saw a flood of files download onto the phone: letters to and from the Mayor's office, funding authorisations to academic institutes, confidentiality agreements related to the ULEZ Expansion from three years ago.

Part of Max frankly wanted to resist looking at them, the sensible part of his brain wanted to type and send "Not interested" to the anonymous sender. And yet he found himself lingering on the files, wondering if there really was something there, something he hadn't seen before, or something he didn't already know.

Suddenly there was a whipping sound and a sharp crack above his head. He swung around and looked up just in time to see a figure tumble down directly towards him from the lion's plinth. It must have been the person sending the files. This is how they were close enough to make AirDrop work. But why where they falling?

Max feebly outstretched his arms to no avail. The faller slammed into him, but much to Max's relief, whoever it was, was either very light, or very good at landing, or both. It somehow didn't feel like he was the victim of a plunging body, but instead being shoved quickly yet gently to the ground; was that a hand cradling his head? The faller deftly bounced off and rolled to the side. It was a woman.

Max parked this realisation for a micro-second while doing a short mental self-diagnostic to see if any injury had occurred. Not a bump, bruise or scratch could he register. It was time to turn his attention to his would-be assailant, "Are you okay?" he asked.

She didn't answer, but she clearly was ok. The woman was crouching low, staring off into the distance. Dressed all in black, wearing trainers, combat trousers, a dark jacket with an oversized hoodie that cloaked her face in semi-shadow. Despite his bewilderment, he noticed her large almond-shaped eyes, deep brown, almost black, hinting at depths of resilience and intensity. Her smooth skin had a golden hue, indicating South Asian heritage. Sharp cheekbones framed a slender nose and her lips settled in a subtle pout, as if perpetually poised between ebullient determination and intimate sorrow.

Suddenly there was that subdued snapping noise again and something appeared to ricochet off the plinth behind her. She barely flinched. But a truly horrifying thought occurred to Max: were they being shot at?!

His stomach churned, his head spun, and Trafalgar Square felt like it was floating in space, tilting on an axis and veering around. His heart was pounding hard, drumming a wild rhythm of fear and adrenaline in his chest. His palms turned clammy, while his body seemed to lose cohesion and go limp.

Real actual gun shots. Being fired at him!

In the middle of London? How could such a thing even be happening? His thoughts scattered with confusion; a blackout beckoned. His face suddenly snapped to the right. Did he just get shot? Or… "Did you, did you just slap me?!" he asked the woman. She ignored his question and instead implored: "Run Max. Run now!"

Max was regaining some function of his jellied limbs, but he was still not quite sure if he got back up by himself, or the woman, relatively petite and seemingly slight of frame, had actually hauled him off the ground and shoved him towards the direction of the street.

Now Max found himself in the path of a taxi that blared its horn, braked hard and pitched sideways on the slippery tarmac. Frozen in fear, Max squeezed his eyes shut and braced himself for impact, expecting the black cab to sideswipe him, but he peeked an eye open to find his face mere millimetres from the halted vehicle. The angry cabby was shouting at him. "Oi! What the fuck are you playing at?!"

Before he could respond, there was another gunshot. Max had no idea where the shots were coming from. He looked frantically around, then back at the plinth where the woman was taking cover. She looked back at him and shouted: "Go! Get in. Go! I'll call you!"

Max, now too numb with shock to protest or question what was going on, reached for the taxi's doorhandle, but the cabby had noticed the gunshot too: "You're having a laugh ain't cha?!"

And with that he sped off, leaving Max standing there exposed to whoever was shooting at them. Still stricken with stupidity, for a couple of heartbeats he stayed planted to the spot and looked across for the woman, but she'd vanished. His legs finally regained gumption and he started running. When he eventually stopped, he realised he had ended up in Piccadilly Circus where the presence of tourists making the most of the damp evening, gave some reassurance.

Even so, Max looked over his shoulder and darted glances at the random strangers milling about. Not having seen his would-be assailant, it was prudent to be suspicious of everyone. With no more gunshots evident, he started to recompose himself when his phone started buzzing. He pulled it out of his pocket and saw it was flashing 'Anonymous'. It had to be the mysterious woman calling.

He hesitated again. It was a bad enough idea to have accepted those files; files that dredged up a past that frankly, Max wasn't sure he wanted to revisit, not now that a new chapter beckoned. But it could also be dangerous to his mental health to reopen old wounds, why pour years of therapy and counselling down a drain, why return to a path that took him to hell and back? And barely back.

Why go back to a place he didn't want to, and where some crazed woman and a brazen sniper awaited him? Who fires a gun in Trafalgar Square anyway? In London. Just down the road from 10 Downing Street and the seat of government itself! How crazy does someone have to be to try to shoot a nobody journalist in a place like that?

Come to think of it, why wasn't this entire area already swarming with sirens and armed response units? Of all the thoughts reverberating in his brain, "nobody journalist" stood out.

Maybe it wasn't him being shot at, after all, but the woman. No wonder the shots seemed to cease when she disappeared. She had been the target, not Max! And now that crazy lady was calling. He didn't need to get involved in anymore ULEZ crap, or indeed the pay-per-mile crap. And Max most definitely didn't need to connect with someone being pursued by a crazed and desperate assassin and get involved in getting-shot-at crap!

There was no need to risk ending up collateral damage, especially not when he had a date with Destination Dubai to look forward to. The phone was buzzing again. Max held down the button on the side until it buzzed no more. He stuffed the lifeless device back into his pocket and headed home.

A couple of hours later, he was sat in front of the

TV, catching up on car videos on YouTube, and devouring a massive pizza. He'd actually been eating a lot leaner and lighter of late, especially since the therapy. But tonight, he needed some comfort food, so he'd picked up this extra-cheese meat feast special on the way home. Whenever he would pause from stuffing it in his face, he noticed his hands still shaking. He put down the pizza and repeated his self-affirmations:

"Positivity is a Choice; I am Prepared to Succeed; I am not Defined my by Past, I am Driven by my Future!"

It wasn't long before Max was dozing off and dreaming of dune-bashing in a Ford Bronco Raptor. At one point taking off and landing with a hard jolt so vivid that he involuntarily woke himself up. For a moment he looked around with alarm. And then suddenly remembered the file dump on his phone.

Who was that woman, and how did she get hold of these confidential files? Another journalist? Or did she work at the Mayor's office? Max tried to wade through his older memories, trying hard to recall faces from the past. Did he know her, or had met her before? She certainly didn't look familiar, and surely he would remember having seen someone as striking as she was.

The most important question of all? How was someone so small and light capable of pulling a six-foot, 195lb man off the ground? She was quick too. And didn't seem at all fazed by someone shooting at her. One thing was for sure, she wasn't someone to be messed with. Maybe the would-be assassin had got her after all, in which case none of these questions mattered anymore.

Max wanted to go back to his sand-bowl dreamscape, but curiosity was getting the better of him, and he switched his iPhone back on. Unsurprisingly the screen blitzed with multiple miss-call and message notifications. He swiped them all aside and pulled up the files.

The previous Mayor, Khalid Siddique, had funded Empire College to the tune of a million pounds, and then strongarmed them to conjure up the research he needed to justify the ULEZ expansion.

But Max knew that. He just didn't have proof. Did this constitute proof? That would depend on if the documents were real and how they were sourced. The emails looked real, especially the ones where Deputy Mayor Mrs Lopez cajoled and virtually threatened the lead research professor to acquiesce to the Mayor's requests. However, this had been reported in the press at the time anyway. It hadn't made any difference.

There were also files proving plans for pay-per-mile road charging were already in place five years ago. There were letters confirming promises of commitments to the City-Fifty group, an international syndicate of Mayors, determined to radically realign city-dwellers' lifestyles, supposedly for the better, but by drastically limiting fundamental human rights and civil liberties, right down to dictating things like how much meat they could eat, clothes they could buy, and holidays they could take in a year. But again, none of this was really new.

Suddenly "Incoming Call" flashed up. It was her again. So, she had escaped after all. Max was almost relieved at that thought, though he didn't quite know why. But wait, what if it was the assassin calling him. He stared at the screen. Maybe it was inquisitiveness, or the sugar rush of the large cola drink that had gone to his head, but he decided to answer. "Curiosity killed the cat, and it might also kill the content creator," he morbidly joked to himself.

"Max? Max Turner? Look, don't hang up. I know things got a bit crazy back there, I don't blame you for not taking my calls, but we need to meet. I have important information you need to see…"

Max interrupted: "Listen Ms… whoever-you-are…"

He'd taken the call, that didn't mean he had to stay on it, certainly not on her terms.

"I've looked at your files, there's nothing new here, there's no, you know, smoking gun so to speak. I don't know what you're up to, but it's pretty clear you're bad news and involved

21

in something very dangerous. Plus, in case you hadn't noticed, I don't do this shit anymore. So, leave me alone and good luck with, er... staying alive!"

Max clicked "end call" and felt both good at his display of assertiveness and bad about coldly cutting her off and not listening to what she had to say. The mysterious woman immediately called back. He declined the call. Then came another WhatsApp: "You said there's no smoking gun, but I can do better. How about a walking corpse?"

What even did that mean? Then another message popped up, it was a location, accompanied by the message "Go see for yourself. Then we'll talk." Max clicked on the link, and it stuck a pin near what used to be called the Brecon Beacons in Wales, but was now unpronounceable. There didn't seem to be anything there, even on street view, at least at first. But sliding the image around suggested the hint of a small structure just off the narrow road, perhaps a cottage.

Clicking on directions confirmed there was no actual way to get there by public transport. And Max hadn't owned a car since the ULEZ Expansion. His car at the time had fallen foul of the ULEZ restrictions, which is why he had initially started his investigation into the expansion.

In fact, Max could have been a soothsayer, had he not been a journalist that is. His predictions had come true, his fears had been realised. Pay-per-mile or not, Central London had already become a mostly car-free zone, with only buses, taxis and commercial vehicles regularly plying the streets there. Older and classic cars had virtually disappeared from the entire city.

And charges had been hiked, the initial £12.50 a day charge had quickly risen to £15.50 while the Congestion Charge had gone up to £20. Emissions-based parking penalised motorists for owning a polluting vehicle, even when it wasn't actually being driven. It would all be hilarious if it wasn't so wretchedly unjust.

Meanwhile even electric cars had been hit with annual tax a couple of years ago, public charging costs had skyrocketed and London had even introduced parking charges at electric chargers, ostensibly so people would not hog the limited spots. This sounded sensible until you realised it added another £5-10 to your charging cost. It was actually about a third cheaper to run your car on good old petrol or diesel now.

To make matters worse, public transport fare rises had persisted, even as the services themselves continued to crumble. Years earlier, while looking at toxic air pollution claims around ULEZ, Max had proven that it was the air in the London Underground Tube Network that was actually dangerous to commuters' health, not that at street level. But no heed was paid and by all accounts, measurements by others had only showed it getting worse, not better.

Targets to reduce car ownership and driving in London were close to being met, and the pay-per-mile charging just announced, would inevitably be the final nail in the coffin when it came to Londoners' freedom to own and drive cars. Most people just used taxis, Ubers and car sharing services these days, tourists used public transport, along with labourers and workers that were needed (but clearly not wanted) in the city to service the needs of the rich. The rich of course drove, or got chauffeured in expensive electric cars.

It's probably more accurate to say most people just stayed at home. Working from their front rooms and ordering anything they needed online, delivered occasionally by flying drones, but more often the compact Drone Karts that almost exclusively populated the city's pavements these days. Particularly in outer London where High Streets had stagnated and shut, and shops had just been converted to yet more residential units.

Where once citizens railed against 15-minute cities, the argument was moot now. The scurrying Drone Karts usually brought everything to you within 10 minutes. That might sound idyllic to some, but to others it was tragic. Social isolation was the new disease, declining mental health was the symptom, loneliness was the diagnosis, and suicides were often the tragic self-administered treatments. The human spirit is not meant to be caged and entrapped at home. The human spirit was suffering.

It was probably a waste of time pursuing any supposed "walking corpse" at this point. It couldn't change the status quo, or stem the course of direction. Surely nobody cared anyway? No, that was wrong. One person did care. The mystery woman clearly cared; cared enough to not mind being shot at.

Max looked down at the map on his phone again. It seemed that a secret location in the middle of nowhere, beckoned. Well, a look-see couldn't hurt. Plus getting back behind the wheel of a proper car appealed. After relinquishing his personal pride and joy, he'd only driven a handful of times, brand new cars on press launches, all of them electric. Excellent devices, but hardly soulful.

To Max, driving cars wasn't just his job; the act of driving itself was something he'd always cherished and found therapeutic. Frankly, driving was fun. It was satisfying. And he missed it. He got up and approached the line of glass cabinets that housed his collection of model cars, and gazed longingly at the beauties within. His eyes fell on one particular black one and he couldn't help smiling. It was a replica of his old car.

He gave it a clean and put it back and sighed at the thought that he'd have to carefully pack all his collection away for storage before flying out to Dubai. Slumping into bed, he actually found himself looking forward to the morning to come with some excitement. A visit to an old friend was long overdue. He'd probably have a decent car he'd let him borrow. Plus, it would just be great to see him again. And then there was the drive itself to look forward to. Sleep came surprisingly quickly.

CHAPTER 2

Stepping off the bus, Max felt the fresh morning air encircle him. Just as he had survived the unexpected dangers of the previous night, the city had weathered the rain and the streets glistened with dampness. A gap in the clouds let the sunrays squeeze through, and he allowed the warmth to bathe his face.

Perhaps it was the renewed sense of purpose as he walked on to his destination, but he felt invigorated and ready to take on the revelations and challenges this day would surely bring. As he navigated familiar streets, he contemplated how his own journey was inextricably linked to this great city. Brief career forays internationally notwithstanding, an invisible but powerful elastic band would always snap him back to the vibrant capital. He felt he was part of its ever-evolving story, and even as he prepared for pastures anew, he could not begrudge his hometown one last ride.

Finally, reaching his destination, a West London car dealership, he surveyed the forecourt and noted it was rammed with sleek and shiny nearly-new machinery, every single car electric, and virtually all on special offer. It was an impressive if uninspiring carscape patchwork of greys, silvers and blacks, punctuated by the occasional white.

Max couldn't help but think back to his childhood when the other kids would head to the arcades, and he'd sneak off to car dealerships and spend hours marvelling at the metal on display. He would take in the shapes, attempt to memorise the specifications and prices, and pretend to not absolutely lose it if, on a rare occasion, a kindly salesman would actually let him sit in a car. Yet nothing on this forecourt caused him much pause as he wound his way through the cars to the main building. Being a car journalist, he mentally scolded himself: "I really should be more interested."

Entering the showroom, he was reassured to find not much had changed. It maintained a clean, crisp décor, with supercar posters adorning the otherwise bare walls, on one side there were cabinets displaying motoring memorabilia, merchandise and replica models, all tastefully displayed. Max immediately noticed a few new additions, recalling how he used to spend ages marvelling at the collection with some jealousy.

The bright LED lights cast a blazing glow over the showroom, accentuating the vehicles displayed within; essentially, they were a few selected higher-spec editions of the motors placed outside. And there at the back wall, behind an expansive desk, was the expansive man himself. Ahmed Abbas, the owner of Abbas Auto Emporium, truly a man of ample attitude, and magnificent magnanimity. A man who was also surprisingly alacritous for a big guy. Clocking Max, Ahmed immediately sprung up from his chair, swooshed around his desk, and thundered towards him, arms outstretched. Max grinned back and braced himself.

"Max Turner! No way!!" Ahmed exclaimed, virtually lifting him off the ground in a warm and mighty bear hug. "Omigod, it's really you yaar! Max Turner... V-Max T himself! It's been too long, yaar. How have you been?"

V-Max T was his "Influencer" name, a handle he used on social media channels, and one that had stuck after he filmed himself maxing out a Lamborghini Aventador at just over 200mph nearly 15 years ago on a desert road in the Middle East. He had later adopted the brand name "Turner Wheels" for his content. But in the car community, he was still called "V-Max T" or just "V-Max" by many.

To be fair, when he was in his 20s he thought it was just about the coolest handle ever, but with a few miles of maturity at more sedate speeds under his belt, the name left him wincing in embarrassment each time it was used. For one thing, he knew his life was lately very far from V-Max – a term typically used as a short form for "Maximum Velocity".

After a hug that lasted for a mini eternity, when Ahmed finally released Max, he recalled his traditional greeting for Ahmed: "As-Salaam-Alaikum!" grabbing his hand and giving it an enthusiastic shake. "How the heck are you, my friend?"

"I'm good bhai! Come, sit, sit, sit. Gimme just one second Max…. Chai, shai hoojai?"

Max took a seat at the desk, while Ahmed, with astonishing grace and speed, moved off to a side door to grab an employee and whispered instructions to him which, to Max, seemed to take a little longer than just ordering a couple of cups of "chai" or tea, would take.

It's possible that the events of the previous evening still had him rattled, but almost inexplicably he felt the tiniest stir of suspicion. However, before his still somewhat dazed brain could analyse the veracity of his feelings, Ahmed had bounced back to his chair behind the desk.

And moments later the doubts were pushed aside as the genuine warmth sparkling in Ahmed's eyes served to put Max at ease, and he found himself grinning stupidly from genuine delight and Ahmed's infectious demeanour. It was impossible not to smile in Ahmed's presence, perhaps that's why he was such a good salesman.

"It's so great to be back here mate. I see you've got a few new additions to the old showcase. Is that a genuine Knight Rider numberplate?"

"Waa! Yaar, you noticed?! You're sharp Max! Yes, yes, I finally got it. Cost me over four grand, but I just had to have it! But that's nothing, wait till you see this…"

Ahmed excitedly reached into a drawer and took out a box, and Max wondered why he flinched for a fraction of a second. Fortunately, Ahmed didn't notice. Max took a deep breath and saw that the box had a combination lock on it. Ahmed opened it to reveal an ancient paper document encased in plastic.

"No way!" exclaimed Max. "Is that really…?"

"Yes, yes, Steve McQueen's actual International Licence! Don't even ask me how much!"

He waved at a Mercedes EQS parked in the showroom and laughed, "It's worth more than that thing!" The pride and glee on Ahmed's face was palpable as he took the licence out of its case and offered it to Max "Go on, I know you want to hold it."

They both laughed as Max gingerly held the delicate document and gasped in awe. Safely replacing the valuable item, and laughing easily, the two continued reminiscing. After a short while, Max turned to take in the expensive lineup of high-end EVs in the showroom.

"So, how's business been buddy?" he ventured.

"Crap!" Ahmed bellowed with laughter while self-mockingly slapping his forehead.

"See these motors, they've been sitting here for months. Nobody's buying anything. And now with this pay-per-mile... Saatiyanas yaar! The trade will just die." He rolled his eyes and shrugged in resignation; Ahmed was a man of pronounced gestures.

"And especially these EVs bhai... nobody wants them! But they're all I can get hold of; the trade is flooded with them. All the petrol and diesel cars get snapped up like that!" He snapped his fingers so loud, the noise echoed back and alarmingly reminded Max of gunshots. He recovered quicker this time.

"But dude, then how are you managing?" he enquired.

Ahmed grinned and leaned back. "Oh, worry-not yaar. This is just one business, I've got other investments too you know, so money isn't a problem," his reply was followed with a conspiratorial little wink. Max tried hard not to misread the gesture, still fearful of deceitful danger and complicity.

"So how come you're here at the showroom then? Don't you need to be minding your other businesses?"

Ahmed was afforded a pause before answering, as the employee he spoke with earlier reappeared with a tray packed with two cups of tea and savoury snacks. Ahmed and the man spoke in Urdu for a bit. Max had picked up a few words of the language over the years hanging out with Ahmed, but not enough to fully grasp the conversation. As the guy turned to leave, he thanked him then turned back to notice that Ahmed was distracted by his phone, clearly texting someone.

Max had no idea what had come over him, but he very subtly slid the tray towards Ahmed, sneakily twisting it so that the cup nearest him, was now the cup nearest Ahmed: "C'mon mate, chai's getting cold."

But he immediately winced on realising that, in fact, steam was still rising off the cups, and the tea was most definitely not getting cold. Without looking up and not noticing the surreptitious switch, Ahmed waved at the tray and responded: "Take, take bhai, just give me a second."

A second later he put his phone down, and immediately grabbed the cup and took a sip. A sharp pang of guilt stabbed Max, as he immediately regretted his shenanigans with the tea tray.

Ahmed had retrieved the phone and was waving it in the air: "I run everything on this yaar, easy-peasy no problem. But you know me, I based myself here because I just love being around these things yaar…" he made a sweeping gesture towards the cars. "You know how it is. Oh, and besides, I did actually entertain a big spender recently."

"Oh yeah?" Max was sipping on the piping hot, delightfully sickly-sweet, thick but super-strong chai, and eyeing the samosas that had also accompanied the chai. Ahmed had already anticipated his desires and offered him the plate. At the same time, Max realised that Ahmed wouldn't allow himself to have one unless the guest accepted it first. He also knew Ahmed's mouth would already be watering in anticipation.

"Bhai, he bought 10 cars from me. Supercars, sportscars, nothing less than V8s, some from my personal collection… my investment collection. No haggling, no bargaining. Yaar, I made a killing. How do you think I bought Steve McQueen's licence?"

Ahmed bellowed with laughter. Max just mouthed "Woah"!

"But Max, where the hell have you been? You disappeared! No phone, no message, nothing. I was so worried about you. But last year I saw you started posting content again on your channels. I was so much relieved!"

"Yeah, I'm sorry Ahmed, sorry I didn't get in

touch with you. I had some issues I had to deal with..."

"Don't worry yaar, I understand. You're here now and I'm so excited to see you. You brought back some great memories." Ahmed grinned warmly back at him.

Max smiled as he recalled all the time he'd just sat around chatting about cars with Ahmed. They'd go and see "Fast and Furious" movies together, absolutely rip them to shreds as they walked out of the cinema, but would always be the first to get tickets for the next one.

Ahmed continued: "Man, what you did back then when the ULEZ expansion was happening. All your coverage, your amazing interviews, all the data and information you put out there! Nobody, I mean NOBODY, did as much as you!

"All the mainstream media was ignoring everything until they realised local elections could be won or lost because of ULEZ, but you... yaar... you were the essential go-to for all the real news and, for me, all the car news and reviews too. What happened bhai?"

The appeal in his voice and his eyes was earnest. Max sighed, took a big bite out of the samosa he found himself caressing, and washed it down with a swig of creamy chai.

"You remember when we last met? You could probably see I wasn't... well, you know, quite right. I wasn't my usual self. When ULEZ went ahead... and in the following days and weeks, I saw my dire predictions come true, and it... well, it all sent me into a spiral of depression I'm afraid."

"Nahi, yaar!" exclaimed Ahmed.

"Yeah, I was in therapy for quite a while, but don't worry, long story short, I'm okay now. And you know what? I've got a job offer in Dubai!"

"Oh wow - that's fabulous news... I'll be sorry to see you go, but good for you yaar, I'm really happy for you! And I'm honoured that you came to see me before you left. You're staying for lunch nah? There's a new Biryani joint opened up a couple of blocks away that I've been wanting to try!"

Max couldn't help laughing, recalling that it was never long before any conversation with Ahmed would turn to food and eating! "Sounds amazing mate, but there's a few things I need to sort out before getting ready to... you know... take off." Max silently admonished himself for stupidly making that aircraft-taking-off gesture with his hand.

"Erm... I was hoping to ask you for a favour.... But I'd understand if you said no... it's just..."

Ahmed leaned over the big desk and somehow managed to grab both of Max's shoulders: "Don't be silly yaar, anything I can do for you would be an honour, tell me, tell me!" with that, he settled back into this chair.

"I need to make a trip out of town, and wondered if I could borrow a car for a couple of days? But you know, a 'proper' car?" He added a reciprocal wink and immediately wondered if it was too much.

If anything, Ahmed's beaming smile somehow beamed brighter. Stuffing down the rest of his samosa, he was already half out of his chair beckoning: "Funny you should say that Max, I think I have just the thing! Come, come!"

He led Max into "The Vault" as he enjoyed calling it. While the showroom and forecourt housed what both Ahmed and Max termed "regular cars", the back warehouse was a veritable Aladdin's Cave of Automotive Treasures. Even the air was special in here, climate controlled to 25 degrees centigrade and ensuring humidity never rose above 40 per cent, it felt warm but fresh. More merch and memorabilia lined the walls, model cars and mementoes packed out the shelves and in one corner was one of the best libraries of motoring books in London.

More memories flooded back for Max. Sometimes in the name of research, often just for fun, he would spend hours back here, not just pouring over the books on the shelf, but sometimes just marvelling at the awesome collection of cool cars parked in here, some of which he had reviewed. Usually, they'd be covered in thick dust sheets, other times they'd be uncovered, resplendent and shiny. Now and then, the curiosity would get the better of Max, and he'd simply remove the covers himself.

Many of the cars back here were part of Ahmed's own collection, some were being traded, while others belonged to friends and clients who needed to store their cars somewhere safe. Of course, Ahmed owned more cars than just the ones here, they were back at his home. Which was a rather palatial farmhouse in Hertfordshire, complete with barns that had been converted to house the cars.

Almost instantly Max found himself playing that old game of "guess-the-car". That one was definitely an E-Type, he thought, this was probably a Lamborghini, and over there, very likely some 50s Americana, with big fins, huge fins in fact. It was easy to imagine Ahmed cruising to the Ace Café in it, or even tearing up the streets in the 1992 Honda NSX-R that Max had stopped to admire. Suddenly he was jolted out of his reverie.

"Max, Max!" Bizarrely, and rather to his own surprise, Max had ducked down in alarm. Ahmed watched him stand back up with curiosity. Max just shrugged and grinned stupidly, not knowing how to explain his actions. "Yaar, what's the matter you huh?" asked Ahmed.

He almost shook his head, but fortunately, it was a rhetorical inquiry, as he turned, waved and continued towards the back of the warehouse, which was a little darker than the rest of the space. "Listen, stop getting distracted. Follow me, I promise something very special."

Max could see Ahmed heading towards some car that sat under a dark dust sheet, but he couldn't quite make out what it was due to his friend's abundant frame obscuring the view. Suddenly Ahmed stopped, rotated, smiled, and outstretched his arm towards a distinctive and oh-so-familiar shape under the sheet.

A compact three-box saloon silhouette immediately gave the game away. Some would dare suggest that it was a generic and unremarkable automobile shape, but to those who knew, it was one of the most iconic cars of the 1980s. And Max knew. He knew very well indeed. Right now, he was struggling with his emotions, he had stopped dead and had to remind himself to breathe as he fought back a flood of sentiment that threatened to reduce him to a blubbering wreck. His mouth was open but no words were coming out, instead, all he could manage was to dumbly stare, point and look back at Ahmed, only to be greeted by his trademark benevolent beam. Max started to reconcile with the only obvious conclusion.

Ahmed just nodded and inclined his head towards it, as if to say: "Go on, go on, you know you want to". Max did. Oh, how he did! And suddenly he was rushing towards it. He grabbed the sheet and whipped it off in one go with a flourish that left Ahmed guffawing loudly.

There it stood. A black 1989 BMW E30 325i SE, a two-door. This one had the optional BBS crosspoke alloy wheels and black leather upholstery. But this was not just any BMW E30. This was Max Turner's BMW E30. Or it used to be...

"This is..." his voice cracked, fortunately, Ahmed completed the sentence.

"Your old BMW!" he moved in and wrapped an arm around his friend's shoulders. "I couldn't bear to part with it, Max. I knew how much this car meant to you. I was so hoping to be able to reunite it with you one day."

Max still couldn't allow himself to speak. Instead, he reached out, running his hand lovingly over the familiar lines of the car, feeling the cool metal beneath his fingertips. Memories flooded back – the exhilarating drives, the whispered confidences, the shared adventures.

Finally, he felt he could trust his voice again: "But I told you to sell it. You SAID you'd sold it.... Ahmed, the money you gave me at the time, it was that money that helped me to survive during... difficult times."

Inwardly he admonished himself for allowing even a hint of suspicion about Ahmed's intentions to enter his mind. "Bhai, don't worry.

I bought it from you. And then I kept it safe for you, until today, when I can finally..." he held out the keys, "gift it back to you."

Only unmatched loyalty and friendship could account for a man buying a friend's car to help him out and then holding onto it for three years only to be able to return it.

"Ahmed, I... I can't believe it," Max responded, "I thought I'd never lay eyes on her again." He clasped the offered keys, still hanging off the original BMW keychain.

"She's in top condition, fuelled up and ready to go. And don't worry about the charges and all that, it's on auto-pay and I'll take care of them. I want you to take it back out there, and drive the wheels off it, just as you used to," Ahmed gently tapped the bonnet and continued, "She's been waiting a long time. Go do what you need to do, and when you're finished, Nihari and Naans are on me!"

Max could almost smell and taste the distinctive thick curry Ahmed had mentioned. He recalled the popular restaurant in Southall where they would often visit. Sometimes in this very BMW. He just stared at Ahmed gratefully. In return, the big man nodded at the car.

He didn't need to be told twice. With a deep breath, and something of a sense of reverence, Max opened the car door and slid down into the driver's seat. As ever it was the scent that hit him first, a heady mix of ancient plastics, rubber, leather, metals and oils. It instantly transported him back to happier days. Max closed his eyes briefly, relishing the sensation. With a steadied hand, he inserted the key into the ignition and turned. The straight-six 2.5-litre engine churned then barked into life and settled into a silky smooth bassy hum.

He laughed out loud. This was real. He was beginning to accept it. Good things could happen to him after all. It hadn't felt like it after the last few years, but it was true. He gripped the M-Sport leather-trimmed wheel with renewed vigour. He noticed daylight flooding in from behind the car. Ahmed had slid open the big doors at the back. Grabbing the gear lever, Max shoved it hard to the left and pushed it upwards, selecting reverse.

He gave Ahmed a thumbs up and a final appreciative smile. In response, Ahmed simply saluted back with a grand 'you're most welcome' gesture. Max instinctively swung his left arm behind the passenger seat and looked back over his shoulder out the rear window.

He let the meaty clutch up and the BMW responded instantly, eagerly, joyfully even, as it lunged out of the warehouse into the light of day and the wide open, mostly empty, car park. A quick J-Turn and he had it pointed towards the exit gate. He snapped it into first and the rear wheels broke traction, spinning up smoke off the cold fresh rubber. Even over all the din, he could still hear Ahmed laughing as he slid sideways out onto the road.

Snatching a little corrective lock and straightening the car, Max grabbed second and worked his way up through the ratios. The engine settled into a deep thrum, and he took a moment to glance around the cabin. The red check lights on the roof console had gone out save for the brake light. He gave the middle peddle a quick dab and the light blinked out. The correct time glowed orange on the trip computer, and even his old phone cradle was still mounted to the top of the dashboard.

He turned on the radio and glanced back through the rear window to see the antenna rise out of the back fender. It was still tuned to his favourite 80s Hits station. Billy Ocean's "When the Going Gets Tough" blasted out the speakers, and Max couldn't help cackling with abandon. Life-is-good moments like this were to be cherished. He was home, back in his faithful steed, and an epic drive beckoned ahead.

After half an hour he was out of the city limits. Wisely staying off the main motorways as much as possible, he figured it would be best to keep a low profile. Besides, the B-Roads were more fun and best to get reacquainted with the feel of this 38-year-old car which still felt tight and eager. He hadn't realised just how much he had missed this car, and not just the car, but the engagement with the act of driving that only an older car could provide.

So much tactility and sensation had been lost in the transition to new technology. Modern cars were frankly better in every way, but the better they got, the more remote they became. They seemed intent on removing you from being connected with the road. Max was relishing every rev, making the most of every heel-and-toe downshift, and delighting in the steering feel.

As he settled into a familiar grove, he started to think ahead to his destination. What exactly would he find there? A walking corpse? What did the woman mean by that? How did he know this wasn't just some kind of a trap? Just as for a short while he had been gripped by the crazy fear that he would be ambushed at the showroom, he hated himself for doubting Ahmed. And then he wondered why anyone would want to target him anyway. He almost chuckled at the pomposity of his own self-importance. After all, what threat could a washed-out old car journo pose to anyone?

About four hours and a coffee stop later, with a mixture of anticipation and trepidation, he rolled to a stop at the side of the road at the coordinates given. The cottage was mostly hidden from the main road by a line of trees. If you didn't know it was there, you would never notice it. Access was only by a narrow path through an unannounced gap in the trees.

Max turned into it and got a clearer view of the house, its pebbled walls weathered by years of solitude. Along with a couple of sheds, it was nestled in a small clearing in the woods surrounded by wild grass and gnarled trees. The rear opened out onto rising hills, aiding to hide it from view from all sides. Whoever lived here, was definitely off the radar and wanted to stay that way.

While clearly not abandoned, the grounds and structures were far from pristine, verging on dilapidated. A crusty old diesel Land Rover Defender was parked outside, mud-splattered and filthy. Only the windows had been wiped indicating the uncared-for vehicle was still in use.

Max sat in his car for a few minutes. Frankly, he was tempted to back out of there, forget the whole thing and just carry on driving, seeking out the best roads he could find. However, he had come this far. So, with some considerable hesitance, eventually, he walked over to the cottage and knocked on the door. A part of him hoped there was no one home.

That hope was shattered as he heard some shuffling noises from behind the door. It was so quiet in this remote location, that there was no doubt that whoever was inside would have heard the BMW roll up the gravel drive. The person inside seemed as hesitant as Max, as it was taking an inordinate amount of time for them to open the door.

Eventually latches and locks were released, the door creaked half open, and a man gingerly moved into view, still half hidden by the door. The dishevelled figure was slightly slumped forward, appearing to be weighed down from neglect and a hint of defeat. His hair rioted over his head and face, a mix of white and grey that wrapped around his head and tumbled into a beard that concealed more than it revealed.

He seemed initially unremarkable, a crumpled old man in a crusty old cottage, but the old suit he wore was a paradox, hinting at a past formality but now just hanging limply from a body that had outgrown its tailoring. The fabric was badly fraying, stained, misshapen and testimony to minimal laundering and marked with the trials of time. Underneath, a jumper that had seen better days stretched awkwardly over his protruding belly.

It was only when the stranger's eyes, the clear sharp eyes behind the unkempt façade, met his, that Max felt a prickling sense of recognition. There was a history in those eyes, a familiarity that rooted him to the spot. And as the seconds ticked by, the shroud of anonymity slowly slipped away, and a flash of realisation struck

Max.

"Mayor Khalid Siddique?" he finally breathed out, almost involuntarily, as the mosaic of memories clicked into place. Mayor Siddique, the slick politician that sold London a spurious promise of cleaner air by charging and fining motorists. The man who strode the global stage as an advocate of urban environmental solutions, was now standing before him in a decrepit ancient house in the middle of remote woods, almost unrecognisable but for the defiant spark still alive in those challenging eyes.

Recognition too, had flickered in Khalid's expression, giving way to a momentary confusion that quickly curdled into anger. The transition was sudden; the supposedly haggard figure retreated a little, overtaken by the rawness of furious revenge. With startling agility, Siddique's hand had tightened around the handle of a cricket bat handily and purposely placed near the door.

"YOU!!" Siddique roared, the sound almost alien coming from the man Max remembered as stubbornly composed. With a sudden surge of movement, Khalid lunged, the cricket bat swinging through the air towards Max, the sharp whoosh of it cutting through the heavy air of surprise, anchored Max to the spot.

While the shock of recognition had paralysed him, the fight or flight reflex had kicked in, and his legs took command and decided to step back, but without the rest of his body in on the plan, that was never going to work. Instead, he found himself falling to the ground, still fixated on the face of the man who'd caused him so much anguish and frustration, and who was directly responsible for his subsequent dive into the depths of despair. It was only in mid-fall that he became aware of the blunt object that swung millimetres past his nose.

Max managed to twist and break his fall a little, but still found himself staring up from the ground as the bat started its swing back the other way, at a dangerously low arc. He braced himself for the impact, but through his half-closed eyes, he noticed a third person run into the frame.

This person moved with assured commitment, and in a single move, looped an arm over to intercept the swing, twisted around and planted a foot directly behind the former Mayor's legs, efficiently bringing him instantly, but surprisingly gently, to the ground, right beside Max in one smooth but quick movement. At some point, even the bat had transferred to the interloper's hand, who was now pointing it as a silent threat to them both to stay down. Max suddenly realised; it was the woman from the previous evening.

"Elie?" came the equally startled voice from

beside him.

CHAPTER 3

Khalid Siddique, during his tenure as London Mayor, launched the Ultra Low Emission Zone (ULEZ) in April 2019, initially targeting the bustling heart of the city. Max, a Londoner by birth, covered the development without taking a definitive stance. He understood London's challenges well – the city, bursting with congestion, was straining under the weight of traffic.

Central London, renowned for its extensive and efficient bus and Underground train network, the latter colloquially known as the Tube, offered robust public transport options. Over the years, London had witnessed a remarkable improvement in air quality. The notorious 'pea-souper' fogs, a grim hallmark of the city's past, had given way to clearer skies. This transformation was credited not only to advancements in vehicle emissions technology but also to the relocation and environmental upgradation of industrial facilities. As for ULEZ, after a couple of years, it was announced that the air was 46 per cent cleaner as a result, and you really couldn't argue with that. So, Max didn't.

However, this result appeared to embolden Khalid to expand the zone further out to the inner London ring roads, the infamous North and South Circular Roads in October 2021. Again, the area in question was densely populated, built-up and still reasonably well-serviced by public transport services. A claim of a further 21 per cent improvement was made.

Max had written an opinion piece and recorded a video questioning whether an improvement of just a fifth was really worth the cost of the infrastructure required for the expansion (such as cameras, signage, road markings and of course enforcement). Especially when compared to the hardship it would bring to Londoners dependent on older cars. And that was before including the financial difficulties it created for smaller businesses that relied on diesel vans, because diesel vehicles just six years old, were no longer viable due to the extortionate daily charge.

The laws of diminishing returns clearly applied to these air quality initiatives. Still, they had gone ahead. And the first expansion had been instigated shortly after the Mayor had been re-elected for a second term. As such, some argued that he had had a mandate for it.

However, others pointed out that he'd pushed it through under the radar when London's electorate was reeling from enforced lockdowns as the world was hit with the coronavirus pandemic, the likes of which had not been seen in modern times. Everyone was too concerned about being killed by the dreaded COVID-19 epidemic to worry about Mayoral elections and ULEZ extensions. Khalid rode a wave of apathy to see his ambitions realised.

While London tried to get back on its feet and people sought to resume their lives, work and businesses, the Mayor even reassured his constituents that that would be it. There would be no further extensions as they would not bring any great improvements, so instead particular hot spots where air pollution was perceived to exceed alleged safety levels would be targeted. To be fair, that sounded logical. The British mantra of 'Keep Calm and Carry On' was duly adhered to.

Until that is, in early 2022, when the Mayor suddenly appeared to change his mind. The lockdowns had left the city's coffers drained and hapless motorists were usually an easy cash cow. A quick consultation process seemed merely a formality, the results of which were duly ignored. There was even some suggestion they had been manipulated, despite overwhelming results indicating the next extension was very much unwelcomed – 60 per cent of residents voted against it, as did 80 per cent of businesses, who would, of course, be hardest hit again, with many already having collapsed under the twin assault of the previous extension and the loss of business during the pandemic.

Yet by November, Khalid confirmed that a further extension to cover the whole of Greater London, in some cases extending the zone right up to the M25 orbital ring road, would come into place by the 29th of August 2023. Enough was enough. This finally sparked outrage.

Not least for Max. Living just outside of the 2021 extension in Wembley, he thought he'd be fine with his non-ULEZ-compliant 1989 BMW, but now he would either have to get rid of his pride and joy or fork out that daily charge which, as he used his car about four or five times a week, would amount to an extra £2500 annually, at least. And that was at the original daily charge of £12.50.

But what began as a personal crusade took on new meaning and purpose as he deep-dived into the Mayor's own independent Impact Assessment Report, which clearly stated there would be negligible actual improvement in air quality, but considerable negative socio-economic impacts on communities living in outer London.

For Max, the next 15 months were gruelling: gathering more data and evidence that disputed the Mayor's claims of saving lives, and improving the health of Londoners; interviewing hundreds of people who would be badly impacted by the expansion and extensively covering the rallies, protests and anti-ULEZ events, as anger and resentment grew.

Max got credible experts involved, ensured the voices of regular people were heard, and accumulated a stack of evidence against the justifications made for the expansion. There was even validation in the form of one London locality's residents voting against a candidate directly as a protest against the ULEZ expansion. Despite all of this, just as the tide appeared to be turning, the London Mayor ignored everyone and went ahead with the expansion regardless.

And Max went drinking with his mates Despair and Despondency.

Victory aside, however, the tide did indeed turn for Mayor Khalid Siddique, and probably not in the way he or others might have expected. Within his party, alarm bells had started ringing about his rocketing unpopularity among Londoners, not just due to the ULEZ issue, but also his perceived failings in the areas of housing, and more seriously, policing and crime. Under the Mayor's tenure, crime rates had soared with the capital's murder rate actually overtaking New York's.

Perhaps it wasn't so surprising after all, that as the Labour Party, in opposition at the time, readied itself to take the reins of national power, as all the pollsters were predicting, it didn't want to lose the jewel in the crown that was London. Siddique, a Labour Party member, was forced aside when his main rival overtook him in the polls, and former actress and activist, Victoria Hartfield was installed in his place. Her fame, charisma and wide-ranging appeal saw her romp home to victory. It didn't hurt that she had also vowed to review the ULEZ extension, an electioneering promise that was duly forgotten once she moved into City Hall's biggest office.

Instead, she proposed a new initiative, claiming it to be a more just and viable 'green' policy. It was termed: Variable Tariff Road Charging. Under this scheme, drivers would be charged per mile, with rates varying according to location and time, escalating notably within Central London. Predictably, the tariffs were heftier for non-EVs and the 'most polluting cars', though electric vehicles weren't exempt either. The unsettling aspect for many was the government's refusal to rule out a nationwide implementation once it had been fully stress-tested in London.

As for what happened to the infamous former Mayor of London? Admittedly he had fallen off the radar, or perhaps most just preferred not to dwell on him too much. It was widely assumed that he would be walking into a plush position with City-Fifty, the coalition of Mayors of major international cities, formed to enforce perceived net-zero-focussed policies on urban inhabitants through legislation and, more ominously, social engineering. During the Mayor's tenure, he had served as Chair of City-Fifty, and had frequently spoken of how his actions in London were crucial in order to inspire other cities to follow suit.

Some had argued that his efforts might be better placed in serving the citizens he had been elected to represent, rather than pursuing internationally advocated 'Green' agendas. While others pointed out that London had already done its bit by leading the way and setting the standards for low-impact urban emissions.

Those more cynical suggested his actions were being leveraged to secure a lucrative publishing deal for his book "Breathing Life Back into London". However, that argument didn't hold when observers noted, with some glee, that the books had been relegated to the "Bargain Bins" within days of hitting the shops.

Nonetheless, most credible were the accusations that his real paymasters would be amply rewarding their loyal lieutenant, and though he was no longer in the public eye, Max, like others, had assumed that the former Mayor was probably living it up in California by now. Yet, as he now realised, the reality was starkly different. Siddique's current whereabouts and circumstances defied all expectations.

Warily, Max and Khalid hauled themselves back up onto their feet, the formerly trim Mayor seeming to struggle a little. The air was still thick with unspent rage, and neither man seemed inclined to break the wary eye contact, a tumultuous mix of caution and disbelief etched on their faces.

But the interloper finally drew their attention. With her hands outstretched, palms facing down in a universally recognised gesture of "calm the fuck down", she intervened with a composed urgency. "Gentlemen, please take it easy... let's go inside, shall we?" Her voice, firm yet soothing, cut through the tension, offering a pathway to a more civil discourse.

With some uncertainty and not inconsiderable doubt and suspicion, Khalid moved back to the front door, nodding at her, yet still somehow staring at Max, a silent exchange of doubt and suspicion lingering between them. He pushed on the door and it swung open with a mournful creak, revealing an interior that seemed to echo the former Mayor's fall from grace. Illuminated by the feeble light filtering through grimy windows and the muted glow of an old, forlorn lamp, the cramped living room seemed to sigh with the weight of failed ambitions.

The air within was stale, a testament to long

days and nights of isolation. The low ceiling appeared to bear down oppressively, the weary wooden beams groaning under the burden of time, standing as silent sentinels to a man once prominent, now seeking refuge in reclusion. The room was cluttered with boxes, some open and others sealed, scattered haphazardly across the floor and stacked against walls in precarious towers.

Amidst the clutter lay stained and ripped clothes, mostly the same grey suits he currently wore, strewn over the boxes, floor, chairs, sofa and indeed any other surface they could be lying on. The disarray was occasionally punctuated by slivers of what used to be white but were now more yellowy. These were vests and y-fronts.

The woman's lips twitched in suppressed amusement as she gingerly lifted a suit jacket, only to find it draped over a pair of stained underwear. She couldn't help but glance back at Khalid, who'd settled into a single-seater settee after tossing aside a dirty plate that had previously occupied the position.

He met her look with a complex tapestry of emotions. At first, there was confusion, which swiftly transformed into a dawning realisation, and then a profound sense of self-disgust. It was clear the revulsion was directed inward, a reflection of his own dismay at the state of his surroundings and, perhaps, his life. A fleeting flicker of embarrassment crossed his face before he quickly averted his eyes, choosing instead to fix a stern, almost defiant stare on Max.

Max moved an empty box off a rickety chair and perched himself on it, equidistant from both Khalid and the woman, who appeared to have made herself comfortable, still sporting the most subtle of smiles. He moved his gaze back to Khalid, the former Mayor continuing to stare at him intently. Frankly, Max was resisting a rising urge to laugh nervously. He still couldn't quite believe what he was seeing.

Mayor Siddique sat, amidst the shambles of his solitude, upright with one hand stretched out on the fraying armrest of his chair and the other still brandishing the cricket bat like a sceptre of his lost kingdom. Khalid looked around at the disarray himself, as if seeing it for the first time. Finally, his eyes, a mix of defiance and embarrassment, returned to meet theirs.

The silence that settled in the room was deafening; dense with unsaid words and a tension that hung in the air like the demons of the past clinging to the ceiling. Max, the woman, and Khalid Siddique sat quietly as if trying to corral the cacophony of questions, buzzing beneath the surface, into something resembling a coherent opening salvo of conversation. It was too easy to burst forth with screamed interrogations. So instead, there was a stand-off of uncertainties in a room brimming with revelations yet untold.

In this vortex of silence, the minds of the two men seemed to be racing in tandem, each one grappling with the weight of what had transpired, and the implications it bore. Their eyes bore into each other, occasionally flicking across the room, but then returning to lock on again.

The woman knew she could break the silence, she knew there was information to be exchanged, she also had a pretty strong feeling, and her sixth sense never let her down, that the time available to them was limited; and yet, she found herself fascinated by the silent mental parrying. To any casual observer, it would have appeared as if two men were sitting in silence, but to her perception, a mighty battle was raging, albeit one in which neither party was landing any blows.

Max finally buckled. He would be the first to speak. He knew he had to be. However, he decided to try and take some satisfaction from not addressing his foe, but instead turned to the woman. In any case, curiosity about the mysterious lady was starting to get the better of him. Up until now, she had been an enigma, the disappearing damsel of the dark.

Max turned to look at the woman the former Mayor had referred to as 'Ellie'. Bathed in the dim light of the cottage, her petite but athletic frame was accentuated by black combat trousers, a matching t-shirt, and a sleek black leather jacket. Black was evidently her preferred choice of wardrobe.

The dim light seemed to curve around her, casting her features in a gentle yet revealing glow. Her skin was a smooth canvas that played a stark contrast to the rugged tactical attire, and her facial contours were a study in contrasts—delicate yet undeniably sharp, as if sculpted with precision to balance on the edge of empathy and intimidation.

Her eyes were pools of intense clarity, glinting with a bright ferocity that seemed to pierce through the stagnant air of the room. They hinted at a well of strength and secrets, suggesting a depth of character forged in fires Max could only imagine. It was an almost feral alertness that lurked within those irises, a latent power that made Max's heart quicken just to meet her gaze. She was the embodiment of allure and danger.

The more he observed her, the more an unsettling realisation crept upon him - the less he knew, the safer he might be, yet the pull of her enigma was irresistible. Nonetheless, as he mustered the courage to break the silence, he found that even the act of speaking her supposed name held a weight, a feeling of stepping into an unknown that was as enticing as it was daunting. "Ellie? That's your name?" he asked, his voice carrying a tentative note, betraying his sudden and unanticipated enchantment with the mysterious woman before him.

She grinned and nodded back, a small, almost imperceptible smile gracing her lips: "Yes, Eleanor actually. Eleanor Rodrigues..." But before Eleanor could say more, Khalid interjected, his voice carrying a mix of annoyance, begrudging respect and perhaps even a sliver of affection. "Miss Eleanor Rodrigues," Siddique began, his voice carrying the formal cadence of his days as a public figure.

"Former Secret Service operative, trained extensively in intelligence gathering, counter-terrorism, and security operations, not to mention," he rubbed the arm she had twisted earlier, partly to emphasise the point, but mostly because it really did hurt, "Multiple combat disciplines."

He shook his head and continued: "Deployed in high-stake situations across the globe, consistently achieving mission parameters, and earning multiple commendations, including a Director's Commendation for thwarting a major terrorist threat to Central London."

Khalid paused for effect and turned to Max before continuing: "That's when I poached her to head up my security detail," and turning back to

Eleanor, "Yup, she was my protection, and here she is all these years later, shoving me to the ground."

Another pause and the former Mayor's face relaxed slightly, replacing open hostility with the vaguest suggestion of hospitality and the charm that won him two elections: "It's so lovely to see you again my dear, how have you been?"

Eleanor laughed: "Two things: firstly, it's been a long time since I've been your bodyguard, and secondly, you're not happy to see me, in fact, you're shaking in your..." she looked down at his feet, pondered and continued "ripped old spa slippers that you've held together with silver gaffer tape..."

Khalid forlornly looked down at his feet and then back up at Eleanor to ask the question he really wanted answered: "How did you find me, Ellie?"

"Oh please!" she taunted, "This used to be one of our old safe houses, it wasn't hard to figure out why it had been taken off the books around the time you... er... 'disappeared'" she replied.

"Yeah... about that..." Max finally chimed in, "So, er... what happened to you then Mr Mayor?"

Khalid turned back to Max, grimaced, gestured at Eleanor and responded to the question with a question, something of a habit, Max couldn't help thinking to himself. "She led you here?"

Before Max could respond, Eleanor jumped in:

"I did, but listen Khalid, Mayor Hartfield has announced she will be implementing road user charging. They're doing it. I think... I believe... it's time for you to come out of the shadows and break your silence."

Khalid looked back at her silently for a few long moments, strangely the annoyance in his expression subsided, it changed to contemplation as he looked down. Curiously when he looked back up at Eleanor, there was a mixture of sorrow and regret. "I'm sorry for what happened Ellie, I truly am."

At first, Max thought it was a generic statement, but the tone and look suggested a more personal confession, aimed specifically at Eleanor. Max looked across at her, but her expression was an example of well-practised inscrutability.

Suddenly Khalid got up, moved across to the kitchenette, and flicked on a crusty old kettle. He grabbed three dirty mugs, emptied them into the sink, gave them an alarmingly inadequate quick rinse and stuffed three tea bags in them, even as he inquired "Tea?". It was rhetorical as he moved across to the fridge, took out a milk carton, sniffed at it and wobbled his head as if mentally confirming to himself that it would be okay.

"You'd better get your phone out Max, I know how much you like to record everything."

Max could barely believe his luck. Of course, he'd had the phone already in his hand, and had been contemplating how to discreetly switch it to video and point it at the former Mayor. Khalid granting him permission to record off his own bat was better than anything he could have hoped for. It wasn't just that, the stooped frame and hunched shoulders appeared to straighten out. The ex-Mayor was recovering some of his former composure. But before he pressed record, Eleanor leaned across and asked him not to film her, Max nodded.

"You have questions Max... I might have answers."

"Thank you, Mayor Siddique," Max began, "I guess the most obvious question would be, why is the former two-term Mayor of London living the life of... well a hermit in the middle of nowhere?"

Khalid laughed. "No, Mr Turner, that is not the question," he finished pouring from the boiled kettle and started to empty the milk carton into the cups. "The question is why, after all these years, you've come all the way out here, to find me."

He brought the mugs back to the others, handed one to Eleanor and found a gap on the vintage coffee table between him and Max to set down a mug for the journalist. Max took one look at the filthy cup and noted the greasy scum that was floating on the top of the tea. He would not be drinking that.

Eleanor on the other, pulled out the teabag with her fingers, gave it a squeeze and chucked it over her shoulder. She stirred the tea with her finger and took a swig. Her actions astonished Max, but Khalid almost chuckled at the behaviour. Turning back to Max he continued:

"And it's because the next part of the plan to end car use and ownership in London has just been announced," Max couldn't help but interrupt, because of what appeared to be a confession to an accusation long-levelled at the former Mayor... "Plan? Mr Siddique, are you confirming that there was a plan after all?"

"Of course, there was a plan," Khalid responded dismissively, but then quickly delivered the punchline, "but it wasn't my plan, as you all thought it was!"

Max was confused, "you mean it was your predecessor's plan?"

Khalid laughed loudly, "We all just follow instructions... we are all just used... we are all just puppets...

"You've said as much in your videos," he told Max. "I've heard it. Oh yes, Mr Turner Wheels, you see? I did watch your videos occasionally."

While Max tried to process the former Mayor's words, Khalid's thoughts appeared to wander. Max decided to change tact: "Mr Siddique... er... Khalid, can you tell me what... what are you

DOING here?"

"Well, that's just it isn't it?" Khalid replied. "Once they were done with me... Well look, I just did what I was tasked to do. Everyone hated ULEZ, you and all the others that hounded me over it. And then there was everything else... just a series of disasters, from the pandemic to crime rates... they just pinned it all on me. I was scapegoated."

Then he laughed out sadly and with irony: "Yup, just pin it all on the Paki" he spat out, anger simmering below the surface of his jovial façade.

He got up, mug still in hand and hypnotically moved towards the window. "But that wasn't enough. A girl who had been an intern at City Hall suddenly came forward with a formal complaint of sexual misconduct. It wasn't true. Ellie knows." He jerked his head towards Eleanor without moving his head from the window.

Max looked across at her and she nodded. But Max was confused about what he was hearing, "Wait, I never heard about any of this..."

"Of course, you didn't Mr Turner, it was a ruse. It was a threat. We handled it. She settled for compensation. I realised she'd been instructed to do so. It never made the news. But my wife found out. She divorced me, and took the house, the kids, even the dog. Took everything. Or maybe I gave her everything... I can't remember, to be honest, it all gets a bit confusing..."

He went silent but continued after a short pause.

"Anyway, if this was merely a threat, imagine what else they could do to me? So, I dropped off the grid, and here I am..." he paused, still staring intently through the window. "...and here you are..."

His tone suddenly changed, sharpened: "Ellie, you said you sent Max here, but he doesn't even appear to know you?"

Recalling that Ellie wanted anonymity, Max stopped recording on his phone and answered for her. "We only met last night, but there wasn't much time for introductions, as we were... being shot at..."

Khalid suddenly swung around. "Shot at?!" Khalid was addressing Eleanor. "But you weren't hit?"

Eleanor grinned: "I got lucky."

Khalid shook his head and returned slowly back to his chair, mug still in hand. "Luck had nothing to do with it. You're good Ellie, but not that good, not when it comes to these people."

He settled back into the sofa and sighed, the energy seemingly draining from his body again, feigned stature lost once more.

"If they'd wanted you dead, you'd be dead. But they didn't... they wanted you to lead them here," he paused, shaking his head sadly. "It's a shame, I thought I had more time," he concluded with an eerie finality.

Max looked across at Eleanor who, for the first time, appeared genuinely confused herself, but her demeanour changed abruptly. From within her jacket, she produced a gun, slid off the sofa, stayed low and crawled over to the window. Max couldn't comprehend what she was doing but was snapped back to attention by Khalid.

"Start recording again Max," commanded Khalid.

Max once again switched on video and pointed his phone at the mayor, but even as he did so, he noticed a red dot appear on his chest. Even as he raised a finger to point at it, he heard Eleanor scream: "Get down Khalid! Now!"

Max dived off the old chair, which duly collapsed anyway under the force of the sudden movement. He lay flat on the ground, terrified. He glanced across, expecting to see Khalid having done the same. Much to his amazement, the former Mayor was still sitting on his chair, calmly taking a sip of his tea. He looked down at Max. "Sorry for everything I put you through Max." Max looked back in confusion.

"Oh yes, I know what you've been through," Khalid told him. "I went through it too. But it's finally coming to an end for me..." Khalid was almost smiling with a kind of relief.

"Khalid! Get down Godammit!" It was Eleanor. "That's pointed directly at your heart, it's a kill shot."

Khalid smiled back. "I wouldn't expect anything less," then locking his gaze with Max, he managed one final word: "Viridis..."

The bullet tore through the air with lethal precision, its impact not merely puncturing Khalid's heart but exploding the mug in his grasp into a spray of ceramic shrapnel. A cloud of fine debris, a mix of dust, stuffing, and the disintegrated remnants of the chair's fabric blossomed from behind him, marking the bullet's unforgiving path through his body and the armchair.

Max flinched as liquid splashed his face, his first horrified thought was blood, but the scent of tea brought a bizarre relief amidst the chaos. A scream escaped him, more of shock than fear, as the reality of being up close and personal with a violent death, hit home.

Khalid Siddique had been the bane of his life, a focus for angst and hatred, but Max had never wished him any physical harm. It just wasn't his way. And now he had just seen him killed, while he was looking right at him.

Max found himself convulsing, he fought down the bile and shuddered. Then he realised he was being pulled from behind the sofa towards the wall. It was Eleanor. Only then did he become aware that more shots were streaming through the windows. He witnessed the mug of tea he had diligently ignored, explode as it was hit.

His gaze returned to Eleanor, but she was trying to get a view out through another window, and instead, his eyes were drawn to the compact, semi-automatic pistol in Eleanor's hand. The fingers of her hand were curled around the matte black gun with practised ease, suggesting a level of familiarity and proficiency that belied Eleanor's slight stature.

Max's mind struggled to keep pace with the whirlwind of chaos that engulfed him. A prominent politician lay lifeless on the floor, while the room had become a gallery of destruction with bullets tearing through the mundane refuge of furniture and personal effects, kicking up a storm of dust and detritus that mingled with the musty air. Meanwhile, a dangerous woman, brandishing a deadly weapon was shouting at him. What was she saying?

"Stay down! Don't Move! I'll be back!"

With incredible fluidity, she moved across the room. Staying low, she ducked and weaved, intuitively navigating a trajectory that she'd already assessed would shield her from the assailant's line of fire. Before he could fully comprehend what she was doing, Eleanor was gone, swallowed by the shadows. A heavy sense of dread settled over him as he realised he was abruptly, starkly, alone.

The sharp crack of gunfire punctuated the stillness again, a stark reminder of the peril just beyond the walls. He would learn later that Eleanor had escaped out of the cottage's back door, having established there was only one shooter. She returned fire. Max could now hear two distinct sets of gunshots. This continued for a while. The room Max occupied fell from the attacker's focus, offering him a reprieve, a chance to draw grateful breaths.

Suddenly the shooting stopped altogether.

CHAPTER 4

Calm had claimed the cottage at last. Several moments passed. Finally, he dared to lift his gaze above the window ledge but found only emptiness. The silence was eventually broken by the distant growl of a high-performance car, fading into oblivion. Max listened intently - a V8 for sure; the staccato punctuation in the deep throaty roar was distinctive. "Hmm... Mercedes AMG," he concluded to himself.

His mind quickly snapped back to his present predicament and he grappled with the thought that Eleanor might have fled, but his instincts countered; she might still be an enigma to him, but so far, she had demonstrated nothing but resolve to protect him. Part of an instinctual response from her training perhaps?

But if that had been the sniper riding away, could that mean that...?

The sight of the former Mayor's inert figure was a grim reminder of what had just occurred. Surveying the room, it struck Max that, save for the shards of glass now littering the floor, it remained largely as they had found it – desperately disarrayed. Except that is, for the smoke and dust that swirled in the light shafts from the shattered windows, and the expanding crimson that was testament to the day's brutality. Nausea crept upon him from the acrid smell of gunpowder and blood; he turned away, swallowing hard against the rising bile.

He needed to get out of here. Slowly he moved towards the door and shakily, cautiously, inched it open, flinching as it creaked. Suddenly a hand from the other side forced it wide open, and Max almost had a heart attack. He pulled back in horror. Every muscle in his body tensing for more violence. Instead, a silhouette loomed —dark against the relative brightness of the outside world. "I told you to stay put and stay down," came the familiar rebuke.

Eleanor stepped into the room, dispelling the dread with her presence. Relief surged through Max, a wave so potent he nearly succumbed to the urge to grab her and hug her tightly. Thankfully she interrupted his reverie.

"It's okay," she asserted, "our sniper friend seems to have scarpered." Crossing the room with measured steps, she knelt beside Khalid, her movements carrying a ritualistic respect. She laid her palm against the cool skin of his face and closed his unseeing eyes, granting him a semblance of peace. She lingered there, her back to Max, in a silent communion before regaining her composure.

Rising to her feet, she faced Max, her expression a complex tapestry of regret and resolve: "This is my fault. Khalid was right, they were after him not me. And I led them right to him."

Max tried to reconcile her: "How do you know it was you? Maybe they followed me?"

"You weren't followed," retorted Eleanor with an uncanny confidence.

"How do you know?" he persisted.

"Because I followed you."

Max wondered how he hadn't noticed. He waved the phone that he was somewhat surprised to notice he was still holding, "Maybe this then? You know, it's easy to track these things, isn't it?"

"Not yours," she responded dismissively.

"What? Why?" he stared questioningly at his phone as if he had just been told it belonged to someone else.

"Because I protected it against tracking." Eleanor was grinning again.

Max was startled and involuntarily held his phone at arm's length, turning it over and studying it carefully. "What? How?"

"Last night. There was an app in the package you downloaded, it activated automatically and made your phone untraceable."

Max didn't know whether to be outraged or grateful. He was frankly a bit of both. "But why... okay look, never mind. How about the old-fashioned triangulation method... it still uses a cellular phone signal right?"

Eleanor looked at him with mock awe: "You're a bit more up on your espionage methodology than I thought!"

She continued more sincerely, "First up, look, please believe me when I tell you I put the app on your phone only to protect you. Secondly, triangulation doesn't give an accurate location. Out here, it could be off by several miles, so nah."

"So, if your phone is also untraceable, and I'm guessing you would have known if you were being physically followed, because, you're what...? Some of kind of superspy...?" ventured Max.

"I prefer 'Covert Operations Specialist'..." Max couldn't help but admire the subtle smile that played on her face with this retort.

"Right, right... but what I'm saying is, how could the sniper have followed you here?"

Eleanor's smile faded: "To be fair, that's actually a good question."

She looked around the room and gave Khalid's body a final glance. "Let's get out of here, someone might have heard the shots and called the police. Hopefully, the SCS will get here before them, but in either case, we don't want to be around. Well, you don't."

"What's SCS? And why not me?" Max asked.

"Site Containment Services… and because they don't know you. You'll be hauled in for questioning."

Even as Max contemplated the implications of that, and marvelled at the existence of an SCS unit, Eleanor had swept past him and back outside. Max duly, and rather shakily, followed, still coming to terms with what had transpired. And then stopped in his tracks.

Parked next to his classic BMW was a brand-new matte black Tesla Roadster. He couldn't help himself. He hadn't seen one for real as it had only just come out: "Woah! Is this yours?"

Eleanor merely nodded, apparently amused by Max's sudden change in demeanour. He started to walk around the car, taking in its sleek low-slung form, alluring pronounced curves around the wheel arches, and the oddly domed roofline stretching back to a pert rear. He was speaking, but to himself rather than her.

"1000bhp, over 250mph, accelerates from rest to 60mph in less than two seconds… wait…' As he knelt at the back of the car, he noticed the slit around the number plate and looked back up at Eleanor. "Omigod, is this the one with the rocket thrusters? Zero to 60 in pretty much one second! This thing literally flies! The price is over

£350,000, isn't it?

"£368,000 actually," Eleanor replied. "But I'm going to jump in with you."

"What? You're not taking this? It's got over 600 miles of range, hasn't it?"

"Not the way I drive it," laughed Eleanor. "But I think I know how they followed me, there's just too many ways to hack this thing, yours on the other hand... Unless you got a physical tracker on. Have you?"

"I don't know, I only picked it up this morning."

"Yes, I know. Your friend Ahmed had it."

"What?! How did you…"

She dismissed his question before he even had a chance to complete it with a wave of her finger, as she intently focussed on her phone while pointing it at the BMW. A few seconds later she seemed satisfied and looked up: "Nah, nothing. It's clean."

Not knowing how to react to that bit of information, Max turned his attention back to the Tesla. Despite himself, he couldn't help but think that it would be one heck of a review, as not many journalists had managed to get their hands on one of these Roadsters yet, and only a couple of the top guys had driven a Roadster with the SpaceX Package.

Resignedly he got into the BMW. Eleanor followed, sliding into the passenger seat: "Oh this is nice! I love the black leather, it's so me."

Max smiled and nodded his appreciation of her approval. The 325i's engine hummed to life, and he manoeuvred it smoothly back out of the driveway. As he swung the car around, his eyes fell again on the Tesla, its sleek form an undeniable presence. The car enthusiast in him stirred - a blend of curiosity, admiration, and a yearning to experience that piece of electric marvel. Plus, as his YouTube channel had been relatively low output for a while, a review of the most sought-after EV on the planet right now, would certainly give it a much-needed revitalisation in views.

Disregarding the awkwardness of the timing, and the fact that the woman he was about to address was a figure shrouded in mystery and danger - a virtual stranger whose life was a catalogue of secrets - he had a question bubbling to the surface, irrepressible.

"Uh, so…" he stammered, trying to sound nonchalant, "once we've wrapped up this whole… situation, do you reckon I could… perhaps bor…"

"Hold on a second," Eleanor murmured, her fingers dancing over her phone. Max watched curiously as her eyes then flicked to the Tesla. Suddenly, the Tesla juddered and then erupted into a raging fire, the explosion sending a shockwave that Max felt in his very bones. He was left trembling, his heart racing a frenzied beat against his ribs.

Unruffled, Eleanor tucked her phone away, a satisfied smirk crossing her features. She turned to Max, her gaze piercing, as if nothing out of the ordinary had just occurred. "What were you about to ask?"

It took Max a heartbeat or two to realise it was Eleanor who had detonated the Tesla: "Er... never mind. Why did you do that?"

"There were some features on there I didn't want anyone discovering. And besides, it's been compromised."

"So, you just eliminate anything that might lead people to you?"

Eleanor picked up the gist immediately and tried to reassure him: "Things yes, maybe, but people, no, of course not!" As she spoke, she put her hand on Max's forearm as his hand rested on the gear lever.

"Oh, my goodness, you're shaking. Are you okay Max?"

"Yes, yes, I'm fine," he replied too quickly.

"Well to be fair, you've just been shot at, and that's two days in a row, plus you've just seen someone being killed and a car blowing up... erm, maybe I should drive?"

"And what about you?" Max countered, "I mean, that was someone you knew, you worked closely with and... I'm sorry, but by your own admission, indirectly you might be responsible for his murder..."

"Yeah, that part's annoying..."

"Annoying? Annoying?! Really? I mean..."

"Well, as I told you Max, he was a walking corpse anyway. Now listen, we need to get moving! I can drive if you're not up to it." Her tone was sharp, authoritative, and commanding. Max automatically complied and selected first gear.

"No, no, I can drive. In fact, I need to drive. It calms my nerves."

They set off in silence. Sure enough a few miles down the road they noticed several all-black Land Rover Defenders racing at high speed in the other direction.

"SCS?" asked Max.

Eleanor nodded, "Very likely." After a slight pause, perhaps to choose her words carefully, she spoke again: "Listen, Max, I'm sorry about snapping at you earlier, you can see we didn't have much time.

"In answer to your question, yes I did work closely with the Mayor for several years. Maybe I regret his death, maybe I don't, I won't get into that right now. But we're trained to compartmentalise these things. Operational priorities take precedence over emotional compromises.

"Besides, there is always time for contemplation later. And if there isn't. Then that's our fault too."

Max felt the chill in her last statement but also noticed that she'd allowed a rare chink in her emotional armour and given him a peak beneath her veneer of efficient professionalism.

Max changed the subject: "Before he died, he said 'Viridis'. Do you know what that means?"

Eleanor nodded: "Viridis Ventures, I often used to take the Mayor there."

"What is it? I don't think I've ever heard of it?" Max responded.

"Doesn't surprise me you've never heard of it," Eleanor nodded. "It's pretty much a stay-in-the-background sort of organisation. Google it and you'll find some blurb about 'championing sustainable development and innovation', applications for investment funds and even a bunch of challenge prizes and competitions to encourage new ideas etc.

"In reality, they have investments in everything from renewable energy to tech start-ups, and even some more... let's just say covert sectors."

"So, what did Khalid Siddique have to do with them?"

"He used to have a meeting there, at least once a month, sometimes more," she revealed.

Max couldn't help the surprise in his voice, "About what?"

"I don't know, my job at the time was just to keep him safe, not to look into what he was up to. But I do know who he used to meet there, and I think it's time to pay him a visit."

She punched the address into Max's phone, now back in its cradle and guiding them back to London. "You up for this?"

Max nodded grimly and pressed down on the accelerator. "Won't it be too late by the time we get back?"

"Nah, this guy works nights. We usually used to go there around eight or nine," she explained. Max nodded.

While he was putting on a brave front, inside he had to admit to himself he was fighting back a tsunami of turmoil, doubt, fear and anxiety. He was tempted to pull over at the next service stop, call Eleanor an Uber and ring his former therapist for an emergency session. But what would he say? That his symptoms had been triggered by a sniper, a dead mayor and an exploding electric car?

And a woman. A woman he barely knew. One he still didn't know whether to trust or be suspicious of. A woman whose bidding he was already doing. A woman who appeared unassuming in presence, captivating in appearance, one who seemed to smile rather a lot, but who calmly dallied with danger and wasn't shy of murderous intent herself.

She seemed like someone you'd feel comfortable taking home to meet mum, but might kill your entire family while you went to fetch the good biscuits. Fortunately, his parents had long passed, and he had fallen out of touch with most of his family and relatives.

They drove on mostly in quiet contemplation. Eleanor had told Max it was safe to use the motorways so they were making good time. The 38-year-old car seemed to be revelling getting back out on the open road. By modern car standards, there was significant road roar from the tyres and wind noise from the door surrounds. But the M20 designated straight-six motor sat happily at high revs, thundering along the tarmac at ease, happily chewing up the miles. It felt almost euphoric to be out of storage and back on the road again.

Eventually, they pulled over at a service stop, for fuel and a bite to eat. Burning with questions, Max again, decided to break the silence.

"Why?" he suddenly asked.

"Why what?" responded Eleanor, happily chomping into an overloaded 12-inch subway dripping sauce.

Max examined his own merely nibbled-at 6-inch Turkey sub: "Why did you contact me?"

Eleanor seemed to take a while to formulate her answer so Max pressed on: "I mean why do you even need me? You seem, if I may say, more than capable of getting to the bottom of whatever... this is... all by yourself."

"I've been following your work for years. At first," Eleanor paused, her eyes narrowing slightly as if ready to gauge Max's reaction, "as a threat assessment when you started talking about ULEZ and covering the protests." Max's raised eyebrows gave away his surprise at that statement, but Eleanor pressed on.

"Anyway, it quickly became pretty clear to me that you weren't any kind of threat."

By contrast, now he felt a tinge of indignation at being so easily dismissed as harmless. He let his subconscious reconcile his conflicting reactions and instead focussed on Eleanor's next words.

"What I did see was someone who was extremely dedicated and earnest about his work." She took another hungry bite out of her colossal sub, Max felt obliged to mirror her with another small bite, but then immediately regretted it. He wondered where his appetite had gone. And then remembered he'd left it back in an isolated old cottage next to a dead man's body. He put down his sub and sipped his coffee instead, trying to wash down the memory of rising bile.

"I want to help you Max. I want to help you complete the story that no one told as well as you did. I want you to have some closure. Before you leave. Yeah, I know about Dubai,"

Max nearly choked on the hot black liquid, "but how..."

Eleanor just laughed and again waved a dismissive hand in the air. "Max, get over it. I know a lot of things. Many things that I'm not supposed to know." She twitched her head a little: "It's kinda my thing."

Another big bite. But the mouthful didn't deter her from continuing.

"There's more going on here than meets the eye, Max. Like you've been saying for years, it's about taking away people's rights, their liberties, their freedom to travel how, and where, and when, they want. Even their desire to own a car. It's all being stripped away, slowly, but surely. And I've seen how the mechanism to make it all happen works, from the inside."

Max was intrigued: "So, if you know... if you've always known, then why not do something about it? Why not... I don't know... arrest them? Can't you do that?"

"There wouldn't be any point. We're talking about powerful forces above the law!" Somehow, she had nearly finished her sandwich and was eyeing up Max's. "Something wrong with your sub?"

"No, no it's fine. I just don't have much of an appetite at the moment."

"Mind if I...?"

"No, be my guess," Max slid his sandwich over to her. "I've had a bite from this side, so you might want to..."

She'd already started devouring it, oblivious to what Max was saying. "You sure are hungry."

She shook her head. "Nah, just high metabolism," she laughed. "Anyway, about this lot, I mean... I suppose I could take them out, but it wouldn't be easy, and things would get very messy..."

Max interjected: "Take them out?" He looked around surreptitiously and lowered his voice. "You mean kill them?"

Again, the laughter. Max couldn't help thinking that with anyone else, this particular personality trait would start to grate by now, particularly considering the circumstances. Yet with Eleanor, it was almost infectious, almost that is, if it wasn't for the gravity of the situation. "Well, I don't mean take them out for dinner, do I?"

Still using his low voice: "So... so you're an assassin as well?"

"I've been known to dabble!" She took a swig of her cola and winked at him. An involuntary chill reverberated down his spine. He sat back and involuntarily grasped the table as if to steady himself. "You're no different from whoever it was that was shooting at us today?" there was resigned dread in his voice.

She looked up at him, enchanting eyes reeling

him back in. "I never said I was, Max."

For a moment he was transfixed, uncertain what to make of her. Suddenly she snapped away and took another bite of what used to be his sandwich: "Thing is, what needs to happen here, is that this lot need to get exposed. The people need to know what's going on, the world needs to see how it's being controlled.

"Of course, these days, that's not so easy. No one believes anything. Even if I put pictures or videos out there, people will just think it's deep fake AI or something. It needs a face. Someone with credibility, authority." Again, the look: "Someone with empathy."

She grabbed her cola again. "And someone who knows how to tell a story. That's you! And I figured you'd relish the chance to do this."

Max leaned forward again and took another sip of the coffee. It was starting to go cold, the tepid bitterness mirroring his contemplation. The story was luring him back, dangled so tantalisingly in front of his nose by the easily convincing but still untrustworthy Eleanor. He was acutely aware that there was no one more suited to uncover its truths and present a credible narrative. His skills, his experience, and his very nature demanded he pursue it. Yet, in the quiet spaces of his mind, a whisper of doubt lingered, questioning what price his psyche, his peace, and his existence would pay in the wake of this truth's pursuit.

As if sensing his very thoughts, Eleanor put down the sandwich and looked at him directly, seriously, earnestly: "I do have to level with you Max. Things could get... well a little dicey. Today might not have been a one-off. I mean... you know... what can I say? Welcome to my world!" She shrugged, giggled, and just as instantly, snapped back to her former solemnity.

"What I can and do swear, is that if you join me on this mission, your life will matter more to me than my own."

Max was certain he'd heard that line before somewhere, a movie perhaps. He wondered how often she'd used it on others. And what price they had paid for subscribing to the hackneyed ruse. Yet, right now, in this noisy service stop, her words felt sincere. Or maybe he bought it because he wanted to buy it. Perhaps he needed to buy it. Regardless, the look she gave him sealed the deal. He took a final drink of his coffee and set it down. "Well, I guess I don't have any other pressing deadlines at the moment."

Eleanor grinned and slurped her cola: "And you know what? I'll even pay for the fuel!"

CHAPTER 5

It was nearly 9pm when they rolled into the relatively empty car park. As per Eleanor's instructions, they parked near the exit and walked over to the main building. Despite being one of the biggest facilities in the Park Royal Industrial Estate, adjacent to the busy Western Avenue, it had the smallest signage. No big-lettered announcement, just a modest, shiny plaque near the main double door, with an engraving that confirmed this was the headquarters of Viridis Ventures.

As Eleanor had suggested, even at this hour the doors were open, and there was still a receptionist. Far from the hush that usually permeates an office building after hours, here an imperceptible sense of activity was maintained. Long after all other workplaces had emptied, Viridis Ventures was still busy doing... whatever it was that it did apparently.

Eleanor confidently strode up to the main reception, an uncertain Max in tow.

"Hi, can you please let Quentin Dubois know that

Eleanor Rodrigues is here to see him? I have some important information."

The receptionist smiled back curtly and reached for her console: "What shall I tell him it's regarding?"

Eleanor lent forward conspiratorially, even though there was no one within earshot: "Confidential. It's for his ears only."

The receptionist merely nodded, as if such statements were normal in this building, and spoke into her headset. Much to Max's surprise, she immediately slid a pair of guest passes across.

"Use these to go through the glass doors, head to lift A and touch these on the panel to get to the right floor, once you exit it's…"

Eleanor cut her off with a wave of her hand: "Thanks, I know where his office is."

Once in the lift, Max started to speak but Eleanor immediately swivelled, quickly put her finger on her lips in an indication to him to keep quiet, then pointed above her head and it was only then he realised that there were cameras. Eleanor knew exactly where to stand so her hand gestures wouldn't be seen.

Once out of the lift, they walked through a darkened and empty corridor where all the doors looked the same, and none had any numbers or signage. Eleanor arrived at a specific door, flashed a reassuring smile across at Max and pushed it open.

The office was a study in understated elegance and professional sophistication. Directly ahead were large windows draped with blinds hinting at the world outside while offering a sense of seclusion. The side walls, cloaked in dark, textured wallpaper, hosted shelves displaying a collection of personal photographs and tasteful decorative items, arranged with careful precision to suggest a man who valued order and restraint.

A crisp wooden desk was off to the side, spartan and meticulously organised. A tall wiry middle-aged man, with curly silver hair and a sharply groomed close-cropped beard, plus a smart rimless pair of spectacles perched on his nose, leapt out from behind the desk, making his way around the desk, arms outstretched, frame slightly hunched over.

"Eleanor, Bonsoir!" Max detected a thick Belgian-French accent. "It is so good to see you again after, oh it has been too long, no?"

With over-exaggerated charm, he gave Eleanor a two-cheek kiss and moved towards Max, but detected some reticence, so greeted him with a two-palm handshake instead: "Mr Max Turner! What an honour to meet you, Sir!"

Max was taken aback. "Er.. thanks. You know me?"

"Why, of course, monsieur, I am, 'ow you say, a beeg fan. Ze moment you walked into ze building, I was excited to meet you," Quentin responded with a wink. Disarmingly, he then grabbed his phone off the table, and held it aloft to face them: "May I get a selfie with ze famous V-Max T?"

Max shrugged but instinctively obliged. Quentin's arm went around his shoulder, he beamed at his phone while snapping away, while Max managed a meek smile. Eleanor watched on amused.

Quentin suddenly switched his attention back to her. "Ah but Mademoiselle, such a delight to see you again. What brings you to my 'umble place of work?"

As he spoke, he returned to his seat and gestured his guests to sit down.

Stony-faced, Eleanor simply said: "Khalid is dead."

Quentin tensed. He clenched his fingers tightly, knuckles whitening—a subtle betrayal of his feigned surprise. Leaning forward, he momentarily pressed his eyes closed, as if pained by the weight of the news. Then, with a swift motion, he removed his glasses, pinching the bridge of his nose while shaking his head in disbelief: "Quoi?! Mon Dieu, c'est pas possible! Khalid... he was a man I deeply respected. We worked togezzer in ze past, you know? He had...

'ow do you say... conviction."

He briefly turned to address Max: "I understand he might not 'ave been your favourite Mayor, monsieur, but his disappearance, it... it troubled me."

As he spoke, his voice wavered theatrically, yet the glint in his eyes, sharp and calculating, didn't quite match the sorrowful tone

Turning back to Eleanor: "I often wondered 'ow he was managing, living out of ze public eye. Et maintenant, to hear zis news, it is very saddening, véritablement."

He let out a heavy sigh, pausing as if lost in thought, then spoke again to Eleanor, who remained stoic throughout his dramatic turn.

"And 'ow did zis happen, if I may ask? It is a terrible surprise, terrible indeed."

"He was shot Quentin, by a sniper. A sniper that nearly killed us as well," still measured and controlled, Eleanor deliberately allowed her voice to rise as she spoke those words.

He launched into a well-rehearsed performance of shock and grief. His frame stiffened abruptly behind the desk as if jolted by the news and he pressed a hand to his chest over his heart, a gesture of dismay. His eyes, magnified slightly by the replaced glasses, widened for a moment before he blinked rapidly, feigning disbelief. He leaned forward, elbows on the desk, clasping his hands together in a display of troubled thought.

"Shot? By a sniper? C'est incroyable! Zis is... it is an outrage! Poor Khalid. And you, put in danger as well! Mon Dieu, the world we live in... it's becoming more dangerous by ze minute. I am... 'ow you say, devastated by zis news. We must find who is responsible! To target someone like Khalid... et to come after you too, it is unfathomable!"

"Was it you?" Eleanor's voice was sharp as a blade, each word dripping with accusation. Max's intake of breath was almost audible, he gripped his chair involuntarily.

Quentin straightened abruptly. "Me?" His voice twisted the simple pronoun into a disbelieving scoff. His brow creased in apparent confusion, a masterful performance of innocence.

"Did you send the killer?" Eleanor pressed, unwavering.

With a fluid motion that belied his age, Quentin half-rose, half-leapt from his chair, moving out to the side of his desk, nearest to Eleanor, and towering above her.

"Me? Comment pouvez-vous..." He trailed off, shaking his head in mocked disbelief. "Eleanor, comment pouvez-vous suggérer une telle chose?" The stress of his apparent outrage causing him to revert to his native tongue.

The hospitable warmth had evaporated, replaced

by cold fury. "How can you accuse me so? How many times have you seen Khalid and I together? Vous savez how close we were!"

His hands gestured emphatically, at one point brushing the assortment of meticulously arranged documents that adorned his desk into unseemly disarray.

Eleanor was not cowed, she shot up from her chair and lunged towards him. The speed of her movement caught him off guard, as she shoved him hard against the wall, at the same time tightening her fingers around his pristinely starched white Charvet shirt and yanking downwards.

In doing so she managed to unbalance him and buckle his knees. She knew she didn't have the weight to pin him against the wall, but by compromising his stance she could weaken his resistance. At the same time, it had the effect of bringing the tall man down to her height, so that she would be face-to-face with him.

His head snapped back, narrowly missing the wooden shelves, the dull thud of skull against plaster sending a shock through him. Seizing the momentary stun that glazed his eyes, Eleanor brought her palm down with a thunderous clap against the wall millimetres from his face, her hand slotting in between the shelf and his cranium. The startling noise and her relentless intensity made him recoil and turn away from her hand.

"Cut the bullshit Quentin! I know how this place works. Have you been sending your people after me?!" she screamed her words into his face.

Quentin's face twitched with indignation. Regaining his composure with some effort, he pushed Eleanor back by levering his forearm against her chest. Stretching to his full height, he loomed over her. "Madame, it has been a pleasure to see you again," he said, the sarcasm in his tone biting. "But I will not tolerate such groundless accusations. Je vous suggère de partir maintenant!"

Eleanor held her ground. "Not before you explain why your goons have been shooting at me. Why did you kill Khalid? What are you up to?"

Quentin's jaw tightened, and his voice dropped an octave, a dangerous edge underlying his words. "Eleanor, c'est le dernier avertissement. Security is en route."

As if on cue, two security guards burst through the door. Max was very alarmed to see they were armed, one of them unholstered his pistol and pointed it at Eleanor. She backed off and held up her hands.

"Have it your way Quentin, but this is far from over," she declared with a steely gaze.

Quentin's lips twisted into a vague smile of tacit

acknowledgement. "Of that, I am certain."

Straightening his crumpled shirt, he turned his attention to Max, the congenial façade slipping back into place as if it had never left. "Je regrette that our first meeting ended this way. I would have relished the opportunity to discuss your remarkable work. Peut-être une autre fois... maybe another time, mon ami?"

Max, uncertain and feeling completely out of his depth, managed a grin and wave as he followed Eleanor out the door: "Sure, yeah uh... anytime mate."

Within minutes they had been marched out of the building and back into the car park. The Two guards took up post at the front door of reception, having concealed their weapons, but intent on ensuring Eleanor and Max left the premises.

Eleanor unwaveringly marched back to the car. Despite his longer legs, Max struggled to keep up with her pace, half looking back towards the guards, fearing they might be chased. Once they got in the car, and Max had started it, he turned to Eleanor, unable to contain himself any longer.

"What the hell was that?!"

Eleanor calmly turned and looked at him enquiringly, but when she spoke, it was an instruction, not a response. "Drive Max."

Once they were out of the car park, Max chimed

up again: "I mean what was the point of that? I thought you knew some kind of clever spy craft? I figured you'd get him to divulge something useful. Instead, you just got us thrown out of the only lead we had… at gunpoint!"

Eleanor grinned as she continued to stare straight ahead. "Sometimes you have to shake the tree to see what falls out."

"What even does that mean? What falls out could very well land on our heads!"

Eleanor couldn't help but let out a laugh at that quip and then responded. "And besides who says we're not going to get anything useful out of this little meeting with my old chum Monsieur Dubois?"

"What?! What? I mean what, what did we get out of this?"

Eleanor simply winked back but didn't respond. So, Max continued. "Well, I'll tell you what they got. They got to know we're on to them? Listen Miss, I may not be some kind of superspy, but surely that's not a smart strategy?"

"Oh please, they already knew that. They've been watching me for a week at least, and Quentin wasn't exactly surprised to see you with me," Eleanor retorted.

"A week?" Max exclaimed.

"What?"

"A week, you said 'a week'?" Max persisted, "How

do you know it's only been that long?"

"Because that's how long I had the Tesla," she was laughing again, but now she had her phone in her hand. Looking down at it, she instructed Max: "Pull over now."

He duly complied. She got out while continuing to look at her phone, and walked around to the back of the car where the exhaust protruded. Max couldn't see what she was doing as she dipped down out of view. Momentarily she popped back up and returned to the passenger door but didn't get in. Max lowered the window and she opened her fist to reveal a small device in her hand. She grinned at Max and said: "They put a tracker on us."

She stepped back a little and looked up and down the street. Bizarrely she appeared to wave and smile at someone down the street. She then dropped the device and crushed it with her boot. Much to Max's astonishment, she made a fist with her right arm, bent it upwards and whacked her bicep with the other hand in a perfectly vulgar "Italian salute" of contempt. She then jumped back in the car: "Drive. Drive fast!"

Max slammed the 325i into first gear, let out the clutch and floored the throttle, the 1989 BMW squatted at the back and chirped its rear wheels. Max sent a silence thanks to Ahmed, having noted that he had swapped out all the tyres on his car for fresh, high-performance, rubber.

Peeling away, he glanced in the mirror; sure enough, a black 2020 Mercedes-AMG C63 bolted out from behind a parked car, 20 metres down the road.

Max knew his pursuer had about 500bhp and was capable of accelerating from rest to 62mph in about four seconds. That, versus his 170bhp and an 8-second or so acceleration time. Max nodded to himself, his jaw set firmly, and his eyes narrowed and focused. "Oh, it is on," he thought.

As soon as the Mercedes got within pouncing distance, Max executed a sharp left turn into the arteries of the Industrial Area. He knew the only way his 80s icon could take on the mighty modern Mercedes would be by exploiting the Bimmer's unerring agility.

The BMW weaved through the maze of buildings, offices and warehouses, its straight-six engine echoing off the shadowy structures. Max was pushing it hard, the car's lighter frame and manual transmission giving him the edge in the tight corners.

In his wake, a rude and raucous Mercedes, ripping asunder the evening stillness with its fully unleashed bi-turbo V8 fury, a sound that Max recognised from earlier that afternoon at the ex-Mayor's cottage. Its thundering torque enabled it to cover ground quickly and effortlessly, but he could see the driver struggling to react to the BMW's sudden direction changes.

Speeding through a narrowing alleyway, Max realised it was leading to a dead end. He slammed on the anchors hard, whipped the steering to the right and pulled the handbrake. The old 3 Series instantly rotated 180s degrees. He knew the Mercedes would be on him in an instant, but rather than play chicken with the brute, he slotted the BMW neatly behind a large heavy steel skip.

The Mercedes ploughed straight past, hard on its brakes, the ABS frantically trying to keep the car pointing straight. Even as Max pulled out and accelerated, the AMG had scrubbed off enough speed to execute a 180 spin under power. The combination of the excessive momentum and larger size, saw it smack its rear into the wall, but the driver managed to regain control and the damage did not affect the drivetrain.

Max had noted all this in his mirror and allowed himself a grin. Eleanor had been holding onto the door handle with one hand and caressing her pistol with the other. She yelled at Max: "Can you do the 180 again on my mark?" Max nodded. Eleanor opened the sunroof. They emerged out onto a wider road, Cumberland Avenue, and found themselves heading towards a roundabout.

They were three car lengths ahead of the Mercedes. Just as Max started to enter the roundabout, Eleanor made the rotate gesture with her gun hand. Max hooked up the brakes, flicked left, then right and pulled the handbrake, coming to a halt, facing back at the approaching AMG. The Mercedes was almost upon them, but Eleanor already had about half her body up through the sunroof, with her gun aiming directly at the approaching car. Two shots shattered the windscreen, neither hit the driver, but it was enough for him to take evasive action.

Trying to swerve away from the BMW, and now blinded by the cracked window, the driver inadvertently turned in towards the centre circle. The roundabout edging was made up of a concentric arrangement of bricks sloping inwards. Essentially this formed a perfect ramp for the now out-of-control and still fast-moving Mercedes to launch itself into an airborne barrel roll, arcing off to the other side and smacking onto the pavement opposite still in rotation. A line of thick hedges caught it mid-roll and halted any further movement.

Eleanor wasted no time. She hoisted herself up out of the sunroof before Max could even absorb what he had just seen, rolled onto the ground and sprinted towards the Mercedes, weaving through strewn wreckage, gun outstretched. He looked towards the once magnificent Merc, now a mangled mess, and saw their pursuer's head bobbing about inside. But the driver's side of the car was jammed up against the hedge and he couldn't get out. Max assumed Eleanor would pull him out through the passenger door.

Instinctively he looked around and down the other roads meeting the roundabout, but the area was completely deserted. He looked back at the car and much to his surprise just caught Eleanor climbing into the Mercedes herself from the passenger door.

There were a few moments of stillness as he strained to see what was going on. Then there was a bang and a flash of light from inside the car. He almost jumped out of his skin. There was no further movement that he could discern. He looked around again, wondering what to do. What if Eleanor had been shot?

Distant sirens were approaching, his mind continued to race. What would he tell them? The truth? Should he make up a story? But what about the guns? And... what about Eleanor? He was gripping the M Sport steering wheel hard, staring at the BMW emblem in the centre boss and breathing heavily.

Suddenly he was startled by Eleanor diving, feet first, in through the side window of the passenger door and screaming: "Go! Go! Go!"

Max sped off, his heart racing faster than the engine's 7000rpm, sweat beads covering his forehead despite the cool evening. He glanced back in his rear-view mirror and saw with some horror, flames starting to flicker in the wrecked AMG. Meanwhile, Eleanor straightened in her seat, clicked on her seatbelt and closed both the window and sunroof. Max looked down at her hand. "Is that blood? Are you hurt?"

"Relax," she grinned and waved the hand in his face, as if that was going to calm him down, "It's his blood, not mine." She nonchalantly wiped it on her combat trousers, leaving garish dark brown streaks on the Ripstop fabric. "Don't drive fast. Stick to the normal speeds and head towards Harrow."

Max obliged but wanted to protest that they would never make it that far. It would not be hard for police to identify his relatively rare classic from the scene of the crime and pull them over. His only hope was that Eleanor wouldn't shoot the cops!

"Did you see all that?" she was saying. Max was about to reply along the lines of "Are you crazy, of course I saw everything," though perhaps in more fruity language, even though he wasn't normally a man prone to foul language. But he stayed his tongue when the faraway look on her face indicated, she was talking to someone else, perhaps through a concealed earpiece.

"You wiped the cameras? My man! Yeah, see you in a bit dude!"

"What the hell?!" blurted out Max. "Who were you talking to?"

In response, she flashed one of her enigmatic smiles at him: "Oh, don't worry, you'll meet him shortly." As she spoke, she produced a phone from her pocket, but it wasn't hers. Retrieving her phone from another pocket, she held the two together and worked quickly, punching at both screens. Max could make out a "data transfer" graphic on the screen of her device.

"C'mon, c'mon!" she was whispering urgently.

"Okay, okay, I have questions..." Max finally cried out, "Firstly, what are you doing?"

"This was the guy's phone, I'm trying to rip the data off it, but they're also wiping it remotely at the same time." She looked back across at him, "Let's hope we manage to get something juicy off it, hopefully more than just porn!"

Max couldn't believe she was laughing again, while here he could feel his hands trembling on the wheel from the rush, the fear and excitement. "Did you shoot him?"

"Damn right I did," she looked at him with some surprise. "That was our sniper friend from the cottage, didn't you guess?"

"Actually yes, I reckoned as much from the sound of his car. But why'd you kill him? Why not turn him in?"

"Don't be silly!" Eleanor appeared startled at Max's naivety. "He wasn't going to confess to anything, and Viridis would have had him out of the holding cell by the morning, if not in a couple of hours. Then he'd just come after us again. And this time he'd do us for certain."

"You sure? How do you know that?"

"Because he was a professional killer. Because he was one of the best," there was exasperation in her voice, but she started to temper it as she continued. "Because I knew him…"

"What?!" blurted Max.

"After I left the Mayor's security team, I joined an independent outfit for a while. He used to work with them too."

"Who was he, I mean what was his name?"

"Doesn't really matter, does it? He's probably burned to a crisp by now." Max didn't know whether to be awed or scared of her apparently callousness. It was the second time today, he started to question whether he should be running with this woman, or running away from her. Talking of which…

"How come we're not being chased by police, right now?"

"Because we're ghosts my dude!" her playful disposition having returned. "We've just been erased from the surveillance by the Ghost Weaver!"

"Are you serious right now?"

"Oh, very much so!" she laughed and inputted a new address to Max's phone mounted in the dash cradle. "Head here."

She returned her attention to the assassin's phone. Sighed. Nudged down the window a little and chucked out the dead man's device. Shutting the window again, she moved her attention back to her own phone.

Meanwhile, Max became aware of a peculiar tang that hung in the car's confined space, an acrid blend of blood and bullets, metallic, pungent, sickening. He found himself shuddering at the realisation. He tried to put it out of his mind and hit the sunroof open button.

As the crisp and cleansing evening air flooded back into the cabin, he took a deep breath and hoped it would be enough to calm his frazzled nerves. He decided the rest of his questions could wait and instead focussed on following the route being indicated, driven by a newfound curiosity about the mysterious "Ghost Weaver".

A short while later, the BMW rolled into a sleepy residential street in North Harrow. Eleanor pointed out a large detached house, unremarkable save for its generous size. At the left was an entrance to a two-car garage. The door started to yawn open even before they had reached it, though strangely Max couldn't see inside. Following Eleanor's instructions to enter, he realised the interior of the garage was shielded from view, even with the door open, by a thick black string curtain.

The BMW passed through unscratched and unscathed, coming to a halt, ticking over steadily and showing no signs of its earlier workout. Max allowed the engine to run for a few seconds before switching it off, just before the garage door rolled back down.

Looking around he realised they rolled not just into the garage but the whole open lower floor of the house. Far from being homely, the cavernous expanse appeared austere and militaristic in its efficiency. Two other vehicles, both covered up, were parked adjacent.

There were crates and various types of equipment lining the walls, all meticulously arranged. There was a kitchenette and some camper beds in the far corner and next to them some gym equipment. At the centre a semi-circle arraignment of desks, stacked with computer equipment, all the displays on. The tech oasis seemingly providing the main lighting in the otherwise dim surroundings.

Among this organised chaos stood a tall, athletic black man in the prime of his early 30s. His hair was cropped close to his head, and designer stubble graced his jawline. His attire was casual yet stylish— a hoodie paired with dark jeans, accented by the iconic black and white Nike Air Jordans. There was an aura of easy confidence about him, and a warm, engaging smile that reached his eyes.

He approached Max with an effortless gait, a hint of natural rhythm in his steps, the street-smart swagger suggesting a man not only assured in his abilities but also one who revelled in the enigmatic allure of his digital wizardry.

"Yo, Max, welcome to the crib," the man greeted with a charismatic tilt of his head, his American accent pronounced, tempered by a melodic twang. "Flux Jaxon, at your service." He extended a hand, which Max took, noting the firm grip.

"So, you're the er... 'Ghost Weaver'?" Max ventured.

Flux chuckled, casting a playful look at Eleanor. "Aw that old handle?" His eyes crinkled in amusement while he grinned and flicked his wrist, glancing over at Eleanor, "Shucks, you told him that?"

Eleanor simply returned his grin. Max couldn't help his inquisitiveness: "You're American?"

"West Philadelphia, born and raised," he winked at him, stopping short of breaking into song. "And before you ask, no, I don't run up the Art Museum steps every morning, but I've been known to hack a mainframe faster than you can say 'cheesesteak'."

"Don't let his laid-back vibe fool you, Max. Flux here was the CIA's best tech specialist."

Max looked over at Eleanor and was somewhat taken aback to notice she'd removed her stained trousers, revealing the sculpted contours of her bronze legs. Her stature was modest, but her physique spoke volumes for her combat pedigree - every sinew toned from relentless training, a stark contrast to her otherwise compact frame.

She spun around, unabashed, her movement fluid and unselfconscious, and bent over to rummage through a crate for fresh gear. In this unexpected pivot, her well-defined posterior, wrapped in form-fitting functional black underwear, presented itself towards Max. The sight struck a dissonant chord in him, stirring an awkward mix of admiration and a sense of intrusion.

He shifted his gaze hastily, a tinge of embarrassment mingling with an unexpected surge of desire. This was a side of Eleanor that undid the semblance of professional distance, making him acutely aware of the complex, multifaceted woman she was - commanding, undaunted, and, in this stolen moment, unintentionally beguiling. He tried to steady his composure. Flux, observant yet discreet, chose to let the moment pass without comment.

"Truth be told, I did kind of set the bar high there," Flux acknowledged Eleanor's statement with a grin, recounting his days with the Agency. "Met this one," he gestured towards her, "on a frigid assignment in Russia."

Eleanor was now half into her fresh trousers,

pulling them up and tightening the belt strap. How did she make such a mundane garment look so attractive, Max wondered? She caught Max's brief but intense glance, her eyes met his with an ember of amusement, silently acknowledging the disquiet she'd sparked. She too let the moment pass and turned her attention back to Flux.

"Yeah, MI6 poached him after that!" she confirmed.

She walked over to Flux and gave him a hug. Max's discomfiture deepened. Perhaps they were a couple, and Flux had just caught him staring at his girl's bottom! But his fears were soon allayed, their interaction suggested a bond beyond romance.: "Now, he's the brother I never had and the wizard behind all our operations; the voice in the ear, you can ALWAYS depend on."

Flux led them towards his control centre: "You two have stirred up quite the day! El, that was nice work at Quentin's place," they slapped palms in a practised synchronised secret handshake ending with a finger pointing at each other. "I've been keeping an eye on our Monsieur Dubois. You should've seen his face when you left - priceless!"

Max's brows knitted in confusion. Monitored? He glanced at Eleanor, searching for an explanation.

She caught his look and a sly smile crept across her lips. "Remember that 'discussion' with Quentin?" she asked, the air quotes almost visible. "While I was... let's say, 'persuading' him against the wall, I left a little something on the shelf. A tiny camera, pointing right at his desk."

"Giving me eyes in the viper's nest," exclaimed Flux as he sat in his chair and swivelled back to his screens, pulling up the surveillance feed on the main monitor. "Check this, our little elf on the shelf. High-def, low-light, and as discreet as a bat in a cave!"

Max's eyes were locked on the live feed flickering across the screen as the implication of their clandestine operation settled in his mind.

"But won't they find the camera?" he asked.

"Sure man, they'll sweep that place come sunrise. But until then, we've got the best seats to the show," Flux replied, tapping the keyboard with rhythmic precision.

"Shouldn't we be listening in?" asked Max.

"Dude, I've been listening in the whole time," Flux assured him tapping his ears. "Nothing much doing in the hood, but I got a feelin the night's young yet!"

As Max processed all this, a sense of solidarity started to replace the fading rush of adrenaline. There was a newfound respect for Eleanor - and Flux - and their considerable abilities. Not to mention their audacity. They, and he dared to include himself already in that thought, had just walked brazenly into the villain's lair, planted a camera and escaped a murderous attack on their lives.

Yet something continued to nag at him. Why? Why was he here? Specifically, why was he here with these two, and what were they really all about? As they settled down to watch Quentin tapping away at his computer, the lull gave Max an opportunity to voice his lingering doubts.

"Eleanor, earlier you said you're helping me find closure," he surveyed the high-tech lair, taking in all the equipment and cars, "but there's got to be more to it than that."

There was a tremble in his voice as he continued: "I saw two people killed today, I've never witnessed anyone get killed before. I was in a real-life actual car chase, and now we're doing proper spy stuff right here," he pointed at the screen. "I need to know, why are you doing this?"

Eleanor's constant smile wavered as she and Flux shared a knowing look. Flux nodded subtly. She always valued Flux's instinct for people.

"My dad was a huge fan of your work, Max" she began, a note of vulnerability in her voice that he hadn't heard before. "He loved cars, lived for them... his name was Lucas Rodrigues."

Max started a little, actually recalling that name from his YouTube comment feed, comments that had always been positive and complimentary, the kind he liked.

"I don't just mean your ULEZ coverage, but all your car stuff, the reviews, the drives... everything," her voice tailed off a little. Max couldn't help but feel he was finally hearing her real voice.

"...and he was fun. Full of life you know. My hero!" she allowed herself a brief smile, perhaps recalling a fond memory.

"Mum and Dad, forever a couple. Eternal love birds those two, frankly it was embarrassing sometimes; right Flux?"

Flux, engrossed in his screens, chuckled: "Man, I kept telling them to get a room!" His voice took on a playful edge, as he turned to Max, bowing his head and looking up at him conspiratorially "Ya hear what I'm saying yeah?"

Max allowed a brief smile but didn't want levity to break the flow of Eleanor's story and quickly returned his attention to her. Her expression grew solemn.

"Covid took my mom..." Eleanor's voice faltered ever-so-slightly as she continued.

Max gasped, empathy overwhelming him, he spoke softly: "Eleanor, God, I'm so sorry..."

She quietened him with a wave of her hand, "It's okay. But Dad didn't take it well. Especially as Covid hadn't affected him too badly... this was before the vaccine came out of course."

Eleanor took a breath before continuing, "He

spiralled into a deep depression. I had to find a way to get him out of his funk. I remembered he'd always promised himself his dream car, but always being the dutiful husband, father, and family man, you know, life gets in the way, and he never got around to it.

"So, I surprised him on his next birthday with a concours-condition 1987 Ford Capri 280…"

Max whistled, he couldn't help himself, "Woah, the final edition Capri! There were only about a thousand of those made! They're what… about 80-85 grand now? Tell me it was Brooklands Green, right?"

Eleanor nodded, acknowledging Max's enthusiasm, "Dad would have been so chuffed to hear you approve of it. Honestly, it gave him a new lease of life, he adored it. He'd take it to car shows, go on drives, went touring in it. He spent two weeks once touring Britain going to all the places he and Mum had stayed at!

"He usually went with his best friend Virendra – both their fathers had emigrated here from Goa in India, and they'd grown up together, pretty much. Uncle Vir was a big support to him after we lost mum."

Taking a deep sigh, she went on, "Then ULEZ comes along, and Uncle Vir… well he had a supplies business, but suddenly he got hit with a stack of fines on his fleet of non-compliant vans. It pretty much collapsed his business overnight..."

She paused for a moment, as if gathering herself for more painful memories. "Uncle Vir committed suicide..."

Eleanor locked eyes with Max, "And can you imagine... I was working as the Mayor's security at the time... the man that introduced ULEZ. ULEZ, which basically killed Uncle Vir..."

Max drew his breath, he recalled how Khalid had expressed regret directly to Eleanor back at the cottage; somehow, he sensed that there was worse to come.

"Dad spiralled again of course. He stopped driving his Capri, because he refused to pay the charges, even though I put it on my account and told him to keep going out in it. But he wouldn't. He was principled like that you know?" she told him.

Max nodded in understanding.

"Yet, he couldn't bear to see it just standing there unused either, so he sold it," she shook her head sadly. Max could see, for the first time, the cloak of unyielding strength she wore thinning, revealing the raw, vulnerable human beneath.

"He lost interest in life, he got ill, he became frail, he'd go to hospital appointments on the bus, and one evening..."

Her voice trailed off as she clenched her eyes shut as if the act could ward off the painful memory.

"After he got off the bus, two muggers assaulted him..." she recounted with a tremor in her voice. Max noted Flux extending a hand for her to grasp as support, solidarity in silence. The sight stirred a mix of compassion and respect within him for Eleanor and Flux.

"The muggers... they left him for dead," she whispered, a storm of emotions swirling in her once vibrant eyes. "He succumbed to his injuries later at the hospital."

The room felt colder as Max covered his mouth with his hand, a gesture of shock and sympathy, muttering, "I'm so sorry, Eleanor. I'm deeply, deeply sorry...

In the quiet that followed, heavy with unspoken anguish, Max inquired softly, "Did they ever catch the muggers?"

"No. The police never caught them," Eleanor's voice turned icy, her gaze distant and fierce. "And they never will."

The unspoken undercurrent of her words suggested a chapter closed. Max watched as Flux, with an imperceptible nod and without a shift of his eyes from the screen, acknowledged Eleanor's resolve with a supportive fist bump. Max couldn't help but shudder as he imagined a furious Eleanor wreak revenge on her dad's attackers.

Max was struck by a profound realisation,

reassessing his initial impressions of Eleanor he inwardly admonished himself for doubting her motives. Her sparkling humour, and her breezy bravado, he now understood; were not just facets of her personality but a shield against a torrent of loss and injustice. His own ULEZ trauma started paling into insignificance, compared to the heart-wrenching losses suffered by Eleanor. The resilience she exhibited wasn't just admirable - it was aspirational.

As Max was about to articulate his newfound respect, Flux's voice cut through the heavy atmosphere. "Oh yo, guys. Eyes on this." His tone held the urgency of impending action. "We might have ourselves some action right here. Check this Eleanor, you thinking, what Imma thinkin?"

Eleanor and Max leaned into the glow of the monitor as Flux highlighted the CCTV feed from just outside Viridis HQ. Two sinister SUVs, a Range Rover and a Defender with tinted windows, crept into view.

"Mayor Victoria Hartfield, and her security," Eleanor confirmed, her tone now laced with a hard edge.

Flux's voice betrayed a gleam of anticipation, the kind that spoke of adrenaline and instinct kicking into gear: "Oh yeah baby, shit's about to go down!"

The moment was a stark pivot from reflection to

action, the quiet before a storm they were about
to willingly step into.

CHAPTER 6

On the screens, Max, Eleanor, and Flux watched as London Mayor Victoria Hartfield swanned into Quentin Dubois' office, her presence commanding as she gestured for her guards to wait outside. To Max's alarm, she chose not to sit at the desk but moved instead to the sofas, which were out of the camera's view.

Catching Max's look of concern, Flux chuckled, "Don't sweat it, man," and with a deft wink, he expertly manoeuvred the controls, panning the camera across to the sofas with a smooth zoom.

Quentin, as ever, was the quintessential charmer, but it was the Mayor who dominated the scene. "That broad's got star quality, no doubt," Flux commented, a smirk on his face.

Victoria Hartfield exuded a mix of silver screen allure and political gravitas, her sharp discerning eyes missed nothing. Dressed in a tailored, maroon business suit, her hair was a study in precision. Her voice, a melody of clear, toffee-tinged English, projecting the assuredness of someone well-versed in public oratory and debate.

She had the air of a seasoned politician able to switch from charming, to empathic, to stern and challenging, instantly, without warning, and often mid-sentence if she deemed it requisite. The dialogue soon took a turn towards the day's dramatic events.

"Now, what was all that dreadful commotion close by to here?" Victoria inquired, her gaze drilling into Quentin, obviously referencing the earlier car chase.

"It was but a trifle mademoiselle, notheeng more," Quentin reassured with a flourish of his hand, his French-Belgian accent thickening under duress. "Je vous assure, j'ai la situation bien en main."

"English please!" barked Victoria.

"I assure you Vicky, I 'ave ze mattair well in hand," he translated.

There was that switch from concerned to stern from Victoria: "In hand?! Quentin you French fool…"

"Belgian, if you pleeze," he interjected, somewhat meekly.

"Can it Quentin!," she roared back. "We just lost one of our best operatives! and I've just had the most wearisome quarrel with the Police Commissioner."

She stared at him probably expecting a response,

but he proffered only a Gallic shrug.

"And what of that woman, Rodrigues, and that journalist fellow?"

"They are undair control," Quentin assured with a dismissive flick of his hand, "they know only enough to be tiresome, notheeng more." Quentin stood, his stature reasserting itself, there was a distinct shift in authority in the room and a silent acknowledgement of the power he wielded when he chose to exercise it. "But should they dare to cross us again, they will, ah, 'ow you say, deeply regret eet."

Victoria, though visibly taken aback, retained her composure. "Concerning phase two, perhaps we should defer until after the election."

"Possiblement," Quentin conceded, his voice mellowing, hands gesturing in a calming manner. "We must speak again, oui, with our associates to cement our... 'ow you say... stratégie. And what about ze investor peetches?"

"As discussed, a room has been set aside at the charity ball for that. Will you talk to the contractors, or should I?"

"Zey may be on our payroll, but zey are at your disposal, my dear. Command zem as you wish," Quentin said with an exaggerated bow.

Victoria abruptly got to her feet: "I must depart. There's an LBC interview awaiting me at a horrendously uncivilised hour in the morning." With a clipped exchange of pleasantries, she swept out of the office, her security detail in tow.

Almost as one, Max, Eleanor, and Flux, lent back in their chairs, exhaling in unison. Flux was the first to break the silence, "About that ball they mentioned... guess who's got a golden ticket?"

"My recently deceased former colleague?" ventured Eleanor.

"Yup!" confirmed Flux. "I mean you were right; it was mostly just porn on his phone, but check this, amongst all that booty, I found these..." He held up a phone to which he had transferred the extracted data and showed it to them both. "London City Foundation Charity Ball, The Dorchester".

Eleanor's response was a playful punch to Flux's arm. "You did good, bro!" Her eyes then danced over to Max. "So, what do you say, mate? Got a tux?"

"I have as it happens," shot back Max, "but what about you? Have you got anything other than that crateful of combat clothes?" he laughed.

Eleanor smiled, her eyes sparkling with an unspoken challenge "Oooh.. let's see, I might be able to dig something up..."

The day had been a marathon of adrenaline, and the long hours had stretched into a never-ending evening. Fortunately, they had most of the following day to rest, before the ball in the evening.

Max had gone home to grab some things and dress up in his off-the-rack Marks & Spencer tuxedo. He tugged the bow-tied while checking himself in the mirror, and giggled childishly while suddenly humming the iconic 007 James Bond theme. He felt sharp and empowered in the suit and channelled the sartorial euphoria to bolster his still rattled nerves. It hadn't been easy to put the events of the day before out of his mind, much less trying not to worry too much about how the evening might unfold.

With a bit of luck and the right timing, they would get close enough to record whatever Quentin, Mayor Harfield and whoever else, were going to discuss about the sinister-sounding Phase 2. Hopefully that would be enough for Max to go public with his findings. Strengthened by the alliance of his newfound friends; the Ghost Weaver, a technological savant, and Eleanor, who defied a singular description with her myriad of skills (Max could not help but resort to thinking of her simply as a 'superspy'), Max's confidence was quietly mounting.

By 7pm he was back at the safe house. Eleanor was ready and met him outside, the very picture of allure. She had shed her usual armour for a guise that stole his breath. She slid into the passenger seat, and he couldn't help but marvel at her grace. She had shed her combat clothes for a sophisticated long black coat and tall black heels. Her hair, usually free and untamed, was now styled in soft waves that framed her face, a face enhanced by artful touches of makeup that seemed to draw the very light towards her. Deep red lips parted in a smile that was equal parts wicked and inviting. Her eyes, rimmed with kohl, held a depth that was both captivating and dangerous.

"Looking smart there Max!" She winked at him, "Shall we?"

Max started with a jolt. "We should," he managed to stutter, his hands fumbling for the gear stick as he tried to mask his sudden infatuation. Eleanor grinned, no doubt catching the unguarded admiration in his eyes.

They parked on Curzon Street, Max Turner shut off the engine of his BMW 325i, its potent hum yielding to the vibrant thrum of London's nightlife. The Dorchester Hotel stood just around the corner.

Eleanor put her gun in the glovebox of the car and stepped out, removing her coat to leave it in the car and revealing the evening's attire - a striking black Versace dress that draped over her frame with lethal elegance. The gown, bold yet sophisticated featured a deep slit along the side of the dress granting a tantalising peek at her sleek legs.

Max, suddenly felt under-dressed, the hubris of earlier evaporating as his rent-a-style stratum met bona fide sophistication and class. He fumbled with his bow tie, his hands betraying the unease that gripped him. "You clean up pretty good," he remarked, attempting to mask his nervousness with a wisp of humour.

Eleanor fixed him with a glance that was both mischievous and piercing, and from somewhere produced an ornate Venetian mask. "Blending in is the key," she reminded him, her tone a blend of excitement and forewarning.

Too late in the day, Max had realised that it was a masked ball. He looked down a little dejectedly at the Batman mask he'd managed to find at the Pound Store down the road from his place, its plastic simplicity a stark contrast to her glittering masquerade.

He couldn't help but feel a wave of trepidation wash over him - not just for the charade they were about to embark on, but also from Eleanor's daunting presence. He suddenly felt underdressed, ill-equipped and frankly out of his depth. The Bond theme previously in his head had somehow been superseded by Gangnam Style.

As they walked towards The Dorchester, he stole another glance at Eleanor, resplendent and unfazed. Drawing a deep breath, he tried to imbibe some of her indomitable spirit, hoping that would be enough to get him through the evening.

In her grasp was a diminutive clutch, its simplicity belying the arsenal it likely contained. With a deft motion that betrayed her familiarity with covert gadgets, she produced a case akin to one for earpods. She popped it open to reveal two discreet earpieces, extending one towards him with a gesture that brooked no argument. "Pop this in your ear," she instructed, her voice low but clear. "We'll be able to stay constantly in touch, and Flux is online too."

Max took the offered device, curiously examining the tiny piece of technology between his fingers before inserting it into his ear. It was a lifeline, a whisper of reassurance that they were not alone in their endeavours.

They entered the grandiose banquet hall having presented their stolen invite and been waved through after a quick security check, Eleanor's clutch only receiving a cursory glance inside. Max gasped as he looked around; it was like stepping onto the set of a period drama. The walls dripped in gilded opulence, catching the lights and casting back vibrant reflections.

Max couldn't help but ponder how the vulgar juxtaposition of affluent display would sit with charities such events were supposed to serve. In his head, he debated conducting a cost analysis of the evening's expenditures versus its actual philanthropic yield.

Such mental calculations were abruptly halted when he noticed a huge digital counter mounted against one wall. It was indicating £968,658 and continuing to clock upwards. He abandoned his line of thought and self-admonished his instinctual journalistic cynicism. With a mental shake, he brought his focus back to why they were here.

Eleanor was speaking: "Let's split up. If you see Quentin or the Mayor, let me know immediately. I just need to know where they'll be having their meeting, once we know that, we can record what they're saying and then get out of here. I've got an audio transducer in my purse that turns walls into ears."

Max nodded in understanding. He was also relieved to see at least one other man had also done as him and opted to be 'Batman'. He felt slightly less stupid in his mask choice which served to alleviate some of the insecurity he was experiencing.

Even so, the crowd they mingled amongst was a kaleidoscope of London's hoi polloi meets the glitterati, some adorned in finery that would normally be seen on the catwalks of Milan fashion week, and others sporting an off-the-peg summer sale special from Primark. A scale of extremes represented pretty much by Eleanor and himself he noted.

As she glided off into the crowd, mask and tranquil smile in place, she was a far cry from the G. I. Jane he had thus far seen in action. It seemed this girl would be as comfortable at the poshest do in London tonight, as she would be on a battle-field.

The atmosphere was a heady mix of the high and mighty literally patronising the proletariat. The masks served as the perfect veil for anonymity, keeping eager selfie-chasers at bay, restrained by uncertainty over the true identities of their quarry.

Was that Emma Watson mischievously casting spells as a Goth Witch? Did Max just brush someone whose posture screamed statesman... a former British Prime Minister perhaps? And the voice behind that Deadpool mask was uncannily reminiscent of Ryan Reynolds, but that would be far too on-the-nose, wouldn't it? Actually, that is something the zany movie star would probably do.

Max's heart started to sink a little. Much as the masks had been useful in minimising the chances of party-crashers like Eleanor and himself being discovered, it also became apparent that it would make their task tougher too.

Admittedly Quentin's accent would be a relative giveaway, and Mayor Hartfield was sure to have an entourage, but much as he searched, he neither visually, nor aurally, was able to identify either of them. To his chagrin, he had to report as much when Flux checked in on comms. Eleanor was quick with her encouragement though: "I know it's difficult but keep searching, they've got to be here."

Dejected, he found himself distracted by the string quartet perched on an intricately carved balustrade, their strings singing sweetly above the hum of genteel conversation. They too were in masks and Victorian-era costumes. They were strangely captivating, but eventually he pulled himself away when he noticed the buffet table. The journalist instinct kicked in - free food was fair game whenever it was available.

Eleanor's voice crackled in his ear. "I've got a six on the big M… am covering. Max hang back, keeping scanning for QD."

Max surveyed the expansive hall, his eyes scanning for any sign of Eleanor's sleek black form or the distinctive tumult that Mayor Hartfield's presence invariably stirred. Yet amidst the sea of elegant attendees, there was no ripple to indicate either of them, no dramatic flurry to suggest the Mayor's penchant for the spotlight.

The buffet table beckoned; a veritable cornucopia of gastronomic delights that seemed to whisper his name. Perhaps, Max mused, Quentin might also indulge in a culinary pause, and he could chance upon him amidst the hors d'oeuvres or the Belgium chocolate! The scents wafting from the array of dishes were too tempting to resist, drawing him ever closer.

A dapper waiter materialised, proffering a flute of bubbling champagne. The golden liquid certainly offered the shimmering promise of liquid courage. But Max declined with a polite nod. Having tangled with alcoholism, he knew he had pulled back from the brink, and he couldn't risk his hard-won sobriety. He dared not touch it, even though he knew it would have helped steady his nerves.

He grabbed a plate and started piling on pickings from the array of finger food on display. Again, the comms came to life. "M's just entered a side room, but still no sign of... oh wait... yup, QD spotted. And in he goes. Right, deploying Tired Damsel."

Max detected that familiar humorous tone, but had to ask, "Tired Damsel?"

Flux's voice buzzed with excitement, the pace of his words matching the quickening pace of the operation: "Ain't no sweat, man," he chuckled, "it's all 'bout Ellie playin' that tired achy-breaky feet game, ya know? Just needs a sec to lean up against that wall, pretend to work out the kinks, take time-out for a tootsie rub. But for real? She's got that clutch pressed up against the bricks. Crank up the volume and listen close—

we're 'bout to tune into Big M's secret broadcast, live and direct from the Dorch!"

Max found he had paused with his hand holding a tong grasping a cheese canape in mid-air, as he tried to comprehend what he'd been told. Eleanor would lean against the wall outside the room, feigning fatigue. As she 'massaged' her feet, the cleverly concealed microphone in her purse would be eavesdropping on the adjacent room. The image of Eleanor, graceful even in pretence, jumped into his head. He was struck by her ingenuity, her ability to turn even the simplest act into a strategic move, and of course her effortless beauty.

"This is what we're catchin', got some fuzz on the line, but chill, I'll try to clean it up," reported Flux. Max heard the static-filled feed coming from inside the room. A mixture of different voices. Victoria and Quentin's were identifiable, but there were others too.

In a few moments everyone seemed to settle down, and Quentin began what appeared to be a pitch:

"Merci beaucoup, laydeez and gentlemen, and welcome. We know your time eez very valuable, but let me assure you, I believe you weel find ze next few minutes to be most intéressant, informative, and above all... très profitable."

He was greeted by an approving murmur from whoever his audience was; safe to assume they were high-rolling investors.

"Ah, so, let me paint you ze picture of ze grand vision of Viridis Ventures, oui? You see, in zis modern era, 'green' is not just a colour, non, it is a lucrative currency in ze marketplace of ideas and, of course, commerce.

"At Viridis, we are riding zis green wave, not just for ze sake of ze environment – although zat is a charming side effect – but because it is profitable, très profitable. Our plan, it is elegant in its complexity. We align ourselves with ze environmental movement, but our true aim? Profits, mon ami.

"We invest in ze green technologies, but let's be frank, it is more about ze image, ze marketability, and most importantly, ze profitability. Green-washing? Peut-être. But consider it necessary for ze business. Ze public, they love a hero, and we, at Viridis, we wear zat cape with pride. But it is easily removable, non?"

There was polite laughter in the room.

"It is not really about reducing carbon footprints; we are selling an ideology, a lifestyle. It's all about ze branding, you understand? This is ze essence of Green Capitalism. We don't change ze system; we exploit it to our advantage. We use ze tools of capitalism – marketing, branding, consumerism – and we paint zem green. We are very effective at... 'ow you say, 'social engineering', yes?

"So, when you think of Viridis Ventures,

remember, you are not just looking at another corporation. You are looking at ze future, both of our planet and your own wallet. In zis age, my dear friends, green is ze new gold, and we are ze alchemists transforming it.

"Remember, in zis world, it is ze clever, ze adaptable who thrive. We are merely playing the game by its rules, and playing it well, if I may say so myself."

Another murmur in the room, but this time laced with perceptible impatience, someone spoke up, but what she said was muffled by the other voices.

"Yes, yes, of course... so 'ow weel we do zis? Weel proof of concept will be exercised right 'ere in London; and our plan eez the most simple itself..."

Loud music suddenly filled the hall, and an announcement was made for a popular TV chat show host who popped up onto a stage, welcomed by loud cheers and applause. He proceeded to woo the audience with self-effacing jokes received by rowdy laughter, announcing sponsors, participants and auction items. All of this additional noise interfered dramatically with the sound pickup from Eleanor's mic, and all they could now hear were snippets of what was being said in the room:

"Yes, absolutely. Rolled out nationwide..."

"But what about..."

"I assure you monsieur, it will…"

"…full authority…"

"…easy, we'll do it with trackers…"

"Non, non, mon amie, not only will they…."

"that's the beauty of it… they'll literally beg us to…"

Suddenly there was a voice, a real voice directed at Max from his left. "Something not right with that?"

He had been focusing so hard on trying to listen to his earpiece, he was still rooted to the spot, tongs in hand, another canapé suspended in the air. Realising this, he hastily placed it on his plate and returned the tongs, turning with an embarrassed grin to face the inquirer.

It was a man, wearing an intricate mask that evoked the sinuous style of a serpent, in a masterful blend of artistry and symbolism. The surface mimicked the texture of scales, and it was painted in iridescent shades of green and gold. It covered the upper half of his face. There was something familiar about the grin below it. Max noticed the eyes inside the black-outlined oval-shaped openings, scanning his face for a reaction.

Max found his mind hunting through the attic of his memories to provide some kind of recall. There was a familiarity to the man's stance. With a flourish, the man lifted the mask, and the recognition dawned on Max. "Josh Burnett!" he exclaimed, his voice a mix of astonishment and relief. Surprised, but delighted to finally see a familiar face, he put down the plate and grabbed Josh's outstretched hand leaning in for a bro-hug. "Omigod Josh, long time! How the heck have you been?"

Josh had been one of the leading organisers involved in the anti-ULEZ expansion protests that Max had covered. He'd been a leading personality in the campaign, frequently being interviewed on radio and TV and turning up regularly at major events to question and heckle the then-mayor, Khalid Siddique.

"I've been great V-Max, how about you?"

Max remembered he was still wearing his mask. "Dude, how did you recognise me?"

"V-Max! Are you kidding?" Josh's laugh was easy, familiar. "No mistaking your stance, my friend. And the bat mask? Perfect for our very own caped crusader!"

With a chuckle, Max deflected the compliment: 'C'mon mate. And by the way, love your mask, that thing's extraordinary!"

"Thanks! It's based on Veles, a mythical Slavic deity of earth, waters, and the underworld... I just thought it looked kinda cool really," Josh's chuckle was rich with an undertone of mischief.

Max joined in the cackling, but something was

off. The mask Josh wore was an expensive masterpiece, constructed from a quality material, it appeared to have gold leaf inlaid, and were those zirconia embellishments? He took a subtle step back to take in the finely cut tuxedo Josh sported. He realised another reason he had had trouble recognising the former campaigner, was because he was used to seeing him in Anti-ULEZ t-shirts and faded old jeans.

"Nice threads... tailored?" ventured Max.

Josh opened his arms and struck a debonair pose. He replaced the mask on his face and confirmed: "Absolutely!" he pulled on his gold cuffs to emphasise the quality of his dress.

Still processing, Max continued the banter despite the questions swirling in his mind: "Looking slick man. A far cry from back in the day marching up and down Whitehall, right?"

Josh's grin held a trace of nostalgia. "And you, V-Max... or should I say, Vanishing Max? You dropped off the radar! Everything good?"

"Yes," Max hesitated, weighing his words. "Just some personal demons to wrestle with, you know?"

"I hear you, those were some days, eh?" Josh's understanding seemed genuine, his tone dipping in solidarity. "So, what's the occasion tonight? On the prowl for a scoop?"

Max's laugh was a touch too forced. "Scoop?

Hardly. I'm here with a... a friend..."

"Yeah, I think I saw her earlier. What a stunner! A bit of a femme fatale huh? V-Max, you sly devil!" Josh gave Max a friendly jab in the ribs.

Max pondered how to respond, instead he just grinned sheepishly and decided to turn the question around back at Josh, "And you? This scene's a bit... well, poncy for you, isn't it? What are you doing here?"

Josh abruptly straightened and gave him a wink through the mask, "Cashing in mate!"

Max was confused, "Huh? I mean you; you were amazing. One of the fiercest campaigners out there. An anti-establishment rebel, I figured you'd hate this sort of thing?"

Josh bowed slightly as if expressing his gratitude at the acknowledgement, yet it somehow seemed unnatural: "You ain't wrong; course it meant I attracted some attention too, right?"

Max continued: "Well I remember some people really went after you at one point, calling you a right-winger, a conspiracy theorist, racist even and whatnot. But you NEVER backed down. You were always proud and defiant!"

"Oh yes, they did accuse me of all that didn't they?" Josh nodded and then looked at Max directly as if gauging his reaction, "I must have been doing something right then?"

Max wasn't sure what to make of that. The Josh

he had known was passionate, unyielding - his actions had always appeared to be fuelled by genuine fervour rather than any kind of ulterior motive.

"And things have been good for me since then, as you can see!" Josh continued.

"I CAN see, and I'm so pleased for you," Max quickly replied, "Nobody deserves a bit of success more than you!" He was beaming, but inside, he was perplexed.

While they had been talking, Josh had put his arm around Max's shoulders, and somehow, they had started walking.

"Some people, in high places, liked what I did I guess, and the payroll got fatter and fatter..."

"Oh? So, what's the gig?" Max probed, masking his scepticism with a curious tilt of his head.

"Well, I followed your lead, my old chum! I did a bit of 'influencing' innit?"

"Social media? You? You could barely take a selfie I remember!" joked Max hoping that the increasing doubts in his mind weren't being telegraphed by his voice. Especially as he realised they had now exited the ballroom and were in a corridor. Ahead two security personnel stood monitoring the hallway, which at least was reassuring.

"No, you're right, but I didn't need to. I had friends, friends like these gentlemen."

Suddenly, to Max's great surprise, one of the guards stepped towards him and stuck a pistol in his side. Max's heart skipped and an unspoken threat chilled him, as he realised he was in imminent and very real danger. "Don't make a scene Mr Turner, Just walk with us," the guard's voice was a controlled murmur, designed to prevent any public alarm.

Flux's voice crackled in his ear, a thread of concern woven through his usual nonchalance. "Talk to me, Max. What's the 411?"

Max's mind raced. To speak would be to disclose his lifeline of communication. He chose silence, nodding subtly to the guard and allowing himself to be ushered away.

The feed from the meeting room was rich with potential despite the noisy interference, but it played on as background noise while Eleanor and Flux zeroed in on Max's predicament. The stakes of their mission had just escalated. The clandestine conversation was heating up and starting to get interesting, but Eleanor's instincts flared; she knew Max was in deep trouble.

"I'm breaking off Flux, going to help Max. Track him and relay," she then addressed Max directly: "Max, don't respond, just listen to me, stay calm and do as they say, I'm en route to your six."

"West corridor, two metres in, on the move," came back Flux's response.

Max glanced back. Josh's eyes met his, a hard glint replacing the earlier camaraderie. With a slow, deliberate wave, he uttered a farewell laced with unknown threat. "See ya... V-Max T."

As Max was led down the hall, he drew a deep breath, trusting in Eleanor's promise, and braced for whatever was going to happen next. Which didn't take long.

Eleanor emerged through the door with the calculated clumsiness of an inebriated prima donna. Clutching a flute of champagne, she feigned a stumble, her movements exaggerated but controlled. "Max, darling... where did you go?" she slurred, her voice an orchestrated mess of confusion and mock hurt. "Leaving me all by my lonesome—how could you?". The words tumbled from her lips, heavy with pretended intoxication, her eyes scanning the corridor under the guise of a drunken befuddlement.

Josh stepped forward to try and intercept, but before he could even speak, Eleanor had become a blur of action. She threw the contents of the glass in Josh's face and with the other hand ripped off his elaborate and weighty mask, twisting it around and using it as an impromptu bludgeon. She struck with the hard edge of the mask, catching Josh right in the neck, forcing a sharp gasp as his breath choked and his knees buckled.

The guard holding Max, momentarily stunned

by her rapid takedown, began to react, shifting the pistol's aim from Max's side towards Eleanor.

With the grace of a dancer and the precision of a sniper, she pivoted on her heel, swinging the mask like a discus, releasing it to fly across the room. It spun through the air and collided with a sickening crunch against the face of the guard holding Max at gunpoint.

The guard staggered backwards, a thin line of blood tracing down from a cut above his eyebrow, the pistol's aim now veering wildly. Eleanor closed the gap in a heartbeat, her hand snatching the weapon away with practised ease. She pivoted, using the guard's momentum to fling him aside as he tried to recover his bearings.

On Max's other side, the second guard, bigger and stronger than the first, reacted sharply. He seized his captive's arm, wrenching it behind his back. The sudden pain shot through Max's shoulder, and before he could resist, an arm snaked around his neck, clamping down in a chokehold. Dragging him toward the emergency exit at the end of the hallway.

Back inside, the first guard had recovered and was now lunging at Eleanor with balled fists. But she was ready, her body swaying aside to dodge the first punch, then stepping in close to deliver a rapid sequence of strikes to his abdomen and throat with the gun she had snatched from his hand. The guard reeled, his attacks faltering as he struggled to keep up with her assault. With a swift kick to the knee, Eleanor brought him down, his body collapsing beside the unconscious Josh.

Eleanor purposefully cocked the pistol she had snatched off the first guard and was about to give chase when Flux's urgent voice cracked through the com: "El, get down now! Shooters incoming!"

Instantly Eleanor dropped to the floor, and two more men burst through the emergency door just as the guard and Max reached it, their shotguns blazing without warning. The elegant wallpaper in the corridor was shredded by a hail of pellets, and the air filled with the stench of gunpowder and torn fibres.

The guards, their weapons emitting wisps of smoke, used the disorienting cacophony to their advantage, dragging Max out into the night. Eleanor, pinned down by the relentless gunfire, could only watch as the door slammed shut behind them, leaving her in a sudden, eerie silence.

She waited, every muscle coiled, ready to spring into action at Flux's signal. "Clear! They've turned, making a beeline for a pair of waiting black cabs," his voice crackled through the earpiece.

Like a sprinter off the blocks, Eleanor catapulted from her crouched stance. Exiting into the crisp night, she just caught sight of a phone being tossed out of one of the taxis, as the doors slammed shut. Without hesitating, she took aim and shot at the driver's side window, hoping the shock of shattering glass would be enough to give them pause. But much to her surprise, the bullet simply bounced off the glass.

"They're armoured!" she reported back to Flux. Both taxis in synchronicity, gunned their engines and the rear tyres lit up, the ripping rotation whipping up smoke. These were not the usual plug-in hybrid electric black cabs. "You seeing this Flux?"

"Specials, but London's full of black cabs; those two are gonna merge with the traffic like smooth criminals in a moonwalk contest," confirmed Flux. "Girl you better get your skates on!"

Eleanor, retrieved the discarded phone, realising it was Max's and that they would not be able to track him. Stuffing it in the clutch that now hung across her shoulders, Eleanor looked around helplessly. She didn't have the keys to Max's BMW. The usual bevvy of beautiful exotic cars was parked out the front of the hotel, but she didn't have time to run back to beat the keys out of the parking valet.

Frantically searching the immediate vicinity, she spotted an Uber Eats delivery rider on an electric scooter turning in from Park Lane. She ran to intercept the rider as he rounded the side of The Dorchester, and positioned herself in the middle of the road, stance wide, her silhouette a defiant barrier against the soft glow of streetlights, she lifted and aimed the borrowed gun with unerring precision.

The sight of such a vision, caused the rider to simply jump off and scarper down a side street. The still-moving two-wheeler wobbled past her, slammed into some roadwork barricades and fell over, sending hot pizzas spilling out onto the cold tarmac. She retrieved the bike, stuffed a slice of Spicy Meat Feast into her mouth, the heat providing fleeting comfort, and raced off in the direction of the cabs. She had no helmet and wore only her flailing evening dress, legs unprotected and the gun jammed between her thigh and the seat. She sliced up Park Lane before veering onto the pulsating artery of Piccadilly.

Eleanor was way behind, but her adrenaline spiked as the Ghost Weaver's voice in her ear guided her in pursuit of the phantoms ahead. Unfortunately, as Flux had predicted, the taxis did pull a vanishing act as they melted into the tapestry of the still bustling back roads of Leicester Square.

"Sorry Ellie, I think they must be rocking rotating license plates or something, 'cause I can't get a fix on their tags anywhere." Flux's frustration was palpable, mirroring the sinking feeling in Eleanor's gut as the urban jungle swallowed the accursed cabs whole. Her chase was done. For now.

Max's return to the land of the conscious was a jarring and disorienting affair. He wasn't sure if he had been punched out, or drugs had been used, but the ringing in his head and a stiff jaw suggested it might have been the former.

An odd sensation indeed, he'd never been knocked out before. He took a moment to assimilate this thought as he willed his eyelids to part, a simple task that seemed Herculean in his dazed state. His vision began to regain focus, not that there was much to see. The reality of his predicament sharpened as he realised he was bound, his wrists fastened tightly behind him with unforgiving zip ties, and his ankles similarly shackled to the cold metal legs of the utilitarian chair he sat on.

He struggled to make any sense of his surroundings. He was in a large room. Maybe a warehouse come to think of it. its full expanse shrouded in darkness that stretched beyond the harsh circle of light he found himself in. Industrial lamps on tall stands cast stark shadows, their cables snaking off into the void like tendrils. In front of him was a desk that seemed to have lived many lives before this clandestine moment, its surface scarred with the marks of heavy use.

There were three men, all dressed in matching rent-a-commando outfits, staring directly at him. One stood sentinel before Max, another lounged on a swivel chair behind the desk, combat boots insolently desecrating the desk's surface. The third perched on the edge of the desk, the relaxed grip on his compact submachine gun doing nothing to lessen its threat, though at least the weapon's barrel was thankfully not trained on Max. Nonetheless, the casual flick of the guard's trigger finger was unnerving enough.

"What the hell is going on here? Who are you? Why am I here? Who tied me up?!"

The ferocity of his outburst took even Max by surprise. He glared up across at the men, his demands for answers hanging in the still air of the warehouse. The intensity in his stare was unyielding as he locked eyes with the man standing before him. He stood bolt upright, muscular and powerful, with a body appearing to be chiselled from granite. Blond army-cropped hair, angular jawline, piercing blue eyes and pale features.

There was a pause - a heavy, lingering silence - before the man responded in a thick accent. "You may know me only as ze Bone-Crusher," the moniker rolling off his tongue with a mix of pride and warning. But it prompted muffled laughter and snorting from his companions. With a sharp pivot and a withering stare, the so-called Bone-Crusher silenced them. From the few words he had spoken, Max had surmised he was German, or perhaps Austrian.

"You vill disclose to me ze information I seek," the Bone-Crusher continued, his voice low and resonating with restrained fury. "or I shall become ze embodiment of my namesake, giving mein comrades here a spectacle zat is most... amusing, ja?" The question addressed to his so-called comrades rather than to him, Max surmised.

"Listen mate," Max found himself talking back, "I don't want any of my bones to be crushed, fractured, bent or broken. I don't know what it is you think I know, but I'm all ears. What do you want from me?"

It would be fair to say that the man in front of him was taken aback by this complete lack of resistance of any kind. In fact, Max was sure he saw disappointment flash across his face. Collecting himself, the man leaned forward, the thick accent more pronounced as he interrogated, "I vish to know vhat Mayor Siddique imparted to you before his untimely demise."

Max stared back and gave himself a moment to think about the gravity of his situation. He was held and bound in an unknown place that could be so vast no one would hear his cries for help, so that would be futile, and the men knew it.

From their clothes, their robust physiques and

demeanour, the men all appeared to be trained operatives of some kind, and not adverse to employing lethal means, as recent events had chillingly illustrated. They were also not British. The main interrogator appeared Germanic, and as for the other two, while they hadn't spoken yet, their features hinted at Southern European.

More alarmingly, while he could still feel the earpiece reassuringly nestling in his cochlea, it had fallen completely silent. His last glimpse of Eleanor was a vivid recollection of her overpowering a guard with effortless precision, while he was being dragged backwards. He desperately hoped she was okay, but logic suggested, she was probably fine.

Inwardly he berated himself for ignoring the inkling that had gnawed at him since their first encounter. As he had correctly concluded at the time, Eleanor had been the intended target, not him. He had warned himself not to get entangled in her perilous world. And yet now here he was, ensnared and facing the prospect of a brutal interrogation. His optimism waned; he was painfully aware of his low threshold for pain.

"Sure, I don't mind," Max replied with a forced casualness. "But I want to talk to whoever's in charge, not you Mr Crusher." The other two started giggling again, this time the frowning man, simply barked at them: "Ruhe!"

Then turning his attention back to Max, trying

to present a failing semblance of civility he spoke with controlled calmness, his accent thickening with each word: "If you vould be so obliging, Herr Turner, I vill convey your information to mein superior, und you can zen be free to leave."

"Listen, Drago, I told you I'm willing to have a nice civil chat about my meeting with Khalid, but to whoever is giving you orders. If I tell you, you might not relay it correctly... it could be... lost in translation."

The snickers from his colleagues returned, this time unabated. The man known as Bone-Crusher didn't bother to silence them and seemed to somehow straighten his already straight frame. "Very well Mr Turner... I'll be back." With that, he swivelled abruptly and walked off into the darkness. Austrian, Max confirmed to himself, definitely Austrian.

He overheard one of the other men whisper to the other, "Drago!" and they almost fell off their perches laughing. "You're-a funny man, you make-a us laugh, Seenyor Turner!" the one on the table shouted at him. Italian, concluded Max.

That amusement, however, turned chillingly serious as the Italian operative's face hardened, the machine gun now aimed squarely at Max. "And listen, if you make any jokes about Italians, I will shoota you. So I suggest you shaddap you face."

Max fought hard to restrain his laughter,

fortunately, the aching jawline at least served to assist in that regard.

Somewhat surprisingly, it was not long before he heard approaching footsteps echoing through the cavernous space. His eyes widened with disbelief as the silhouette of Mayor Victoria Hartfield materialised from the inky darkness. She approached Max, stepping into the spotlight as if onto a stage; her gown from the evening's ball still draped elegantly around her. She was a stark contrast to the empty surroundings. His bruised jaw dropped open involuntarily.

Stunned to see her, Max couldn't help but wonder how long it had been since he had been at the charity ball. The absurdity of the scene was stark, the Mayor in her ballroom finery, glowing in the gloom of the warehouse, and him, strapped to a chair, dishevelled and downcast in the spotlights, despite still being dressed in his tuxedo, bow tie even now in place; too formal for the desolate setting, yet paradoxically underdressed for a confrontation with the city's most formidable figure.

"Ah Mr Max Turner, we meet at last!" Victoria spoke, her voice theatrical yet laced with a steely undertone.

Max stared at her trying to recover from the surprise of her appearance. Recalling that she had once been a 'Bond Girl' he simply couldn't help himself. He saw an opening for levity - or perhaps a gambit for time: "Mayor Hartfield... Do you expect me to talk?"

Victoria paused mid-stride, her stare sharpening as she assessed his quip. The warehouse's dim light played across her features, momentarily softening her stern visage into an almost playful expression. "Very amusing..." she conceded, the ghost of a smile on her lips, "But wrong film, that was before my time Mr Turner!"

She stepped up close and surveyed him. Leaning down, her proximity enveloping him. Her face drew near, close enough for the air around Max to become perfumed with the distinct mix of her powerfully scented perfume, laced with the rich, warm undertones of aged brandy, likely sipped earlier in the evening. The potent combination was as intoxicating as it was disarming, a stark contrast to the sterile chill of the room they occupied. Her eyes, sharp and calculating, held his in a steady gaze as her hands rose to his neck. Max tensed, expecting to be throttled.

Instead, she deftly loosened his bow tie and unbuttoned the top buttons of his shirt, her palm briefly resting against the warmth of his bare chest beneath. Moving her face across to his cheek, lips almost brushing past his, her breath grazing his cheek, she murmured into his ear: "There now Mr Turner, isn't that more comfortable?" Her voice was a soft caress, belying the threat that lay beneath.

Suddenly she pulled back, but not before letting her hand slide all the way down to his groin, before straightening and once again staring sternly down at him, seemingly surveying Max from head to toe. "My, what a tangle we find ourselves in!"

She turned to the Austrian: "Why am I here Stahl?"

He seemed caught off-guard, not ideal for a man in his profession: "Ah, Madam Mayor, I vas under ze impression you vanted to have vords vith ze captive?"

"Moi? Speak to this fellow? When I could be at home sipping a nightcap, thinking about that nice young waiter that served me a delicate amuse-bouche... a sliver of smoked salmon atop a hard, ripe cucumber..." she suggestively extended and rolled out those last few words.

Victoria's mind seemed to wander. The mercenaries glanced at each other in a mixture of amusement and befuddlement. Max wondered if the Mayor had been celebrating a little too hard after her meeting earlier that evening.

Eventually, she seemed to snap out of her fantasies, "Oh but tiresome duty calls, doesn't it?" Suddenly she waved a questioning hand at Stahl: "Well?"

The tall Austrian visibly started: "Madam?"

Victoria's command was sharp, her tone brooking no argument. "Untie him! And bring him closer to the table. If we must engage in conversation, let us at least afford each other the courtesies of civility."

"Immediately, Madam Mayor," the Austrian mercenary affirmed with a crisp nod to the two subordinates who promptly lifted Max's chair and repositioned it adjacent to the desk, snipping through the zip ties that bound him.

Victoria sat in the swivel chair behind the desk. Much to his surprise, she spun fully around with a flourish before returning to the desk, slamming both palms on the surface, her gaze piercing into Max's with a commanding intensity: "Right then Mr Turner, let's get down to brass tacks, shall we? You're going to tell me everything Siddique said before his untimely departure."

For a moment Max just glared back at her, taking in the extraordinary woman before him. A former Hollywood starlet, turned activist, turned politician, turned evil villain straight out of a movie.

"Untimely you say?" Max shot back with a cold edge, massaging his wrists trying to restore circulation after finally being freed from his restraints. "Why don't you tell me first why you had him killed?"

A brief flash of fury contorted Victoria's

perfectly sculpted features before smoothing into an expression of patronising pity. "I hold nothing but the deepest regard for the vital initiatives enacted by my esteemed predecessor. His passing is nothing short of a tragedy for our beloved capital," she declared, her voice dripping with feigned grief as she dipped her head in a theatrical gesture of grief.

Max stared back at her, uncertain what to make of the performance. It was almost convincing: "This isn't a press conference Madam Mayor," he finally responded.

Eleanor raised her head, she was grinning: "No, that's tomorrow, Max!" She laughed.

"Did your scriptwriters come up with that, or is it all improv?" Max asked, "You actually seem to be enjoying all this."

Victoria leaned back in her chair: "Well I've had a good night, haven't I?"

"I wouldn't know Madam Mayor…"

"Oh, wouldn't you? What about that cute little friend of yours, would she know?"

Max didn't respond but continued staring at her, with what he hoped would be a look of unmoved defiance. In return she leered at him somewhat lasciviously, appearing to peer down his open shirt. "I was hoping our first meeting would be under less… vexing circumstances. But you have thrown yourself into the deep end, my dear boy."

There was no question Victoria was drunk, but what Max couldn't ascertain was did that make her more or less dangerous? The Mayor was displaying more than a hint of infatuation with him, perhaps he could work with that; or was it all just a ruse? A masterful act by a woman accustomed to switching personas at the drop of a hat? She was a woman used to getting whatever she wanted, but also at making people believe the role she was playing.

Yet, there was the possibility that her guard was down, that she might slip and expose the secrets he had sought. Max stole a cautious glance at the armed mercenaries nearby, their watchful eyes reminding him of the delicate dance he was engaged in.

"I'm not the one holding people at gunpoint Madam Mayor…"

"Oh please… my friends call me 'Vicky', you can address me as Victoria for now, and we'll see how the evening progresses, shall we?"

"What do you want from me… Victoria? You obviously had me abducted at the ball, why have you brought me here?"

A flicker of sober determination cut through the mellow sheen in Victoria's eyes, as if she could snap in and out of her roles at will. "What did Khalid tell you?"

Max hesitated. He shook his head and moved

back in his chair, putting up a last show of resistance. Stahl moved forward and slammed a fist hard down on the table right in front of Max with a thunderous crash, denting the metallic surface, a brute force demonstration meant to shatter any lingering defiance.

Max's eyes snapped to Stahl's menacing smirk as the fist recoiled, primed for its new trajectory intended to connect with his face.

Time to throw the towel in. Max raised his hands in a gesture of capitulation, redirecting his attention to Victoria, ready to bargain with the only currency he had. "Alright, alright! He said something about... Viridis Ventures."

He saw a flicker of acknowledgement in her expression. He decided to play his hand: "He mentioned you... said you were just a puppet..."

Victoria rose to her feet, her face a storm of indignation: "I'm no puppet, Mr Turner!" She bellowed, the words ricocheting off the cold warehouse walls. Her manicured finger jabbed towards Stahl, "This is what puppets look like, and I, Mr Turner, I am the Maestra pulling the strings!"

On her silent cue, Stahl lunged forward. His fist, a mallet of flesh and bone, crashed into Max's gut. Air whooshed from his lungs, and he doubled over, desperately trying to recover his breath, fighting back the convulsions of shock ravaging his body from the sudden unanticipated violence. Taste and vision mingled in a mesh of pain; iron flooded his mouth, whether from bile or blood, he wasn't sure.

The last time he'd been punched like that was when he got into a fight over a girl with his then-best mate, Nick, back in Sixth Form. The long-buried memory resurfaced unbidden – a foolish scuffle over who, Judy? She wasn't even all that now that he recalled her. Suddenly, bizarrely, he found himself wondering what might have become of Nick.

The absurdity of the thought amidst his dire predicament was almost laughable, a small, absurd rebellion against the darkness encroaching on his consciousness.

"Was there anything else? Was there anything else Mr Turner?" Victoria's shrill voice eventually penetrated through the fog of agony.

Max tried to lift his head as his breathing began to steady. He looked up towards her but was momentarily further blinded by the light from the lamps. Bubbles floated across his vision and a grotesque distorted image of the Mayor materialised. Despite the pain he was in, Max made the potentially fateful decision to press on. The stakes were high, potentially fatal, but if this was his end, why not go out knowing what it was all about at least?

"Phase 2..." his voice was strained, harsh, a

gravelling whisper, and he realised he was dribbling onto his trousers. He fought to regain control and moved back in his chair.

"What was that? What did you say Max?" Victoria had sat back down again and was leaning forward, her presence like a cloud of frost over the table. "Speak up, Max. What about Phase 2?"

"Phase 2... Khalid mentioned Phase 2," Max coughed and spluttered, but continued, trying hard to restore a normal breathing pattern, "he was about to tell us about Phase 2 when you..."

His eyes flicked to Stahl's impassive stance, a silent sentinel of impending doom, and a prudent edit formed, "er... I mean... when someone shot him."

A transient gleam of triumph flickered across Victoria's features. "Phase 2, indeed. It's regrettable that Khalid won't witness its fruition. But it's for the collective welfare, Max. Envision a rejuvenated London - clean, salubrious, secure - a veritable haven for our progeny."

"Sounds idyllic," Max retorted, his voice laced with a sardonic edge, grimacing as he tried to affect a chortle.

Victoria smiled diabolically: "Max, Max... oh my dear V-Max T of Turner Wheels fame, how greatly you misunderstand me, how little you think of my motivations, how sadly mistaken you are!"

She was in full theatrical monologue now: "Can you not grasp the grandeur of the vision? Small children happily frolicking about our great city, no fear of being run over, no chance of being sickened by the heaving toxicity in our air... Oh and the elderly, shuffling about, doing... whatever it is that useless old people do while not contributing to anything..."

"Children and the elderly don't live in the middle of the city," Max was starting to recover his voice and his mettle. "Nobody does, they've been priced out, only the rich can..."

"Yes, yes... well you know, they have no place in a centre of commerce and trade anyway, they just get in the way of all the money to be made, don't they?" she retorted.

"That's the plan? Get people to leave the city?!" Max's tone was accusing now, his resolve hardening.

"No of course not. Phase 2 is about making money, and it's about control!" finally came the revelation.

"Making money? For you and your... what... covert syndicate? And what becomes of people's liberties, their sanctity, their autonomy, their psychological well-being?"

Victoria's reply was quick and sharp. "You fail to see the larger canvas, Max. This is about crafting a legacy, the long-term vision for the city, the country, and wouldn't you know," suddenly she affected an American accent for no obvious reason "actually the whole goddamn planet!"

Max recoiled internally at the gravity of her admission; he had no riposte for the abstraction of an ego so fervent with self-righteousness. It was a vision that blinded her to the untold hardship it would inflict on ordinary citizens, a misguided ambition poised to unravel into a tapestry of turmoil.

Abruptly, she sprang up from her chair, signalling the end of their tedious exchange. "Nevertheless, it's inconsequential. You shall not witness the fruition of this... this glorious purpose!" With a grandiose sweep of her arms, she turned to leave. But then, as if on a whim, she pivoted sharply back towards him, a sinister grin spreading across her face.

"Oh, and in response to your original question..." she paused and channelled the notorious Auric Goldfinger from the renowned Bond film, her voice deepening theatrically, "No, Mr. Turner... I expect you to die!"

Her laughter echoed through the space, a celebration of her perceived cleverness. She directed her next command to Stahl, ensuring her distaste for violence was unmistakably clear: "Do wait until I have departed, Stahl, as you know I abhor such barbarity..." She tossed Max a fleeting, contemplative glance, before adding with a hint of perversion, "Oh, and bring me the bow tie will you Stahl? There's a good fellow."

Stahl accompanied her into the darkness, to ensure her safe exit. Max felt the stark reality of his perilous situation; he was unrestrained now, but the Italian had trained his weapon back on him again.

"I'm-a very sorry for you, Mr Turner, you're-a funny guy, you know that? Eh, any last-a requests I can-a grant you?" His accent was thick, his words rolling off his tongue with a playful lilt.

Max glanced up with a resigned nod, "yeah, could I borrow your car keys?"

The Italian burst into hearty laughter, nudging his companion: "You hear-a this guy? Funny to the very end, eh?" He turned back to Max, shaking his head with amusement.

"Sorry, my friend, but-a nobody touches my car."

Starting to come to terms with his impending fate, Max decided to fill the remaining time with the one thing he always genuinely, truly loved to do - car chat. "What do you drive? Let me take a wild guess... a Lamborghini Revuelto?"

The Italian chortled. "Ah, Che meraviglia! That would-a be the dream, eh? But I'd need to bag a few more kills-a to afford that," he waved his gun in Max's direction again, chuckling at his own dark humour. "Don't worry my friend, if I kill-a you first, I'll never hear the end of it from the angry Austrian!"

"Wouldn't dream of making Drago unhappy..." Max jested, eliciting more laughter from the duo.

"So, what do you drive then?" Max prodded, curious despite the dire circumstances.

The Italian whipped out his phone, showcasing a photo with pride: "Guarda, just-a got it last week..."

It was a fiery red Alfa Romeo Giulia Quadrifoglio. "Four years old, only-a 25,000 on the clock. Snagged it for under 40k. What'd ya say?"

"Wow, she's a beauty," Max nodded approvingly. "Seems like a steal at that price. So, about those keys...?"

"Funny guy!" The Italian shook his head, still grinning.

Stahl, AKA the Bone Crusher, returned from the shadows, his presence immediately stifling the mirth. With a steely stare and no need for words, he approached Max, his gun at the ready. "Forget your silly fantasies, Vitale. Zis kill," he motioned to Max with a sinister grin, "vill get me behind zhe vheel of an AMG GT."

Max offered a nod of respect to the choice of car, then tightly closed his eyes. The ominous click of the hammer pulling back filled his ears as he tensed, and braced for the end.

CHAPTER 7

Suddenly Max's earpiece crackled to life. "Close your eyes and turn away from the West Wall now!" It was Eleanor's voice, bringing unexpected hope in the face of certain death.

The message, however, puzzled him. 'West Wall? Which one is the West Wall?' he blurted out loud. Opening his eyes, he anticipated Stahl's puzzled expression quickly transforming to realisation and then to action as he swung the gun right.

"Ah, so that's the West Wall," Max thought to himself. He took the momentary distraction as an opportunity to drive off the chair to his right and flatten himself on the floor.

An explosion rocked the warehouse, bricks and metal erupting into the warehouse, as a huge bin lorry burst backwards through the West Wall. Its heavy rear steel structure acting like a battering ram, tearing through the wall and scattering debris. The lorry, clearing the newly-made hole and debris, executed a sharp 90-degree J-turn, sliding right. Its driver's cabin swung around, halting mere meters from the desk in a cloud of dust and rubble.

The Italian and his colleague, jolted from the shock of a 30-tonne truck careening into the warehouse and swinging toward them, scrambled for their guns. But it was too late. Two precise shots rang from the driver's cab, extinguishing their lives instantly.

The door half-opened and Eleanor screamed at Max, "Get in!" Stahl had already fired several shots, but they had all ricocheted harmlessly off the lorry's sturdy rear. Stahl then saw Eleanor, who was already firing at him. He rolled behind the desk to dodge the bullets, and from there poked his gun over the tabletop to return fire.

Max seized the moment, sprinting around the back of the lorry and vaulting into the passenger side of the cabin. Eleanor unleashed the torque of the electric lorry in forward gear and got the rear wheels spinning on the smooth warehouse floor. The vehicle kicked its back end across, its motion whipping away the desk, leaving Stahl exposed. He simply stood and continued firing even as the bullets pinged off the back. Eleanor pushed her door ajar and returned fire, but from that angle, she knew there was no chance she would hit him.

She floored the throttle. As the heavy lorry lunged forward, Stahl, driven by desperation, sprinted after it. He leapt and managed to latch onto the back of the vehicle as it hurtled forward. However, his elation was short-lived as he realised Eleanor was threading the truck back through the hole it had entered from, only she was doing it sideways. Stahl was on the side that would impact what was left of the old concrete wall. Knowing the impact would be devastating, he relinquished his grip and tumbled back onto the ground in frustration.

As Eleanor masterfully guided the lorry in a sweeping drift, its broad side slammed into a line of parked cars opposite the wall writing them off. Max, peering out, noticed one of the crushed cars was indeed a red Alfa Romeo Giulia Quadrifoglio, and for some reason, he felt a little sad about it, recalling the excitement in the now-dead Italian mercenary's voice. He was less sorry to see that another was a Mercedes AMG SL Roadster, very likely Stahl's car. Looking back out of his window, he caught sight of Stahl emerging from the hole in the wall, regarding the departing truck and smashed cars with unrestrained fury.

Eleanor kept going. Max realised they were in Shoreditch in East London. Eleanor hauled the big vehicle through alleyways and slammed on the anchors near a Waste Facility, alongside similar trucks parked in a row.

"Let's go Max, time to ditch the lorry!" she instructed crisply.

Max hadn't been able to speak thus far, still reconciling how close he had been to dying and then witnessing the death and destruction unleashed by a rampant Eleanor. As he flopped down from the cabin, Eleanor was already by his side and dragged him over to the scooter she had hidden behind a tip. "You okay Max?" she asked, her tone soft.

"Er... yes, I think so. I... I... You saved me, Eleanor. That guy was about to..." Max's voice trailed off, still in disbelief. Eleanor smiled back comfortingly but moved again towards the bike with some urgency.

"There's no time for chit-chat – hop on, now!" Her voice was sharp as she swiftly ripped off the delivery compartment from its mounting on the back of the scooter, clearing just enough space for two to squeeze tightly onto the little bike. Max clambered onto the diminutive two-wheeler behind her, his arms reflexively encircling her unexpectedly firm waist. He could feel the heat emanating from her body, fuelled by adrenaline, through the delicate fabric of her evening gown. This warmth was in sharp contrast to the chilling brush with danger he had narrowly escaped moments ago, making the contact all the more striking and surreal.

"Hold tight!" she barked and sped off so sharply, that Max had no choice but to cling even more tightly to her. She raced through the late evening streets at fearless speed, cutting corners, leaning hard over to the point where several times Max caught his breath, convinced they would crash. There was no chance to form the semblance of a coherent thought, never mind converse at the breakneck pace. In an astonishingly short time, they arrived at the road where they had parked the BMW.

It had been clamped.

After surviving a violent kidnapping, a brutal interrogation, a near-death experience, a harrowing escape under gunfire, and a terrifying ride on a scooter through the city streets, Max's nerves were beyond frayed. He stood there, staring at the clamp in disbelief and frustration. "What the actual fuck?! Who clamps a car at night?!" He yelled with exasperation.

Eleanor peered at the sticker plastered on the windscreen. "High Emission Parking Penalty," she read aloud, her voice tinged with sympathy. "Looks like there was a maximum four-hour free stay for 'more polluting cars'."

Max threw his hands up in bafflement. "Now WHEN did that become a thing? How does that even make sense," he pleaded with no one in particular, "when it's parked, it's not even putting out any emissions!!" he yelled, boiling over with unbridled emotions.

In a sudden gesture, Eleanor stepped up and wrapped her arms tightly around him. He was trembling, the adrenaline and cortisol from the night's events still coursing through his veins. Caught off guard by Eleanor's unexpected embrace, Max's initial resistance melted away. He leaned into her, his body shaking, as the comfort of her hold released a wave of endorphins, soothing his jangled nerves. Gradually, his shaking subsided, and he wrapped his arms around her in return.

Eleanor gently broke the embrace and looked up at him. "Better?"

Max nodded as he found his breathing normalising and racing heartbeat settling into a familiar rhythm, "Thanks Eleanor, I didn't know it, but I needed that…"

"What's this now? Our second or third date?" she cracked a small smile, lightening the mood, "My friends call me Ellie, I think it's okay for you to do the same."

Max grinned back and nodded, but fought to suppress the unwanted memory of another who'd said something similar earlier to him, except her friends called her Vicky. Shaking off the thought, he turned his attention to the sticker and clamp on the BMW, trying to focus on the immediate problem at hand.

Eleanor was scanning the street intently when her eyes settled on an Audi R8 supercar parked nearby. In her hand, the spent pistol transformed into an improvised hammer, poised to shatter the car's window.

"What are you doing?!" Max asked.

Eleanor glanced back at him, a hint of sheepishness in her expression. "Er... we need a ride..." she admitted.

"Ah, yes..." Max turned back to his BMW, his expression a mix of ruefulness and affection for his cherished car. Eleanor caught his look, and it stirred memories of her late father and the moment he had confessed to selling his beloved Ford Capri.

She had exerted a calming influence on Max, but she also knew he had been taken far from the comfort of his normal life. In some ways, the BMW 325i was his tether to normalcy, a symbol of stability in the chaos swirling around them. It was important. Sighing with understanding and empathy, Eleanor decided against the Audi and returned to the BMW, retrieving a lipstick from her clutch.

"Keep a lookout," she instructed as she knelt beside the yellow clamp encasing the BMW's wheel. The clamp, a standard London Triangle, was secured by a hardened steel chain, 10mm thick. With the lipstick, she marked three links in the chain and then reversed the stick to reveal an emitter concealed beneath the cap. Pressing a button, a concentrated laser beam shot out, targeting the lipstick markings. The chain links fizzled under the intense heat, melting away and releasing the clamp.

She stuffed the clamp, along with the window

sticker she had also peeled off and, oddly, the pistol, into a recycle bin nearby, "it's out of bullets anyway", she told Max as she walked back to the passenger door of the BMW. "Shall we?"

Max hesitated just before sliding into the car, his eyes finding Eleanor's across the roof. The intensity of his gaze was palpable, a mix of profound gratitude and an unspoken connection. "Eleanor... Ellie... I... you saved my life... thank you, El..."

Eleanor's grin, radiant and reassuring, cut through the gravity of the moment. She raised a hand in a gentle, silencing gesture, her eyes sparkling with an unspoken understanding. "Get in, Max, we've well overstayed our welcome, and I need you to fill me in on what happened."

As they drove back to Flux's safe house in Harrow, Max relayed the harrowing details of his ordeal since regaining consciousness and finding himself bound and vulnerable in that stark room. To his surprise, Eleanor's reaction to the Mayor's involvement was more muted than he had anticipated.

"It's a real shame we weren't recording the conversation between you and the Mayor," lamented Eleanor.

"Yeah, that would have been some evidence for sure," mused Max.

"Unfortunately, the earpiece doesn't have tracking capabilities, and it's reliant on phone signals – either yours or mine to function..." Eleanor explained.

"And they took my phone off me," Max said, now understanding the communication breakdown.

"Which I retrieved," Eleanor revealed, patting her clutch, much to Max's relief. "When I got close enough, I knew you'd be able to hear me before I crashed through the wall..."

"Except I had no clue which one was the West Wall!" laughed Max, finally starting to recover his sense of humour. "But how did you find me?"

"Simple, we followed the Mayor!" Eleanor explained. "Anyway, back at the ball, most of what we got was Quentin pitching Viridis to... I guess a bunch of would-be investors," she filled him in. "It was mostly just blah, blah, blah..." she said illustrating her point with a playful hand puppet gesture.

"However, they kept referring to some upcoming event that was going to change everything, no idea what, but it might be connected to something else that was mentioned a couple of times, 'Project Imperium'."

She continued: "It seems to be a pivotal point for Phase 2. Flux is trying to find out whatever he can, but there's something else..."

She paused, biting her lip in hesitation. Max, sensing her reluctance but driven by a growing impatience and curiosity, prompted her. "Go on,

Ellie..." he urged.

"Your friends back at the warehouse... the goons?" she finally spoke.

"What about them?" Max asked warily.

"I know those goons, well the head goon at least."

"Stahl?!" Max felt a knot of apprehension in his stomach. Stahl didn't seem to be the sort of person Max would want an ally hanging out with. Then he recalled the sniper that Eleanor had killed the day before.

"You knew the guy from yesterday too? You seem to know all the people trying to kill us," Max inadvertently threw a suspicious glance her way. She caught his look. He tried to laugh it off nonchalantly.

"They were both part of the Eclipse Squad," she confirmed.

"The Eclipse Squad... are you serious? That's a real name?"

"I'm afraid so," she remarked, shrugging. "They're an elite group of international operatives and commandos. It's a covert organisation that specialises in political activities, contracted from the shadows and usually working there too. You know... anything from standard protection work, to manipulating political outcomes, and even bringing out about regime changes."

"Damn!" reacted Max, taking a sharp intake of

breath. "But how do you know them," he feared what the answer would be, even as he asked the question.

Eleanor hesitated, then admitted, "Because after leaving the Mayor's office, I worked with the Eclipse Squad for several months."

She fell silent, giving Max time to react. For his part, he somehow wasn't all that surprised. He realised she was waiting for a reaction, but after all he had been through, seen and learned in the last three days, the fact that Eleanor used to work as an international political assassin, seemed to be the least of his concerns right now.

"You're not... still contracted to them, are you?" he ventured.

She shook her head. "Nah, I hated working with them. So, I went independent and teamed up with Flux a couple of years ago. Mostly I specialise in protection and security these days, but..."

Sensing that Max was okay with her revelation, she felt confident enough to bring back some levity to the conversation, "depends on who's paying and how much," she added with a wink. "Being independent means that Flux and I get to choose."

"I'm flattered."

Puzzled, Eleanor turned to face Max, "huh?"

"That you chose me," he was grinning. "But as for

paying, I have to warn you, I'm broke!" he warned her.

"That's okay, we'll just break your legs," she shot back, a wicked smile playing on her lips.

"I'm really not sure if you're joking… or not!" Max responded pretending to be fearful.

Laughter filled the car, breaking the tension that had settled between them. Max still felt a pang of awkwardness though. Thankfully, the safe house was just a few blocks away, a welcome respite from the night's revelations and dangers.

The shutter went up as soon they approached. Parking and emerging from the car, Flux stuck up an arm and pointed a finger down at the table next to him, an assortment of pizza boxes spread out on it. "Yo, my peeps! Come and get some of this cheesy goodness. And brace yourselves, I got a mix of news - some dope, some not so chill."

Max, feeling a wave of nausea, excused himself for the bathroom. The events of the evening had taken their toll, and he couldn't suppress the urge to vomit. After a few agonising minutes of heaving, he splashed water on his face, finding a semblance of calm. His hands still trembled, but less violently now.

When he rejoined the others, Eleanor had reverted to her trademark black fatigues and boots, and was munching into a slice of pizza. Flux spun around in his seat rising to greet Max with a warm, brotherly embrace. "Man, you good? Heard things got kinda hairy out there."

Max sank wearily into a proffered chair, the weight of the past days heavy on his shoulders. "Understatement of the year," he murmured. "It's fair to say not just tonight, but the last few days have been nothing like anything I've experienced in my life."

Flux's usual buoyancy seemed dampened by concern. "Yo, Max, for real, I feel like I dropped the ball, man. Should've had your six. This high-octane spy game ain't your usual jam, I should a known that."

Max reached out, grasping Flux's arm in a gesture of solidarity. "Hey, Flux, don't worry man. You've been amazing..." His voice trailed off; appreciation evident in his weary eyes.

He picked up a slice of pizza from a box, stared at it, but then put it back down again. "I gotta be honest guys, and you know this of course, but I am totally out of my depth here, way, way outside my comfort zone."

He picked up the pizza again, but didn't take a bite. "I'm not used to... I'm not equipped to do what you guys do. It's been tough. I'll be honest... you probably already know this, but... I've been in therapy for the last few years. Just started piecing my life back together when you literally dropped into my world." He gestured towards Eleanor with the pizza.

He contemplated taking a bite as Eleanor spoke:

"I understand Max. I'm sorry to have done this to you... perhaps it's time that..."

Max raised a hand, the slice still untouched. "No, no, listen. I'm all in, all the way. Ride or die as someone once said.

"For the first time in years, I feel like I'm being true to myself," he continued. "That moment with Stahl, gun to my head... I was at peace; you know... I was okay with whatever was about to happen. At least I would have gone out trying to do the right thing."

Max put the pizza down again. "I guess, what I'm really trying to say is that... I'm not always going to be able to keep up with you guys, but I promise to do my best."

Eleanor nodded understandingly. "Max, you're doing more than just keeping up. And I think you'll be surprised at what you're capable of. This journey you're on... we're on... it's a path to something more. Redemption, maybe." She bit into her slice, then washed it down with beer. "That's if we manage to stay alive long enough!" she added with a wry grin.

Max's expression faltered slightly, but Eleanor chuckled. "Lighten up, Max! A little gallows humour never hurt anyone."

Flux spoke up staring at the slice dangling in Max's hand. "Hawaiian, not your thang, huh? We got some pepperoni action and classic Margherita too."

Max stared at the pizza sadly, "You know Flux, I'm actually starving mate, but I've just been hurling my guts out…"

"Bro, that's just standard operating procedure!" Both Flux and Eleanor laughed out loud.

Eleanor spoke up, "Fill him in Ghost Weaver."

Flux swung back around to his array of screens. "A'ight, listen up, y'all. First things first, your protest pal Josh? Man's got more dirt than a landfill - gambling, drugs, domestic abuse, you name it. And the dude was drowning in debt before he got mixed up with your anti-ULEZ crew. But check this – his luck turned around faster than Flash in the Speed Force! Bank accounts ballooned with a couple mil by the time ULEZ went live."

Max sifted through his memories of Josh, trying to reconcile this new information with the man he thought he knew. There was never a hint that he was anything other than a personally affected and ardently active supporter of the cause.

Yet he had been a ringer from the start, colluding with Khalid directly most probably since even Eleanor wasn't aware of him. It appeared he was hired to bring deliberate discredit to the cause by subtly voicing just a few specifically controversial views. That's all it took.

"Yeah, dude was a plant from the get-go," Flux continued. "Stirring up the crowd, tossing out wild views to make y'all look bad!"

Max wondered who else might have been on the generous City Hall payroll.

Flux leaned forward; his tone serious. "As El told you, about that eavesdrop sesh, we didn't get much juicy goss, but we do know something's cooking; something big's about to go down. They kept yakking on about Phase 2."

Eleanor picked up the thread: "I think it's fair to say Phase 2 is aiming to take away cars for good, that's evident from your tete-a-tete with the Mayor. So, we need to know what that second phase is, but we got nothing solid, except..."

"Except?" perked up Max, "There is another lead?"

"Not quite," continued Flux, "but from what was being said, whatever the event is, it's gotta be part of 'Project Imperium' - whatever that be! And whatever that be, it be buried deep and I mean deep, in the most obvious spot you'd never think to look."

Max's brow furrowed in confusion, "Viridis?" he offered. Eleanor made the distinctive incorrect answer gameshow buzzer noise. Flux flicked his wrists, "Ah dude, so close! Think about your date this evening my man."

Max glanced across at Eleanor, Flux just shook his head, "Not that one".

Suddenly it hit Max, "City Hall?"

"Bingo buddy! That place, before it was the Mayor's crib, was The Crystal, so-called because it's like this giant crystal carbuncle sprouting out the ground. You know what else? It belonged to Siemens."

"What?" Max was astonished that he hadn't known that".

"Yo, so here's the 411 - the tech giant dropped a mega-serious server deep down in a bunker at their old digs. We're talking isolated, off-the-grid kinda stuff. Short story: ain't no way I'm cracking that nut from here; it's an in-person job only."

"I guess that explains the £35 million or so that was spent on the move," chimed in Eleanor. "The move felt completely unnecessary at the time, and was a logistical and security nightmare," she shook her head. "I should know, I project managed it! But now it makes sense, it was a better place to hide secrets!"

"You betcha," Flux nodded in agreement.

Eleanor stood, her gaze fixed on the array of screens. "Flux, hook me up with some visuals on The Crystal and the area around it." With a few clicks and swipes, Flux brought up detailed images and maps.

Eleanor scrutinised the screens, her mind racing. "I know this building well, and I think I know how to get down there, but it ain't going to be easy," Eleanor was studying the images on screen as she spoke.

Max, having nibbled tentatively at the pizza, decided that the pineapple really didn't work for him after all. "Er... Ellie... do you have my phone?" he asked.

Eleanor, deeply engrossed in the screen, gestured towards a nearby desk without looking back. Max retrieved his phone and powered it on.

"Servers run hot, so there's this hardcore aircon system down there, and a vent shaft running up to the roof. It pops out around here..." She jabbed at a point on the screen, her hand lingering there as she pondered their next move.

Flux, peering at the building layout, chimed in, "Yo, scaling this bad boy ain't hard. Suction gloves and you're like a badass Spider-Woman. But here's the catch – you're gonna be out in the open, clear as day. Ain't no sneaky way to do it without getting spotted from the outside... AND the inside."

Max, trying to get a word in, interjected, "Um, guys, I got something on my phone that could maybe..."

"Max, hold up a sec, please? I've just have to brainstorm this thing." Eleanor cut him off, her attention still fixed on the screen, "No fortress is impenetrable," she muttered to herself.

Max shrugged and sat down, quietly watching the intense strategizing between Eleanor and

Flux carefully from his back-seat vantage point, while tentatively trying a slice of Spicy Meatfeast.

She jabbed at the image of the cable car line that passes across the Thames near the building. "This! I can use this," she declared with determination.

Flux nodded: "Grappling gun and zipline?"

"Negative," responded Eleanor, "We'd have to stop the cable car, and that would draw attention. No, I'll need to jump it."

Flux let out a low whistle, "Dang, girl, you plannin' to take a leap of faith, huh? You wanna float like a butterfly and sting like a bee, don't cha?" Eleanor winked at him.

Flux scratched his chin, thinking. "At the closest spot it passes the building on the way down, it's only a few metres from the rooftop, but fit as you are, and you fit, don't get me wrong El, you ain't gonna make that jump without a run-up... or... hmm... I don't see no jetpack lying around here, though I did say we should get one, didn't I?"

Eleanor ignored him: "How about if I make the jump from higher up?"

Flux pulled up some more info on the cable car: "Okay, check it, that bad boy's cruising at about 90 metres high, at its peak, a whole 30 metres above the rooftop. So, we're looking at a 45-degree angle for your drop."

Eleanor flashed a confident grin and they continued rapidly outlining the plan. Max focused intently on following their train of thought.

"I'll need a speedwing…"

"Woah Ellie!" called out Flux with concern, "those things are notoriously hard to control… use a base-jumping chute, surer bet."

"I thought they were rated for a minimum of 150 metres…" Eleanor replied

"Then girl you gonna set yourself a new record," grinned Flux. "Don't worry, I got you, I'll crunch the numbers."

Despite her uncertainty, Eleanor conceded: "Yeah, you better, and double… triple-check them, the slightest error and I'll either end up in the drink or splattered on the side of the docks!"

She pointed again at the screen, focusing on a specific section of the rooftop. "I'll aim to land here, and the shaft entrance is over this way, roughly 20 metres, right?"

Flux leaned in, his eyes scanning the layout. "Looks more like 25 to me."

Eleanor nodded, mentally adjusting her plan. "Okay, so I'll need some gear to cut through, an abseiling kit, and those suction gloves you got - could come in handy."

Flux's eyes lit up with an idea. "Yo, I got this cool little signal relay gadget. You can set it up on the roof. Once you're down in the server room, just plug in and I'll do the rest remotely – hack in, find the file and download it. Easy peasy."

"Cool," Eleanor acknowledged. "I'll hoist myself back up, and then I'll need the grappling gun to fire a zipline down to the docks... how's that boat of yours Flux?"

"My Gemini? Oh yeah, she fine, sleek as ever and ready for some action. We'll be waiting for you by the water, engines humming and all set to jet!"

Max felt breathless witnessing the back and forth and hearing the plan formulate. They even did the secret hand-shuffle thing again in conclusion. Max decided to drop his bombshell.

"Guy's, that's amazing. A truly spectacular plan! Really! So daring, so dangerous, so like daredevil stuff and all that!"

Eleanor and Flux looked at Max in amusement and mocked a little bow. But then Max waved his phone screen at them: "And so unnecessary... I might have an alternative; we could just go to this new car launch I've been invited to there, tomorrow evening. Might be a bit easier?"

Flux, unable to contain his excitement, quickly snatched the phone from Max's hand. As he scrolled through the details, his face lit up with a wide grin. "Oh man, this is dope! Ellie, you just got relegated to Plan B, looks like we're switching gears to Plan A. This one's got the style and the smarts!"

Eleanor, leaning back against the desk, let out a small sigh, a mix of relief and bemusement crossing her face. "You had this in your back pocket the whole time?"

"I did" replied Max.

"So why didn't you…"

"I tried…"

"Yes, you did…" Eleanor was shaking her head.

"But you said…" protested Max.

"Yes, I did Max." Eleanor conceded.

"So, Ellie, will you be my… cameraman? Er… I mean camerawoman?"

Eleanor glanced at Flux who put up his hands instantly, "Girl, I got no objection!"

Eleanor's eyes met Max's, a playful spark in her gaze. "Then I will Max," she laughed.

The three shared a moment of light-hearted camaraderie, a welcome break from the stress and danger that seemed their norm. Max, reassured by their support and the new plan, couldn't help but feel a growing sense of anticipation for what the next day would bring.

CHAPTER 8

They went by tube train, alighting at Canning Town station and walking up to City Hall, the building that was formerly known as The Crystal. The evening air held a gentle warmth, wrapping around them as they approached the distinct, angular glass structure.

It stood bathed in a dazzling array of lights, its façade reflecting a myriad of colours that seemed to dance across it. A brand-new car company, Edison, had its brand flags fluttering gently around the entrance, confirming the evening's takeover by the fledgling Chinese motor manufacturer. The fifth new player from China to enter the UK market this year alone. Sat just outside on a raised round platform and under a heavy cover, was an example of its new car, teasing the imagination of onlookers.

The setting sun cast its final golden hues over the Thames, creating a picturesque backdrop that rivalled the luminous vibrancy of The Crystal. Compared to everything around it, the building's unique angular design gave it a futuristic appearance, which seemed to make it the perfect venue for the unveiling of a car that promised to blend retro novelty with cutting-edge technology. A compact city car hinting at a design ethos reminiscent of bold 1970s 'folded-paper' wedge-shaped styling, yet presented with a 21st-century sheen.

The conference and exhibition space commandeered for the car launch was clearly visible through the glass frontage on the right of the main entrance. Flashing their invite and directed through security with relative ease, they were met by an eager Press and PR executive.

"Sorry, I think we're a little late..." apologised Max.

"No, no, you're just in time; the presentation is just about to begin," the PR lady assured them with a professional smile.

They followed her towards the darkened seating area. There were four further models of the new car, the Edison Model A, waiting to be unveiled, placed around the room and on each side of the main stage, lit up by strategically placed spotlights designed to accentuate their appearance. A large screen dominated the centre of the main stage, no doubt where the promo film and presentation slide shows would be shown.

Opting for discretion, Max chose a vacant seat in the back row, mindful not to cause a disturbance among the other journalists already seated and focused on the proceedings as they began. Meanwhile, Eleanor was directed along the side aisle close to the front to line up behind several other camera operators who'd already set up the tripods and equipment.

As she carried her kit, a momentary misstep caused her to stumble near a security guard, who quickly reached out to steady her. Grateful and slightly embarrassed, Eleanor offered him a warm smile and a quiet thank you, while deftly slipping his security pass into her pocket without him, or anyone else, noticing.

She swiftly set up her tripod and camera, expertly hooking it up and initiating a live feed to the Turner Wheels YouTube channel. Max, watching from his vantage point, saw the notification pop up on his phone. He quickly checked the feed and gave Eleanor a thumbs-up. She glanced back and returned the gesture, playing her part to a T.

The room buzzed with a diverse crowd of industry insiders, journalists, VIPs, and Edison dignitaries eager to showcase their new electric marvel to the UK market. As the lights dimmed further, signalling the commencement of the presentation, a hush of expectation settled over the assembly.

A charismatic host sprang onto the centre stage, smoothly handling the introductory formalities.

Shortly thereafter, he welcomed Edison's CEO and President to give his speech, and everyone found themselves focusing extra hard to decipher his heavy Chinese accent as he drew out the preamble before the premiere.

In the meantime, Eleanor had navigated her way towards the back of the room, ostensibly in search of the ladies' room. However, as everyone's attention was drawn to the proceedings on stage, she seized the moment, and adeptly used the purloined security pass to slip through a restricted access door and onto the back-office.

It was eerily quiet, the Mayor's staff having departed for the day. Familiar with the building's layout from her past tenure here, Eleanor knew her access would be limited. Sure enough, having emerged from the lift into the basement, once she reached the server room door, it stubbornly refused to yield. Unfazed, she dug into one of her pockets and pulled out her favourite lipstick.

Back upstairs, on the opposite side of the room to the camera crews, Max noticed several dark-suited personnel peering across at the camera area. One of them was looking down at his phone apparently trying to match what he saw with the cameras aimed at the stage.

A cold realisation dawned on Max; the live stream of the car launch on his YouTube channel had inadvertently alerted them to his presence.

These guards (could they be Eclipse Squad?) were trying to identify who was filming it. He quietly reported this development back to Eleanor and Flux, alerting them to the developing situation.

Eleanor's voice crackled through the earpiece, reassuring yet focused. "Don't worry, I'll be in and out of the server room in just a few minutes, and we'll be out of here. They're not going to cause a commotion while the Edison bigwigs are blabbing on."

"But the signal relay - it's still on the camera, right?" Max's voice held a tinge of anxiety. "If they try to cut the feed, they might stumble upon it."

Flux's voice cut through, oozing confidence. "Chill, Max. I'm watching the hall. Looks like the black suits are holding station. Stay calm, stay low... we got this bro."

Below, Eleanor's lethal lipstick had done its work and cut through the lock. She slipped in, keeping the lights off in the server room, so she'd barely register as a shadow on the CCTV inside. She slipped on a pair of spectacles enabling her to see better in the dark, found a terminal and slipped in the remote interface.

"Oh, we live baby!" came Flux's jubilant exclamation, "I'm in and I'm hunting down Project Imperium."

Back in the hall, Max, distracted by the updates in his ear, was caught off guard as the room erupted in applause. The music swelled, and the audience stood as the covers were whisked off, revealing the Edison Model A. He stood too, less for the car and more to keep an eye on the personnel at the side.

"Oh, I gotcha!" Flux's triumphant voice echoed in Max's ear. "Download commencing, give me 30 seconds and we'll have what we need."

That was the good news. The not-so-good news was that the hall's lighting was in that instant turned up to full brightness, illuminating the entire space for photographers to capture the dignitaries and the newly unveiled car. The bright lights also left Max suddenly exposed. And much to his dismay, he recognised one of the guards, it was Stahl! Even worse news, Stahl had spotted him.

Max was just about to relay this back to Flux and Eleanor but before he could speak, he received a clap on the back and for a moment he was certain his heartbeat had simply given up and stopped.

"V-Max! How the devil are you?" The familiar booming voice belonged to a fellow journalist; one he had shared countless press drives with. The sudden recognition drew the attention of other journalists, those who remembered Max from his more active days on the automotive media circuit in the years before the counselling.

To his astonishment and immense relief, Max found himself quickly surrounded by old friends and colleagues, all eager to catch up after his long absence. While photographers were busy snapping the senior execs and the cars, the group around him knew it would be several minutes before they would get access to the cars, and the unexpected reunion became a welcome distraction. Shielding him from Stahl, they bought Max precious time and stayed the advance of what were now confirmed to be Eclipse Squad operatives.

Gratefully engaging in the small talk, Max listened as Flux's voice crackled through his earpiece: "File secured, El's on her way back to you. I see you got yourself a handy human shield, man. Keep those guys talking; those suited goons won't make a move while the V-Max lovefest is in full swing!"

On this rare occasion, Flux was wrong. Stahl was losing patience, perhaps still stinging from the loss of his Mercedes that Eleanor had left a mangled mess back in Shoreditch.

"Please make your vay to ze cars now for ze viewing, ja?" Stahl barked at them, a little too loud and abruptly, with strained politeness, his thick Austrian accent accentuating the oddness of his command, causing a ripple of unease among the meek members of the media, a few of whom rotated towards him in astonishment.

Out of nowhere and much to Max's surprise and relief, Eleanor popped up holding her secondary camera. She grabbed Max, pulling him through the group with a determination that took him off guard. They brushed right past Stahl, Eleanor shooting a defiant glare at the simmering mercenary.

"C'mon V-Max, we need to get some footage inside one of these cars. We're streaming live!" Eleanor announced loudly, feigning urgency to secure an exclusive spot in one of the Edison Model A cars.

Even as the Edison execs were still finishing with the staged smiles and handshakes, Eleanor had barged through the crowd pulling Max behind her and they clambered into one of the cars on stage. Before anyone could protest, she slammed the doors shut, switched on her camera's auxiliary light and started filming, the bright light warding off any potential intruders or protestors and signalling to onlookers that they were broadcasting live.

"Tell us what you think of the interior of the Model A, V-Max T!" Eleanor prompted, her voice carrying the excitement of a live broadcast. Max, reflexively drew on years of experience reviewing cars and seamlessly transitioned into an automatic critique of the Model A's dashboard controls, seating position, practicality, materials employed, and overall build quality. All the while, his mind raced with questions about their next move.

Meanwhile, Stahl, standing outside, was equally consumed with thoughts about Eleanor's next step, torn between waiting them out or acting on his mounting anger. He was frankly livid and Eleanor's challenging look had wound him up, just as she knew it would. He hit the button on his coms, "Trigger ze fire alarm now," he hissed into the microphone, his voice laced with authority and frustration. "Don't argue, just do it!"

The ceiling lights flashed urgently, and a blaring alarm erupted, sharply curtailing the proceedings. Chaos ensued as guards and staff, including some of Stahl's men, began herding people out through the fire exits with practised urgency. Meanwhile, Stahl, with calculated precision, had his bulkier henchmen form a semi-circle around the front of the car that Max and Eleanor were in. This not only served to hide them from the view of the rest of the hall but also effectively trapped them within the vehicle.

Stahl had positioned himself deliberately at the very front of the car. As the crowd began to filter out, driven by a rising tide of mild panic, he slowly pivoted to face them. His features contorted into a grin, but it was one that twisted the very essence of what a smile should convey. Instead of warmth or friendliness, Stahl's smile only accentuated his menacing presence. It grotesquely magnified his intimidating demeanour, rendering him even more unsettling in appearance.

"Kurt Stahl," Flux was on the coms again, "the Slayer of Salzburg, he's known as. Not to freak you out, but he's one nasty dude. Seems like even his mama must a hated him when he was born and he just been taking it out on the world ever since."

Eleanor couldn't help herself and started grinning. This seemed to displease Stahl and served to extinguish his sinister smile, rendering his expression even more malevolent. Max realised then, that Stahl's ugliness wasn't just skin deep, it was etched into his very being.

Aware that the live stream was still on, Max just stared blankly at Stahl, still not speaking out loud his real thoughts, but instead just rattling off the performance stats of the Model A "… and that sort of power in this little thing," he turned back to the camera, "equates to a pretty terrific acceleration time of zero to 62mph in an extraordinary 3.5 seconds…"

His voice trailed off as he noticed Eleanor fastening her seatbelt, an act that seemed almost surreal in the current setting. "But will it do the same backwards?" she quipped from behind the camera, with a hint of mischief.

"What?" he looked over at her in confusion. She was still grinning at Stahl, but snapped her head around to Max, glancing down at the gear selector and then giving him a wink before turning her attention back to the tall Austrian and continuing the stare-off.

Max paused to allow himself to accept that what he thought Eleanor was suggesting, was indeed genuinely what she was suggesting. He glanced at the rear-view mirror. He couldn't see much as they were still on the stage. He had noted earlier that the ramps on which the car had been driven up were still in place, but they were at the wrong angle; he knew also that directly behind him was the glass frontage of the building he had been trying to peer through on their way in.

He secured his seatbelt and spoke out loud looking directly into the camera that Eleanor was still pointing at him. "Hey guys, have you ever fantasised about driving a car through a window? Well, I have!" He engaged reverse gear, looked over his shoulder, then back at the camera and winked. Eleanor was laughing enthusiastically and nodding her head, as she flicked the feed over to the external camera still capturing everything from the tripod it had been left on, anticipating the spectacle they were about to create.

The big Austrian also seemed to sense their plan, his face contorted in rage and he started yelling in his native tongue as his balled fists flew down in rage towards the bonnet in a futile attempt to stop them. "Was?! NEIN! Stoppen! Das geht nicht!

Hör jetzt auf! Scheiße!" he cried. Max, seizing the moment, flipped the boost paddle and stomped on the accelerator pedal.

With its electric motor immediately responding, chucking a ton of torque directly to the rear wheels, it zipped back and flew off the stage completely missing the ramps, landing hard on the floor, just long enough for the wheels to grip and deliver another burst of breath-taking rearward acceleration, smashing through the glass façade, onto the paving beyond and the racing up onto the mound of grass outside, before Max remembered to cut the power and slam on the anchors, while spinning the wheel to the right forcing the front of the car to arc around, stopping half up the hillock.

Having been one of the first evacuees from the building, the PR lady that had greeted them was now running furiously towards Max, frantically waving her arms in dismay at his actions with their precious display model. Looking in his rear-view mirror, another figure bearing down on him fast was, he noted with some trepidation, the hulking Stahl.

Despite the escalating situation, Max couldn't resist a bit of theatrics. He flicked the down button on his window and shouted at the approaching PR lady, "Terribly sorry! I've just got to get the jump on everyone else with a scoop on the first review of the Model A!"

Meanwhile, Eleanor kept the camera rolling, transmitting a live feed from inside the car to his channel. She anchored herself against the backrest of her seat, foot propped up on the dashboard. "Max, your views just spiked like crazy!" reported Flux laughing, "now get the hell outta there!".

Max floored the right pedal again, checking his mirror to find, much to his astonishment, that Stahl's looming figure wasn't there. Just as the wedgy little Model A, skipped over the top of the mound, he noticed that the display car that had been parked outside was also on the move. It was Stahl.

"As you can see guys, this thing is whippet-like fast, and can turn on a sixpence, yup even going backwards!" Max started reporting to his live audience which was growing by the second.

His plan to steer the car out onto the road was thwarted by solid poles acting as a barrier. Reacting swiftly, he manoeuvred the vehicle through a narrow gap, accelerating down the pavement instead. He sped past the cable car station and veered left towards the road. But as he did so, he caught sight of Stahl emerging from the street, barrelling toward him on a direct collision course.

With quick reflexes, Max swerved sharply to the right, steering towards a set of descending half-steps that led to a lower walkway beside a floating hotel. The Model A agilely hopped down onto Dockside Walk, narrowly avoiding a collision with Stahl's oncoming vehicle. Stahl overshot and hurtled down the adjacent steps, his vehicle perilously close to tipping over.

"I'd say the steering on this thing is pretty sharp and responsive," Max narrated to his viewers, maintaining his reviewer's persona amidst the chaos. "Though, for my taste, I'd love some feel and a slightly heftier weighting to the helm!"

Navigating past the Good Hotel, as it was named, there was a set of narrow ramps about two metres wide, installed for accessibility, directly ahead adjacent to the left wall. They were tightly squeezed alongside sets of staggered steps on the right. Max skilfully threaded the Model A through the narrow ramps, bouncing from one to the next.

In contrast, Stahl opted for the steps, relying on brute force to propel the car forward, but he was still losing momentum in comparison with Max's smoother progress. Having nearly rolled the car once, Stahl refrained from attempting a direct sideswipe due to the concrete ledges separating the ramps from the stairs.

On his livestream, Max continued his improvised review: "The ride is a little firm, but it does manage bumps very well, with good damping on the rebound."

Approaching the end of the section, Max faced

an imminent dead-end with a building directly ahead. His initial plan was to execute a sharp left turn, again trying to get to the road. However, his path was blocked by a cluster of tourists. Swiftly recalculating, he jinked right, narrowly slashing right across Stahl's path, before continuing left along Dockside Walk. The sudden intrusion of the car sent tourists scattering, their leisurely strolls under the soft glow of the evening lights, cruelly interrupted.

"It's actually very good on rough surfaces, and extremely agile... love the way this thing changes directions!"

Ahead, a set of historical 1962 tubular steel-based dockside cranes loomed. Max skilfully angled the Model A to pass snugly between the cranes' towering legs. In contrast, Stahl, less precise in his driving, scraped the side of one of the legs, damaging the Grade II listed structures.

"The all-around visibility is just stellar in this thing," Max continued, "You can place the car exactly where you need and keep a keen eye on the action behind you too!"

Max burst into the open expanse of the main courtyard in front of London's ExCel, near the imposing Sunborn Yacht Hotel. He skilfully steered around Royal Victoria Square, taking a sharp left along the paved section, skirting the grand steps leading up to the Western Terrace of the exhibition centre, which loomed to his right.

Behind him, Stahl took a more aggressive approach, cutting a diagonal line across the grassy square, bounding down the shallow stepped edges. He almost caught up with Max but lost some traction on the dewy surface.

"The grip really is very tight on this thing, there's hardly any understeer, and minimum propensity to slide." continued Max on camera.

Finally hitting the tarmac, Max steered right into the elongated roundabout of the Western Gateway, where show visitors were usually dropped off. He deftly dove into a gap in the barriers at the end, cutting left towards the car park. Stahl, momentarily caught off guard by the abrupt direction changes, had fallen slightly behind but was quickly closing the gap.

"Hey guys, I do hope you've enjoyed this exclusive, high-octane first test of the astonishing new Edison Model A EV," Max declared, raising a thumb and smiling directly into the camera as he pulled a sharp right into Sandstone Lane, then veered into the first car park entrance. I'm giving it a V-Max T Thumbs up! But do let me know what you think in the comments. Don't forget to Like, Share, and Subscribe, and I'll catch you all in the next video – thanks for watching!"

Eleanor cut the feed and checked the stats as Max expertly navigated the vast car park under the ExCel exhibition building. "That was brilliant,

Max! We're sitting at about 150,000 views and it's still rocketing upwards and looks like you just gained another thousand followers... oh wait, make that more than two thousand! " she laughed out loud. "Turner Wheels is back in business, baby!"

"Thanks, Ellie," Max responded, skidding the little car around a reversing vehicle, causing Stahl to slow further and widening the gap between them. "But any bright ideas on how to shake off Stahl would be appreciated right about now!"

Eleanor quickly assessed the car park layout and directed Max through the labyrinth, expertly cutting between the parked vehicles. They weaved their way to the far side of the expansive parking area, gaining some precious distance from Stahl. Spotting a narrow gap between two large SUVs, Eleanor gestured sharply, and Max deftly manoeuvred the car into the tight space, switching the EV off immediately.

However, the car's automatic lights, which had flicked on upon entering the indoor park, remained stubbornly lit. As Stahl sped past, scanning for them, the glow of their taillights caught his attention. Slamming on the brakes, he reversed back, stopping ominously behind their hiding spot. With a menacing grin, he caught sight of Max and Eleanor looking back at him and raised his gun in their direction.

Behind Stahl's car was a grilled wall, with the Dockside Walk just beyond. "Duck down and reverse hard, now!" Eleanor commanded.

Max complied, once again the Model A demonstrated its alacrity, and barely slowed as it connected with the side of Stahl's stationery car, and pushed it relentlessly towards the wall. Stahl, in a frenzy, was firing his gun, shattering the windows of Max and Eleanor's car. The bullets flew perilously close but missed them.

With a sickening crunch, they rammed Stahl's car into the grilled wall which gave way and flew backwards, across the path, tipping over the guard rails beyond and plummeting into the dark waters of the Thames below. Stahl's car followed, its five-star crash-safety rated passenger cell, and particularly the side impact protection beam in its door, simply tearing the barrier railings asunder and his car pitched off the side of the now unprotected ledge and tipped over into the river below.

In a final desperate act, Stahl kept shooting as he went over the edge. Max's car almost followed him over, but the brakes grabbed a hold of it just as the rear axle cleared the edge. One of Stahl's final bullets pierced through the floor of Max's car, puncturing the EV battery and igniting it. Max and Eleanor abandoned the Model A. As they leapt out, the front of the car lightened, and it began to pivot on its middle, now teetering on the ledge.

Eleanor rushed to the edge and peered down through the smoke that was already billowing from the bottom of the car she had just been in, the thermal runaway effect causing the fire to spread through the battery pack.

Below she could make out Stahl, crawling desperately out of the driver's door window of his car. Max had also gone to the guard rail on the other side of the car and also witnessed Stahl struggling to crawl out of his sinking Edison. Much to his surprise, his car which was still see-sawing uncertainly on the ledge next to him, suddenly dipped its rear and slid down. With Stahl halfway out of the window, Max was horrified to see the Model A fall directly on and crush the Austrian assassin, just as the rest of the car erupted in flames.

Coughing and covering his mouth, he looked across to where he thought Eleanor would be, but she was walking up from behind him. He realised with some horror, that she must have given the unsteadily perched car a little "helpful" shove.

She looked down and then back at Max. "Well, he always did have a fiery temperament," she quipped.

He turned to her, a mix of shock and confusion in his eyes. "Did you just...?"

"Me? No Max, you did all the work on this one.

Losing out to a civvy like you, must've really... crushed him!" she laughed. Max stood, struck with dismay, and grappling with the possibility of his direct role in a man's death.

"Snap out of it, Max!" Eleanor shouted, her voice cutting through his thoughts. "We need to get out of here, fast!"

She then spoke into her coms, already running back into the car park, dragging Max behind her: "Flux?"

"I got you, El," Flux's voice crackled over the comms. "I cut the cameras, but boosting another car ain't gonna be wise right now. ExCel's locking down. The building's being evacuated – I suggest you find the flow and go with it guys!"

They found a stairwell and quickly ascended to the main atrium, where crowds were being ushered towards the exits. Swept up in the flow of evacuees, they made their way out of the West Entrance and joined the stream of people heading towards Custom House station.

Managing to find a pair of seats on the train, Eleanor looked over to see Max's hands shaking uncontrollably, a physical manifestation of the day's intense experiences. For her part, she was pumped, and frankly ready to go another round with any would-be assassin that might appear, though none did, somewhat to her disappointment.

However, she couldn't help but feel a surge of

guilt. She had pulled Max, essentially a civilian into her world of espionage and danger, into a maelstrom of political intrigue, death and violence - an ordeal that would test even the most seasoned operatives.

The car chases across London had broken every single traffic law in existence and several more that hadn't even been invented yet. Although to be fair, that was an area where Max had handled himself on par with, if not better than she would have, and she was highly trained in tactical and precision driving techniques, not to mention that since childhood she'd been influenced by her petrolhead father. Her respect for Max's resilience grew, even as she grappled with the responsibility that she felt for exposing him to such peril.

Eleanor's gaze lingered on Max, whose eyes seemed lost in a distant void, reflecting an inner turmoil she knew all too well. Not just because she had been there herself many times in the past, but because she was privy to the depth of his mental struggles having read the confidential psyche files she had asked Flux to obtain. The information laid bare in those pages had revealed a man wrestling with demons far more profound than she had initially realised. It was a testament to his strength that he hadn't completely broken under the weight of recent events.

Max, sensing Eleanor's watchful eyes, pulled himself back from the edge of his introspective abyss. He offered her a faint, somewhat strained smile. His hand, still trembling with a mix of adrenaline and anxiety, sought refuge by clutching tightly at the fabric of his jeans. It was a small, almost subconscious attempt to ground himself. Eleanor observed the subtle battle playing out within him, a mix of admiration and concern etching itself across her features. Max turned away in embarrassment, pretending to ascertain where the tube train was stopping next.

She had put him through the wringer, and she knew it. Yet, Max had risen to the challenge remarkably, displaying courage she hadn't anticipated. It was a daunting journey for anyone, let alone someone grappling with the shadows of past traumas.

She moved her hand across and put her palm over his still trembling fist. Her touch was a silent offer of solace. She pulled his hand free of its desperate grasp of his jeans and cupped it with her other hand.

Max, visibly surprised by her gesture, looked at her with a mixture of gratitude and self-consciousness. Sure enough, the shaking began to ebb away under her steady hold.

"You did amazing Max..." Eleanor whispered, leaning closer to ensure her words cut through the rumble of the train, "I know I'm putting you through hell here, but I couldn't do any of this without you. I'm asking a lot though… if you want out, just let me know."

Max's response was a gentle head shake, his voice tinged with resolve despite the ordeal. "I'm okay, Ellie," he assured her, though his eyes hinted at the whirlwind of emotions he was sorting through. "I just need time to process… it's all a bit surreal you know?"

For the remainder of the journey, they sat in companionable silence, Max drawing comfort from Eleanor's firm, reassuring grip. His gaze occasionally drifted, lost in thought, but always returning to the grounding presence of Eleanor's hands clasped around his.

An hour or so later they arrived back at Flux's place; the air was thick with the electric buzz of excitement. Flux, animated and spinning in his chair, greeted them with a fervour that was contagious. "Yo, yo, yo, folks! This stuff is the shit right here!" he exclaimed; his words punctuated by dramatic gestures. "This Project Imperium stuff, it's big – like, real big. And London's just the start, it's like just a test bed for what's coming."

"And what is coming Flux? What's phase 2," Eleanor leaned in, her curiosity piqued.

"Ah my dudette, phase 2 – well they gonna take away the cars. I mean not like outright banning 'em, but making it so only the select few, the high and mighty, can have them, you hear what I'm saying?"

Max nodded, connecting the dots, "Forcing everyone else onto public transport...?"

"Exactly brother; but you got to follow those threads and see where they lead back to." Flux continued, his hands slicing through the air.

"It's a total monopoly play. Viridis and their cronies, they're everywhere – trains, buses, you name it. They build 'em, run 'em, even mop 'em. It's like they're trying to be the puppet masters of mobility, the sellers of sustainability, with sticky fingers in pies that ain't even come out of the oven yet. Welcome to Green Capitalism 101!"

Max's fingers moved rapidly over his phone's keyboard, absorbed in typing.

Eleanor, observing his intense focus, voiced a note of caution. "Might be a bit premature to go public with all this, Max."

He paused and looked up, "No.... you see... ever since our recent, well, near-death experiences - can I say that?" Eleanor nodded while Flux simply rotated his cap to the front, a silent gesture of intrigue. "I've been compiling a running blog post," Max continued, "a sort of dossier on everything we've uncovered so far."

A sudden realisation seemed to strike him, and he quickly added, "But hey, don't worry. I haven't mentioned either of you, this place, or anything that anything that would compromise you..."

Eleanor feigned shock; her voice filled with mock outrage. "Max! Are you trying to hog all the glory for yourself?"

For a moment, Max looked genuinely mortified, until both Eleanor and Flux burst into laughter. "Dude, your discretion is much appreciated," Flux said with a grin.

Eleanor chimed in; her tone serious but her eyes twinkling. "Yeah, we're best left in the shadows. That's our domain."

"And that's exactly where we need to stay," Flux concluded, his voice carrying a mix of jest and earnestness.

"I figured as much," Max said with a sigh of relief. "So, what I'm doing is setting up a posting schedule. If I don't change the posting time each day," he paused, the weight of his words sinking in, the stark reality of their situation echoing in the silence, "for whatever reason, then everything we've found so far will automatically go public."

Eleanor and Flux exchanged a glance, a silent communication passing between them. "Smart move, my man," Flux commended, turning back to his array of screens. "But hey, there's something else you might wanna consider adding to that bombshell blog of yours."

"What's that, Ghost Weaver?" Eleanor beat Max

to the question, her curiosity evident.

Flux leaned forward, his fingers hovering over the keyboard. "There's this one folder inside Project Imperium. The file name's just a date; Sunday, August the 8th, 2023, four days from now. But man, it's locked down tighter than Fort Knox. Triple encrypted, double-wrapped in security, and I bet my last dollar it's rigged to self-destruct if a hacker tries to crack it open."

"You can't get in Flux?" Eleanor asked, her tone laced with a mix of surprise and challenge.

Flux pulled back, drew air in through his teeth, shook his head and looked back at her, feigning offence, "Bitch please!" Eleanor smiled bashfully. "C'mon, El! You doubtin' the Ghost Weaver? Girl, you must've forgotten who you're dealin' with. I'm the dude who had the bigwigs at Langley sweatin' bullets, thinkin' their HQ was 'bout to be dust in the wind."

He swivelled his chair to face Max, a mischievous glint in his eyes. "True story, man. Had 'em on lockdown for hours, thinkin' all hell was 'bout to break loose, you know?."

Turning back to Eleanor, his expression softened to a mock-serious tone. "A'ight, a'ight, I know that's supposed to be hush-hush." He gave a resigned shake of his head, jerking it towards Max, "Tch, guess you gotta off him now, El."

Eleanor glanced at Max, a playful grin on her lips. "Maybe later, Flux. He's still useful alive." She gave Max a reassuring wink.

Flux swung back to him, "Bro… what you think you heard… you did not hear. Capisce?"

"So, Ghost Weaver," Eleanor interjected, bringing the focus back to the task at hand, "how long do we need? An hour? Two?"

"Girl, I'm a genius, but I ain't no genie! This thing is clamped up tighter than a Victorian Queen's chastity belt, but give me a few days and I'll charm those metal bloomers right off this babe!"

Max reclined in his chair and sighed somewhat dejectedly. He waved his hand in a gesture of frustration. "A dead ex-mayor, assassins lying cold, me nearly meeting my maker… I've lost count of how many times… plus, a wrecked warehouse, City Hall needing new glazing, not to mention two brand new Chinese show cars now junk at the bottom of River Thames… and forget about me ever being invited to a car launch ever again… On top of that, a Belgium hellbent on profiteering and a former Hollywood actress now transformed into a murderous mayor… What have I forgotten?" Max thought for a moment and then clicked his fingers, "Oh of course, a deadly murder group of killing machines… what did you call them?"

"Eclipse squad…" Eleanor interjected softly.

"Yeah, the Eclipse Squad, at Madam Mayor's beck and call, with our pictures on their phones' wallpapers, and flat-out keen to eclipse our lives right now," Max stood, his movements amplifying his frustration.

"And still, in the wake of all this chaos, with all that we know now, even this file we stole from the Mayor's office – which sceptics could say we conjured up – we're still short of any real concrete proof that would topple Viridis, Hartfield, Imperium, and their entire phase 2 operation!"

He collapsed back into his chair, exhausted from his tirade, the weight of their predicament bearing down hard on him.

Eleanor was looking at her phone and held it up towards him, "On the bright side, your subscriber count's nearly doubled and your Edison Model A review has gone viral - it's already at a million views!"

She sported a grin, but Max only shook his head. Flux chimed in, "Too soon huh?"

Max's mood softened at the sound of Flux's voice, and he let out a half-hearted laugh. "Yeah, bro, definitely too soon."

"But you know, Max, I doubt even Jeremy Clarkson's ever pulled off a review quite like this. You might just break the internet!" Flux added.

Max finally gave in to curiosity, checking his phone. His notifications, which he'd muted, were now overflowing. Hundreds of them. He opened his Facebook, inundated with messages and updates. One particular post caught his attention, and he sat upright. "Look at this – there's a protest on Whitehall tomorrow, rallying against Pay-Per-Mile..." He handed the phone to Flux. "Organised by the same group that did the anti-ULEZ events."

"You should be there, Max," Eleanor suggested, peering at the screen Flux handed her.

"Are you sure that's a good idea?" Max pondered.

She looked up, "Shake the tree, remember?"

"Yeah, okay," he nodded thoughtfully. "But what about your Eclipse goons – won't they just do me on sight?" Max expressed his concern.

Eleanor's eyes flicked to Flux, "Time to cash in a favour, don't you think, Mr Jaxon?"

Flux's response came with a knowing smile, "Way overdue, Ms Rodrigues!"

CHAPTER 9

The morning sun cast a warm glow over the iconic skyline of Westminster, its rays glinting off the recently renovated and resplendent Big Ben Clock Tower. Amidst the bustling crowd of tourists, Max and Eleanor melded seamlessly with the throngs converging on Parliament Square.

Eleanor was a striking presence, impossible to overlook. She sported a form-hugging white T-shirt emblazoned with the infamous smiley face from Watchmen, creating a stark contrast against her skin-tight, dark red jeans and pristine white Nike trainers. Large, dark Vivienne Westwood sunglasses obscured most of her face, adding to her conspicuous appearance. A red Phillies baseball cap, worn at a jaunty angle, completed her ensemble.

With a casual air, she slung her backpack over one shoulder and positioned herself with theatrical flair beneath the imposing statue of Winston Churchill. Adopting a boisterous Philadelphia accent, ostensibly to tease Flux, who she knew would be listening in, she called out to Max, "Yo dog! Snap a pic of me with ol' Winston here, will ya?"

Clad in his signature brown jacket, Max, with a satchel slung over his shoulder holding his camera equipment, couldn't help but chuckle at Eleanor's over-the-top antics. He played along, his camera capturing her as she struck a series of exaggerated poses, pretending to engage in an animated conversation with Churchill's stoic statue. Each click of the shutter served as a brief interlude from their recent, tumultuous escapades.

Max found himself captivated by Eleanor's infectious energy and whimsy, even as he knew that her seemingly carefree demeanour was an act, just a means to an end. Though he wasn't quite sure what that was at this precise moment.

Their stroll through the square was punctuated with similar high jinks, Eleanor's loud behaviour and exuberant frolicking drawing glances from passers-by. Max couldn't help but admire her ability to command attention, her every move seemingly choreographed to ensure they were noticeable amidst the sea of tourists.

Beneath Mohandas Karamchand Gandhi's statue, Eleanor launched into an extraordinary impersonation of the iconic pacifist leader of the Indian independence movement. With dramatic flair, she rattled off a series of poignant quotes, straight from memory:

"Freedom is not worth having if it does not include the freedom to make mistakes."

"Strength does not come from physical capacity. It comes from an indomitable will."

And with a climactic flourish, she concluded: "First they ignore you, then they laugh at you, then they fight you, then you win."

Max, filming her performance, admired the relevance and poignancy of her chosen quotes, subtly mirroring their current undertakings. When he looked up from his camera, he became aware that a small crowd had gathered around to watch her performance.

Not missing a beat, Eleanor darted over to Nelson Mandela's statue, beckoning the burgeoning crowd to follow. There, she launched into another uncannily accurate rendition, this time embodying the legendary anti-apartheid revolutionary and former President of South Africa:

"No one is born hating another person because of the colour of his skin, or his background, or his religion. People must learn to hate, and if they can learn to hate, they can be taught to love, for love comes more naturally to the human heart than its opposite."

The crowd listened in rapt attention, drawn in by her perfect rendition and the power of Mandela's words.

After a while, they found themselves on a bench indulging in ludicrously overpriced ice cream. Max sat upright, nursing a modest two-scoop tub, while Eleanor lounged against him, her body twisted casually so her legs stretched along the bench's length. Max finally voiced his curiosity, "Eleanor, what's with the tourist act? What exactly are we doing here?"

Eleanor responded with a leisurely lick of her ice cream, her gaze sweeping across the crowd. Behind her seemingly relaxed demeanour, her eyes were darting around with hypervigilance. "It's simple, really," she said, her voice smooth and unperturbed. "We're making a show of ourselves, trying to catch the wrong kind of attention," she grinned. "We're waiting to be taken."

Max's spoon hovered in mid-air, frozen in a moment of realisation. His interest in the mint-choc-chip ice cream waned rapidly. The notion of being 'taken' once more held no appeal after he was nearly shot in the head by Stahl last time. "Taken? By who exactly?" he asked, his voice tinged with a mix of apprehension and curiosity, the supposedly pleasant day out, suddenly taking an ominous turn in his mind.

"By him," Eleanor subtly indicated with a slight nod of her head, gesturing discreetly with her ice cream cone. Max's attention shifted to where she was pointing. From the bustling throng of tourists, a tall, ruggedly handsome man in a dark blue suit materialised, as if he had been there all along, yet remained unnoticed until he chose to be seen. The suit he wore was sharply tailored, accentuating his sturdy build. Beneath it, a crisp white shirt was paired with a slim black tie, and his shoes, polished to a mirror shine, completed the ensemble with an air of meticulous care. There was a certain military poise about him, suggesting an underlying readiness. A slight bulge under his blazer hinted discreetly at the presence of a concealed weapon.

He moved with an effortless grace, exuding a quiet confidence. As he approached, Max noticed the man's calculated movements: a subtle adjustment of his cuffs and the faint, knowing smirk on a jawline that had clearly seen significant action. A closer look revealed a slightly crooked nose, suggesting a past not unfamiliar with physical altercations.

The stranger reached them and without pausing he gently shifted Eleanor's legs off the bench to make room for himself. Sitting down, he surveyed his surroundings and straightened his tie as he moved in tighter. Close enough so he wouldn't have to raise his voice too much to be heard above the noisy crowds.

"Hello Ellie, causing a commotion as always I see!" he greeted her in a voice that was both low and crisp, resonating with an unmistakable air of familiarity. "Didn't you ever learn anything in Spycraft 101?" he added, a playful reprimand in his voice as he turned to face her more directly.

Inexplicably, Max felt a twinge of discomfort at the man's proximity to Eleanor. He edged towards the end of his side of the bench to give Eleanor more room, but she didn't budge away from the man's encroaching presence. There was an unspoken cordiality between them.

"Hey Dalton, how's it hanging?"

Eleanor's tone was teasing as she momentarily shifted her attention from her ice cream and her expression switched to mock concern as her mouth fell open, "Oh, I'm terribly sorry... I should've asked 'how's it healing' right?"

Dalton recoiled slightly, visibly stung by the remark. He retorted with a blend of sarcasm and flirtation, "Fully operational, my dear Ellie. Care for a... demonstration?"

Max studied the two realising they had a history together, the veiled jabs were both intriguing and unnerving, and he found himself pondering how well he really knew Eleanor, who continued to surprise him. He chose to remain an observer, keeping his thoughts to himself.

"Maybe another time Jake," replied Eleanor winking at him. "Right now, I'm getting far more pleasure licking this delicious ninety-niner!" She extended her tongue and worked it slowly, lasciviously from the base of the ice cream to the tip. Max shifted uncomfortably.

Dalton's stern demeanour cracked into a brief chuckle. "Well, you might want to hurry it up, because he who is never wrong, wants to see you."

Eleanor grinned, turned to Max, lowered her glasses for a moment and winked at him, "I thought he might."

Dalton's next words were curt. "Ditch the civvy."

Eleanor's response was immediate and firm. "Civvy comes with," she declared, her tone leaving no room for argument.

She smoothly facilitated introductions. "Max Turner of Turner Wheels, meet Jake Dalton, an... er... old work colleague."

Dalton extended a hand towards Max with a grin that was both charming and calculating. "Pleasure mate!"

Max, slightly taken aback by the unfolding scenario and Jake's earlier casual dismissal of him as a 'civvy', cautiously returned the handshake. "Likewise," he responded, his wariness palpable.

Much to both men's astonishment, Eleanor, seizing the moment, finished her ice cream with a single dramatic gulp, having removed the flake, which she offered to them. They shook their heads almost in unison, so she devoured the crumbly chocolate while throwing the wafer cone in a nearby bin.

"Let's go Dalton, we haven't got all day; we still have the London Eye to do and we might even take in a boat ride later!"

"Certainly Ellie, follow me." He led Eleanor away, and Max hastily joined them, quickly ditching his tub, its contents largely uneaten, in the same bin.

They strode past Westminster Abbey and along Victoria Street, veering into an unassuming side road. There, they came upon a nondescript café that blended into its surroundings - the sort of place you wouldn't notice unless you already knew it was there.

Max and Eleanor found themselves being silently ushered to the dimly lit recesses of this ordinary establishment. As they navigated their way through the maze of tables, the low hum of casual conversations and the clinking of coffee cups created an ambient soundtrack to their approach.

The back of the café, shrouded in shadows, offered a stark contrast to the lively atmosphere at the front. In this secluded area, a solitary figure sat at a table, his presence commanding yet enigmatic.

Dressed impeccably in an expensive suit that whispered of sophistication, in one hand he held a phone, casually scrolling through, while the other cradled a steaming cup of coffee. The man was clearly of Chinese heritage, his smooth clear skin meant his age was hard to determine, but the streaks of grey in his carefully groomed hair, and the lines of wisdom etched around his eyes, suggested a man in his upper middle years. His posture was both relaxed and purposeful, exuding an aura of confidence and authority.

His dark eyes, sharp and perceptive, flicked up from the phone screen as Max and Eleanor approached, appraising them with a discerning look. A hint of a smile touched his lips, revealing a charismatic blend of warmth and calculation, "Ah, here we are," he said, his voice smooth and resonant, redolent of an Oxbridge education, betraying only the merest hint of a Chinese intonation. "I trust you found your way without too much trouble?" His question was rhetorical, the faintest trace of amusement in his tone.

"Good morning Director Wong," Eleanor responded, "it's good to see you again Sir". Max was taken aback by her sudden switch to formality and deference to the seated man, who was evidently someone she respected.

The man gestured to the seats opposite him, "Please do pull up a pew, won't you?" His voice carried an air of polite command.

They obeyed and Jake took up a seat to the side. From here, he maintained a vigilant watch over both Max and Eleanor, as well as the café's entrance, his eyes constantly scanning and assessing.

Wong, while ostensibly addressing Eleanor, directed his words to an unseen presence. "And greetings, Mr Jaxon. I trust you're in fine fettle, my dear fellow."

Eleanor's smile hinted at an unspoken conversation. After a brief pause, she relayed Flux's message, "He says, 'Good to know the master of the game is still playing the board. Regards from the digital den.'"

Noting Wong's wry smile and quick nod in acknowledgement, she turned to Max, "This is Director Wong Lei, he was my boss at the Agency; Director Wong, this is Max Turner," Eleanor completed the introductions.

"Yes, of course, I'm well aware of your fine work," Wong offered Max a firm handshake, "it's lovely to finally meet you, Mr Turner."

Max returned his warm smile and watched as Wong Lei purposefully set his phone down on the table, face down and aligned with precision. He adjusted his coffee cup to match, then lifted his gaze, giving Max and Eleanor his undivided attention. Even in this simple act, Wong exuded an aura of effortless command, a dominant presence.

"So, Ms Rodrigues, my dear Ellie," Wong began, his tone laced with a mix of sternness and forced joviality, "we have a deceased mayor in a bullet-riddled cottage, a wrecked Mercedes in Park Royal accompanied by a deceased Eclipse Squad operative, another operative... rather crisply pressed found between two brand new cars at the bottom of the Royal Victoria Docks, and let us not omit a written-off refuse collection vehicle and a warehouse sporting a new architectural feature."

Wong's recounting of the chaos Eleanor was seemingly responsible for, was delivered with punctilious poise, yet there was restrained irritation in his voice, hinting at an underlying disapproval.

"That bin lorry was NOT written off..." Eleanor began, a hint of protest in her voice.

Wong raised a hand, halting her mid-sentence, his forced smile unwavering but his eyes sharp. "As the proverb goes, 'to fish in troubled waters', my dear?"

"Wong, listen to me," Eleanor leaned forward, her voice lowering to a serious, compelling tone. "We're onto something significant, involving Mayor Victoria Hartfield and..."

"Viridis Ventures, and our friend Quentin Dubois..." Wong interrupted, "Yes, I know..."

"Are you also aware it was one of those dead assassins that eliminated Siddique? On Quentin's direct orders!" Eleanor wasn't backing down, and showed no surprise at Wong being privy to her activities. She knew he was a man who liked to remain apprised of all goings on, either within the agency's remit, or any extracurricular activities. Plus, the Agency liked to keep tabs on all its former operatives.

"He shot at us too!" Max interjected, recalling the harrowing start of his adventure in Trafalgar Square, but then hesitated, unsure if he had overstepped. He glanced apologetically at Eleanor, who nodded encouragingly.

Wong turned his attention to Max, his expression changing subtly to one of formal contrition, "I am sincerely sorry, Mr Turner, for what you've been through." Wong gave him an understanding nod before turning back to Eleanor. "But you; you've been giving me quite the migraines; the havoc you've wreaked, is not easy to brush under the concrete carpet, despite the extraordinarily efficient efforts at concealment of the Ghost Weaver."

"Break the pots and sink the boats, innit?" retorted Eleanor, flipping Wong's penchant for proverbs back on him.

Wong noticed Max looking a little confused and explained, "The proverb refers to a general that ordered his troops to destroy their cooking pots and boats, signifying commitment and a point of no return," he elucidated, shifting his focus back to Eleanor. "Are you at the point of no return, my dear?"

"Way beyond it, Wong," Eleanor replied with a

resolute tone.

"Careful Ellie, do not make this personal," warned the Director. Max realised he was alluding to the death of Eleanor's father. "Remember, Wong is never wrong." He used his catchphrase with a mix of seriousness and a trace of humour.

Eleanor's lips curled into a brief smile at Wong's familiar phrase, a touch of warmth breaking through her stern demeanour. She recovered quickly and hardened her expression again.

"I can blow this thing apart; I know your hands are tied Director, I know how this works, but mine aren't, and I will serve you Hartfield's head on a platter," Eleanor responded staring at Wong fiercely.

"I hope you don't mean that literally," he responded, "though I fear you actually might." He sighed and leaned back slightly, his fingers interlocking in front of him in a contemplative gesture. "Mr. Dalton, would you mind giving us a moment?"

Jake Dalton cast a hesitant look at Eleanor and Max before nodding to Wong and reluctantly moving away. Once assured of their privacy, Wong leaned forward, his voice dropping to a more confidential tone. "Ellie, you know I always have your back, but there's only so much chaos that can be caused before the higher-ups start hunting for necks to roll. And one of those necks could very well belong to your favourite Chinaman," he made an act of slicing a finger across his neck.

"On the flip side, if you can deliver on your promise..."

"We're close Director. Somethings going down on Sunday, I don't know what yet, but it's shaping up to be a major incident, possibly a terror-level threat," Eleanor disclosed earnestly, her eyes searching Wong's for any hint of additional information. "Have you picked up anything on your end?"

Wong shook his head, but his expression was inscrutable. "Sunday, you say?" Wong shook his head thoughtfully, "nothing that I've been made aware of as yet, but that's not uncommon. Sometimes we're a little late on catching the chatter, you know how it goes. Tell me Ellie, what do you need from us?"

Eleanor paused, considering her next words carefully: "Keep the heat off Max and me for a few more days?"

Wong gave a decisive nod. "Consider it done," nodded Wong.

"And... if you can, get Hartfield's hounds off our backs? The Eclipse Squad very likely have a kill order on us, not least cause I took out two of their top guys," she added.

Wong let out a deep harrumph, his mind

turning over the implications. After a moment's contemplation, he replied, "Alright, Ellie. I'll call Victoria in a moment. I'll spin a yarn about bringing you back into the fold to help manage our 'errant journalist' here." He gave Max a wry smile, adding, "Pure subterfuge, of course, my good Sir." Turning back to Eleanor, "She won't buy it, but she'll be obliged to keep hands-off, at least for a while."

Max, sure that he would be speaking out of turn, nonetheless had a pressing concern of his own he wanted to raise, "er... Sir... about the Edison guys..."

Wong grinned, "Oh, you'll have no trouble from them!"

Max was confused, "hey? I... er... ruined their car launch, and destroyed two new Model As, not to mention smashing a hole in the side of the Mayor's building, and the ExCel...?"

"Mr Turner, Edison apparently adore you right now; your video is on 10 million views and rising. It seems the Model A is trending thanks to you. Frankly, money can't buy them that sort of publicity!

"As for the damage, I agreed with the mayor to concoct some story about two ex-operatives having a vendetta against one another that got out of hand," he looked across at Eleanor and winked, then returned his attention to Max, "... and that you, my dear fellow, just got caught up in the whole thing!" Shrugging he addressed Eleanor again and concluded, "The rest was hushed up in all the usual ways... interests of national security and all that... you know the routine."

Abruptly, Wong reached for his phone, a silent signal that their time was up. "Now, if you'll excuse me. And Ms Rodrigues, and do send Dalton back in, He's probably making a spectacle of himself loitering outside, and we can't have that."

Eleanor almost saluted in response, "Thank you, Director, I owe you one."

Wong chuckled, "Just put it on the tab Ellie. Oh, and Mr Turner..." Max paused to give the formidable man his full attention. "'A journey of a thousand miles begins with a single step,' I bid you good luck, and happy hunting, Sir."

Eleanor tugged at Max's arm before he could think of how to respond, and led him off. Sure enough, outside they found Jake, pacing up and down the pavement. "Your leash is being pulled Dalton, better get back in there."

Jake started to head back in, then paused and spoke gently with an undertone of concern, "Watch your six out there Ellie." She acknowledged him with a nod, and leaned in to give him a kiss on the cheek, "You too Jake, it was good to see you again."

As they walked away, Max found himself

grappling with an unexpected surge of jealousy. The emotions caught him off guard; he hadn't fully admitted, even to himself, the depth of his developing feelings for Eleanor. While he wrestled with a curiosity about Eleanor's past with Jake, another pressing question lingered in his mind, demanding to be asked.

"Can we trust him?" he asked.

Eleanor glanced over with a raised eyebrow, "Which one?"

Max paused for a moment, considering. "Actually, either of them," he replied, his tone reflecting his uncertainty about both Jake and Wong.

Eleanor couldn't help but let out a chuckle at his response. "Trust them? No, not really. I wouldn't trust either of them as far as I could throw them. But right now, Max, we don't really have a choice in the matter."

Max mulled over her words, a wry smile playing on his lips. "I don't know Ellie, I reckon you could chuck them pretty far actually!"

Eleanor's laughter rang out, bright and infectious, as she quickened her stride. "Come on, Max, let's get you to that protest!"

As they neared Whitehall, Eleanor's tone became more serious. "You go on ahead. I'll be watching," she instructed before swiftly disappearing into the crowd. Max glanced around, but Eleanor had faded away as effectively whisper in a hurricane.

Approaching the front of the bustling crowd gathered at the gates of Downing Street, Max was taken aback when an impromptu cheer broke out: "Turner Wheels! Turner Wheels! Turner Wheels!" The chant echoed through the air, energising the atmosphere.

Several protesters broke away to warmly greet him with embraces and handshakes. Their faces lit up with a mix of surprise and joy at seeing him. They peppered him with questions about his whereabouts, and his wellbeing, some even asked if he still had his iconic BMW. Max found himself as delighted as the ones asking, to be able to answer, that yes, he did have the car.

Suddenly, Alex Harrington, a prominent figure in the anti-ULEZ movement, grabbed a loudspeaker and put an arm around Max. "Ladies and gentlemen, for those who don't know him, this is V-Max T of Turner Wheels. He's an outstanding journalist, a huge YouTuber, and genuinely one of the good guys. He did so much for us during the ULEZ expansion protests. Let's show him some love!"

The crowd's response was thunderous, their cheers and applause echoing off the buildings. Max scanned the crowd, pleased to see familiar faces joined by many new ones, swelling their numbers to several thousand strong.

As the cheering subsided, Alex leaned in towards

Max, lowering the megaphone. "So, V-Max, you up for giving a speech?" he asked.

Max considered the offer, questioning how far he wanted to wander back down the rabbit hole that had traumatised him so much four years ago. Yet, here he was, amidst a sea of eager faces, all looking to him for inspiration. With a resigned nod, he accepted the loudspeaker and faced the crowd. His heart pounded in his chest, his thoughts racing.

Max stepped forward, he hadn't prepared anything; this was going to be off-the-cuff, from the heart, raw and unrehearsed.

"Hey everyone," he began, his voice wavering slightly with a mix of nerves and adrenaline. "Thank you for such a warm welcome. I'm just a guy who loves cars, and who believes in the freedom they offer us. And this pay-per-mile scheme... it's more than just extra costs. It's about what it really represents, you know?"

A murmur of agreement rippled through the crowd.

"It's like, we all know the world's changing, right? We need to be greener, and I'm all for that. But there's gotta be a balance. The answer can't be to just charge us for every mile. That's not fair, especially for those of us who... well, who rely on, and need our cars."

The crowd's enthusiasm buoyed Max, giving him the confidence to continue.

"Think about it. Cars aren't just machines; they're a part of our lives. They are more than just transport. They symbolise our freedom, our ability to move about, to live our lives. Modern cars are cleaner, and more efficient. The shift to electric vehicles is making air pollution arguments increasingly irrelevant.

"They say they want to extend our lives by a few days, months, a handful of years, but at what cost? At the cost of our freedom, our happiness? Have a heart, Hartfield!"

The crowd loved that, a few picking up the cry and returning it, "Have a heart, Hartfield!" Max felt empowered, riding the wave of the crowd's energy.

"Life's about more than just existing; living is about experiencing, exploring. Cars help us do that. And yes, we need to care for our planet, but that doesn't mean we should travelling across it!"

He thought this might be a good place to wrap it up, but the chorus of agreement from the crowd encouraged him to continue.

"This new scheme... it hits the little guy the hardest. The daily commuter, the parents doing school runs, small businesses... We're all feeling the pinch. And isn't it ironic? We need our cars to work, to earn, to live, and now they want to charge us for using them?!

"Look, we're not against change. We're not against doing our part for the environment. But let's do it in a way that's fair, that doesn't stifle our freedom to move, to explore, to work, to make our, and our loved ones' lives better. We need solutions that don't make life harder, more miserable and leave us poorer.

"Finally, okay, I'm gonna plug V-Max T and Turner Wheels on social media, because... well, there's more to all this than meets the eye, but you're all smart people and you already know that, so I'll just say, keep following my content... there's more to come! Guys, thanks so much for listening. Let's keep driving towards a better future, together."

As Max soaked in the third round of thunderous cheers and applause, his spirits lifted. The crowd's chanting of "Turner Wheels" filled the air, revitalising him. Eleanor's voice echoed the chant through the coms, adding to his newfound energy. Even Flux expressed his admiration, "Yo Max, you just rocked that mic, man! True orator in the house!"

"Yeah, that was a great speech Max," Eleanor agreed.

Max was about to respond when Alex, his face alight with admiration, approached him for a congratulatory embrace. "Max! That was just brilliant! So, mate; are you back?"

The question made Max pause. It wasn't just

an inquiry; it was a moment of self-reflection. From thinking he had left all this behind and was ready to move on, to plunging back in. The answer, he finally realised, was obvious. "Yeah, I'm thinking I'm back!" he declared, a sense of determination in his voice. Alex's grin widened, mirroring Max's own sense of resolve and excitement.

Max reached for his satchel, "Right then Alex, now that I am back, better get to work and do some interviews; you up for being first?"

"Absolutely!" Alex responded with a smile. "Let's do it mate."

Max set up his camera gear and mic and having got a few words with Alex, and one of the other organisers, began weaving through the crowd, engaging with various protesters.

Meanwhile, Flux's voice crackled through the coms, offering a strategic edge to Max's impromptu reporting. "Yo Max, keep them interviews flowin', man. I'm runnin' some slick voice analysis here – we'll catch any posers or big shots hidin' in that crowd. You're killin' it, dude. Just keep that vibe pumpin', aight?""

Max nodded to himself, feeling a renewed sense of purpose. As he moved through the crowd, his confidence grew. He was back in his element, doing what he did best – connecting with people, sharing their stories, and giving a voice to their concerns. The energy of the protest, the passion of the people, it all felt right. He was indeed back.

Amongst the interviewees, Max encountered a diverse array of individuals. Most were passionately articulate, others just expressed deep concern, and a few seemed to be there more for the sense of solidarity than for a clear understanding of the issues. Many were simply grateful that someone was taking the time to genuinely listen and convey their concerns to a wider audience.

All interactions were cooperative and appreciative, except one. It was Eleanor's voice that alerted Max, speaking into his earpiece from an unseen vantage point. "Max, there's a woman to your right, about five-foot-six, brunette, curly hair, late 20s, dressed in a black waistcoat, white shirt, blue trousers, and blue trainers. She's holding a 'No to PPM' placard. You see her?"

Max, momentarily pausing between interviews and feigning a check of his equipment, spotted her. "Yes, I see her. But it looks like she's coming to me."

"Oi, Mr. Wheels, right?!" the woman approached him, her voice tinged with a robust East London accent.

"It's Turner, actually," he greeted her with a welcoming smile. "Turner Wheels is my channel, but you can call me Max," he replied, offering a handshake and raising his camera, "would you be up for doing an interview?"

"Nah, I don't wanna be on no camera. What I wanna know is what's your game mate?" she countered, her voice dripping with suspicion.

Max was taken aback, it was the last thing he had expected to hear, "I'm sorry? What?"

In his ear he heard Eleanor, "Flux, are you getting this?"

"Already on it," Flux responded promptly, his voice indicating he was scanning her voice and running her profile.

"I mean you mate, you're a bleeding hypocrite ain't cha?" the woman persisted, her tone accusatory.

Max shrugged, "Miss, I really don't know what you're on about."

"You just talked about saving the planet, right?"

"I said we need to look after the place we live in…"

"Whatever… point is, you believe in climate change, and I saw you just posted up an electric car review, it's got like millions of views, you love 'em. Mate, you're not one of us; you're just another woke lefty, trying to make us look bad!"

Max, trying to remain diplomatic, responded, "I'm here to represent all motorists. I believe in our right to own and drive cars without being priced off the roads. But I also think we need to find a balance with environmental concerns…"

"You don't know what the fuck you're talking

about mate, and I don't trust you; you're just here to mock us, to make us look like a bunch of idiots!" The woman was attempting to stir up dissension in the crowd against Max. However, it backfired. Several protesters, recognising Max's genuine intent, stepped in, creating a buffer between him and the agitated woman.

She retreated and seemed to melt into the crowd. Max tried to see where she went, but quickly lost sight, though he thought he caught a glimpse of Eleanor, but his attention was soon drawn by others who were keen to engage with him.

"Don't worry Max, I'm on her," he heard Eleanor. It had been her he'd spotted, after all.

"Oh, this girl raising some red flags right here," Flux spoke up, "She's a ghost on the usual searches, which means trouble. Digging deeper, and uh oh, what have we here? El, I think this girl be running with your old gang."

"Eclipse Squad," Eleanor deduced swiftly. "Flux, I tagged her. Do you have a fix?"

"Heading south to Westminster..." Flux reported.

"Max, you with us?" Eleanor asked, urgency in her tone.

"Absolutely!" responded Max. He hastily waved his goodbyes to the protesters closest to him, and headed down Parliament Street, hooking up with Eleanor who was waiting for him further down.

He noticed she had somehow switched back into a zipped-up black jacket, the red cap replaced by a more inconspicuous black one.

"Eastbound," Flux updated them, "passing Portcullis House... wait... she's stopping there."

Eleanor and Max had caught up, but waited beside the building while the woman paused in the central reservation of the road. They took cover in the shadows cast by the towering columns of Portcullis House which served as a work extension to the Houses of Parliament. The iconic Big Ben loomed above them, a silent witness to their covert operations.

"I've got eyes on her now, Flux," Eleanor whispered into her comms.

The woman was near the crossing, mimicking the actions of tourists as they took selfies with Big Ben. Yet her glances towards the entrance of Portcullis House betrayed her true intent. After a moment, she continued her journey, crossing the road and heading in the direction of Westminster Pier.

Max started to move, but Eleanor's firm grip halted him. He turned to her, questioning, only to see her nodding towards a figure further down the road. Max froze as he recognised Quentin Dubois. The woman had been waiting for him.

Cautiously, they tailed Quentin and the woman, maintaining a discreet distance. The pair descended the steps to the pier, turning right towards the ramp that led down to the boats. The two ahead of them, deliberately kept several members of the public between them, so as not to appear together and made their way to the far end, gate E, to await the Eastbound Thames Clipper Uber Boat.

The waiting rooms had glass walls, and there was a relatively small queue of people waiting inside. But to enter would mean that Eleanor and Max would be spotted immediately. Remaining outside, however, risked making them too obvious.

Without warning, Eleanor spun Max around, enveloping him in a tight embrace. To any casual observer, they were simply a couple lost in a moment. But this strategic position allowed Eleanor to surreptitiously monitor Quentin and the woman, still appearing to wait separately for the boat.

"Er... is this the right time Ellie?" Max whispered with a hint of amusement, playing along with the ruse though, understanding what Eleanor was up to.

"Hey, even I need a hug sometimes, right?" Eleanor quipped; her tone playful yet focused.

"What you kids be up to huh?" Flux's voice crackled through the earpiece, teasingly.

"Shut up Flux, I know you got eyes on!" Eleanor retorted.

"Ghost Weaver sees everything; you know that sis!" he responded.

Max meanwhile found himself sinking into the extended embrace. The nearness of the extraordinary woman, her scent weaving a spell over his senses, offering comfort and somehow a respite from the abnormality of the absurdly surreal day - make that, days - he was having.

Eleanor sensed the change in his demeanour and raised her head to look up at him, her eyes meeting his. Mortified that he had overstepped the boundaries of their feigned closeness, Max started to withdraw. However, Eleanor gave him a reassuring smile and pulled him tighter with a gentle firmness, snuggling her face into his chest for a brief, serene moment, before subtly shifting her attention back to their subjects.

"Boat's arrived," she whispered.

"What?" Max, momentarily lost in the embrace, stuttered, "Oh! The boat, right." He started to turn, but she held him in position.

"Wait…" Eleanor's eyes were locked on their prey, as she picked her moment. "Now, let's move."

They discreetly tagged onto the back of the queue to follow them onto the boat. Fortunately, the staff split the boarding, with the first half of the queue being directed to board from the front and Max and Eleanor boarding from the rear, passing through a small outdoor seating deck and into the main cabin. This proved useful as they witnessed Quentin grab a seat quickly as the boat started to fill up, the woman immediately sliding in next to him, as if she was just another random passenger.

The 125-foot catamaran, capable of ferrying over 200 passengers, bustled with activity. Several people were ordering snacks at the small café placed centrally. Quentin and his companion had chosen seats nearby. Max and Eleanor found a couple of places at the rear, a perfect vantage point for surveillance.

"Flux, please tell me that tracker was the new MicroPin 300 and not the old NanoTrak ZTs we had?" she leant across to explain to Max, "The new ones have mics."

"You know Ghost Weaver's cutting edge, right?" he laughed, "you really think I'd roll with anything but the latest? Piping sound through now… it's not great though, they be whispering."

The woman's voice was faint but clear, Quentin's responses more distant and distorted. Most of the conversation was the woman relaying back her experience with the protesters and her interaction with the Max. Quentin seemed keen to find out if Eleanor was there, but the woman hadn't seen her. Frustratingly, they didn't discuss 8th August, nor reveal any other useful information by the time the boat arrived at Blackfriars Pier and Quentin disembarked.

"Should we follow him?" asked Max. Eleanor was thinking, "No," she decided, "we know where to find him, let's stick with the girl."

Shortly after the boat continued its journey, the woman got up and walked to the rear, possibly heading to the toilets. She moved along the opposite aisle to where they were seated, exiting onto the open back deck. Eleanor watched intently, "Count to ten, then follow me," she instructed Max before heading back and slipping out the door at the end of their aisle. Max caught a glimpse of her hand reaching inside her jacket.

He counted silently and duly followed. Outside he found Eleanor casually sitting with the woman on the wooden bench seat at the very back of the open section. There were fewer passengers on board now. Eleanor was smirking at him, but the woman appeared to be grimacing in pain and at an awkward angle. As he moved closer, he noticed Eleanor had the woman's arm twisted around her back; he also noted the subtle bulge of Eleanor's gun pressed against the woman's ribs through her jacket.

Approaching cautiously, Max took a seat on the other side of the woman, effectively trapping her between them. "Well, hello again! Fancy meeting you here," he called out over the roar of the engines, the speeding boat's foamy wake behind them sending occasional splashes of water against their necks.

"Vhat do you vant from me?" she demanded in a Spanish accent, dropping the feigned London intonation she had obviously gleaned from watching EastEnders, the TV soap. Eleanor glanced across at Max and nodded as if to let him take the lead.

"What were you doing at the protest today?" Max asked, his tone steady.

The woman slipped back into her faux London persona: "Waiting for you my luv, I'm a big fan innit? Ere, listen, can I get a selfie wiv ya?"

Max played along, "Maybe later darling..."

"You're with Eclipse, aren't you?" Eleanor cut in sharply, her grip on the woman's arm unrelenting. The woman reverted to her native voice, "I could play dumb, pero I know very vell that you know who I am."

"What are your orders?" pressed Eleanor, her voice stern.

"Only vatching and speeling the beans back to them," she responded, her tone laced with a mix of pain and defiance. Feeling Eleanor's grip tighten, she let out a sharp yelp, "Ay! Okay, okay! They vanted me to shake theengs up at the protest, pero your fans, Señor Turner, they are too devoted, no?"

"Project Imperium – what is it?" Max interjected, seizing the opportunity to probe deeper.

The woman shrugged nonchalantly, her attempt

at feigning ignorance almost convincing. "Project Imperium? Qué es eso? Sounds like some fancy perfume, no?"

"What's happening on 8th August?" Max tried again.

For a fleeting moment, fear flickered across the woman's features, her mask of indifference slipping. She quickly composed herself, shrugging once more, "No sé!" But both Max and Eleanor had seen it – the brief flash of panic in her expression. She was definitely hiding something about that date.

Eleanor's demeanour shifted as she relaxed her hold, gently guiding the woman's arm back around while maintaining a firm grip on her hand. With a deceptive smile, she addressed Max, "It seems we've made a bit of an error, Max. She's just a low-level Eclipse grunt, probably clueless about the big picture." Turning to the woman, she added sweetly, "We'll let you go at the next stop. Sound good?"

The woman had taken offence, "How 'bout I smash your stoopid face in, you beetch, does that sound good, huh?" she spat back with fiery intensity.

The Eclipse operative's face suddenly contorted in pain, while she fought to stifle down a cry of pain. Max, bewildered, saw Eleanor's face was tightened with strain. Glancing down, he was horrified to see the woman's little finger bent grotesquely out of shape. Eleanor had snapped it.

"Maldita puta!" the woman spat at her, her eyes welling up with tears, she bent down in pain. Max was staring at Eleanor in protest, which momentarily took her attention off the woman, who suddenly rammed an elbow into Eleanor's stomach and swung her fist up into her face. None of these actions were enough to incapacitate Eleanor, but it bought the woman just enough time to raise her feet against the seats in front and push herself up and back far enough to launch herself overboard into the Thames.

Eleanor sprang to her feet, her hand darting towards her jacket pocket. Max, quick to react, clasped her arm firmly, halting her action. "Eleanor, no!" He pointed upwards urgently. They were just gliding out from under Tower Bridge, straight into the full view of a crowd of onlookers perched above. Any action now would draw too much attention.

The woman had chosen her moment flawlessly, leaping into the Thames' murky waters just as they were shielded by the bridge's shadow. Now, as they emerged into the open, a line of tourists on the bridge, cameras in hand, were eagerly capturing the boats below.

With a deep breath, Eleanor retracted her hand, leaving the hidden gun untouched. She replaced frustration with a poised smile and began waving cheerily at the onlookers. Max, catching on to her cue, mirrored her actions, offering friendly waves to the tourists above.

Astonishingly, none of the other passengers seemed to have noticed the woman's dramatic escape overboard, it had been so quick.

"We have a tracker on her right?" asked Max.

Eleanor pointed at the river, "Dead in the water," she lamented, "literally."

"Well, that was all a bit of a waste of time," Max commented, still smiling and waving. Eleanor sat back down; her expression pensive. "Not entirely," she countered thoughtfully. "She did tell us something crucial," her voice low but intense. "Whatever is planned for the 8th of August, it's big, real big. We need to uncover the truth, and we need to do it fast!"

CHAPTER 10

Late into the night, back at base, Max and Eleanor huddled around Flux and his array of monitors, flickering with data, newsfeeds, files, and bespoke apps. Max, despite considering himself relatively tech-savvy, couldn't begin to fathom the complexity of Flux's setup. The air was heavy with the scent of stale coffee, emptied Chinese takeaway boxes, and the tension of unanswered questions. They had been at it for hours. Desperately trying to figure out, what was being planned on 8th August, which was approaching fast.

Flux was in full flow, his voice a mix of frustration and focus. "Yo, we got a whole mess of stuff goin' down on the 8th, but nothin's screamin' 'it's me!' you know? We're talkin' concerts, political rallies, some high-flyin' corporate meetings. Yo, we even got the BBC Proms at the Royal Albert Hall, and check this - London Film and Comic Con at the ExCel. Man, I was thinkin' of rockin' Agent J from Men in Black this year!" he lamented.

"But gotta say, none of this is ringin' alarm bells. None of it feels like it's connected to our bad guys' plan, ya feel me?"

Eleanor, leaning forward, her eyes scanning the screens, was less quick to dismiss any possibility. "Right now, Flux, we can't afford to discount anything. All of these could easily be a cover for something more sinister."

Max, his attention glued to his phone, was cross-referencing dates. Suddenly, his fingers paused, and he looked up with an expression of realisation. "Wait a minute, guys! The EuroBall Rally's big start is happening on Regent Street on the 8th. They'll have high-profile cars, celebrities, and huge crowds... could that be it?"

Flux was already pulling up videos and images from past EuroBall Rally events. "Oh man, it's all high octane and high rollers, a real spectacle. It's kicked off here in London a bunch of times. Yo, check this out, the Hoff was there with his Knight Rider car one year... now that's dope!"

Eleanor, her arms folded, paced a little. "It's a spectacle, alright. Perfect for making a statement, but... what kind? A bomb threat? Kidnappings? A mass shooting? Or maybe just a protest against it?" She trailed off, voicing the uncertainty that hung in the air.

Flux, leaning back in his chair, pondered aloud, "Blow it up? Nah, too drastic. Protest? C'mon... boring!"

Max chimed in, "The EuroBall always gets crazy attention, especially on social media. It's like a magnet for YouTubers, Instagrammers, Influencers..."

"Could be a distraction then? Misdirection? Everyone's eyes are on the shiny cars while..." Flux's voice trailed off.

"While what?" Eleanor's question was rhetorical, echoing the room's collective thought.

A tense silence filled the room, punctuated only by the soft hum of computers and the occasional sip of coffee. They were on the cusp of unravelling something, a thread waiting to be pulled, but the full picture remained tantalisingly elusive.

"Quentin?" Max said, setting his coffee mug down with a determined thud. "He's got to know something. And you did say we know where to find him, right?"

"My little spy on the shelf went dark ages ago," Flux confirmed with a shrug. "So, El, what's the play? Plant another bug, or do we go in more... direct?"

"Got any eyes on the outside, Flux?" Eleanor inquired, leaning towards the screens.

Flux quickly pulled up external CCTV feeds from the roads outside Viridis Ventures headquarters. The screens flickered to life, showing quiet streets. "Looks like an off-night," he observed, "might be an easy in."

"On it... Max, you coming?" Eleanor was already gearing up, her movements swift and purposeful. Max nodded, his expression firm.

She then turned back to Flux. "I'll need the Infil Kit Bag."

"In my van, Ellie," Flux tossed her the keys. "And yeah, better take the van. Max's Bimmer? They'll spot that a mile off."

"Where's it parked?" Eleanor caught the keys effortlessly.

"Back-alley, two doors down," Flux pointed in the general direction. Eleanor threw the keys to Max. "You're driving."

Meanwhile, she was arming herself, securing two pistols, checking the ammunition, and stuffing deadly-looking machine guns, a rifle, and a shotgun into another kit bag.

"Er... you think we'll need all that, Ellie?" Max asked, his tone laced with concern.

Eleanor flashed a confident wink. "Can never be too prepared, especially when dealing with my old Eclipse buddies."

As she prepared, Max was reminded that they were indeed heading into the lion's den itself. Viridis Ventures, the shadowy organisation pulling the Mayor's strings, and protected by a lethal squad of commandos who, thanks to Eleanor and Max's actions, had more than enough reasons to be hostile.

Minutes later, they rounded a corner and there it was – a huge van hidden under a cover. Eleanor deftly unclipped the catches and gestured for Max to help pull off the sheet.

To his amazement, beneath lay a 1983 GMC Vandura G-Series, but not just any old American van. This was an extraordinary replica of the famous A-Team Van driven by B.A. Baracus, Mr T's iconic character from the hit 1980s TV show. The van boasted a two-tone black and metallic grey paint job, highlighted by a red stripe and a matching red rear spoiler. Max's jaw dropped in recognition of the star vehicle.

"The A-Team van!! Er… this is hardly inconspicuous!" he exclaimed, eyeing the van.

"Wait till you start it," replied Eleanor, "it's hardly quiet either!" Eleanor chuckled. And she wasn't wrong. When Max fired up the engine, it roared to life with a rumble that would have made Mr. T proud, and most likely had woken up the entire neighbourhood too.

Eleanor hopped into the passenger seat, and Max, still in awe, turned to her. "I'm guessing this isn't exactly stock?"

"Far from it," Eleanor beamed. "Supercharged 6.2-litre V8 LS9 motor, about 650bhp, 800Nm of torque. It's got a six-speed auto, KW Coilovers, Eibach anti-roll bars, a strengthened chassis, and massive Brembo brakes." She added laughing, "It

NEEDs them!"

Max felt a surge of excitement – whether it was from being behind the wheel of the legendary A-Team van or the thought of driving a 650bhp beast, he couldn't tell. Maybe it was from listening to Eleanor rattle off specs and mods like a full-on petrolhead. If forced to confess, he would have had to admit, that alone was something of a turn-on.

As he revved the engine, the van rocked with power, the engine barking its warning and he couldn't help but grin. Frankly, he felt like a child again. If this night was to be his last, what a way to go out!

Max pulled the column-mounted gearshift down into drive and turned to Eleanor, imitating the unique and iconic style of Mr T, "I pity the fool that gets in our way tonight!"

Eleanor shot back with her own impression of the famous actor, "Let's move, sucker!"

They thundered through the desolate streets of early-am London, swiftly reaching Park Royal. The Viridis building, a behemoth of corporate aspirations, stood strangely silent against the night sky. "It's too quiet," Eleanor muttered, her eyes scanning the vacant parking lot. There was no sign of security or any activity, the windows dark and lifeless.

"I gotta say," Max peered up at the building as they rolled to a gentle stop just outside the car park, "looks deserted, doesn't it?"

"Maybe, but let's not drop our guard," Eleanor replied, stepping out and grabbing her kit bag. They cautiously circled the perimeter, avoiding a direct approach to the main entrance. Finding no resistance, Eleanor led them to a side door. She quickly disabled the alarm with one of Flux's gadgets, then cut through the lock and swung open the door, her SIG Sauer P365 pistol at the ready.

She wouldn't need it. The inside was as deserted as the outside. They walked through empty corridors lined with abandoned desks and disconnected phones, the silence amplifying their every step, echoes from a place abruptly abandoned.

Taking the stairs up, as they arrived at Quentin's former office. The room was empty, stripped of all but a single, out-of-place item. In the centre of the desk sat a plastic green rose, its vibrant hue stark against the barren surroundings. Eleanor picked it up, examining it closely.

Max glanced around warily. "I half expected some sort of trap when you touched that," he admitted.

"Run a sweep, Ellie," Flux's voice crackled through the comms.

Eleanor set down a compact device from her bag where the rose had been. It emitted a brief flash of lights. "All clear," she announced after a moment. "No bugs or hidden cameras."

She replaced the rose on the desk, her gaze lingering on it.

"Symbolic, perhaps?" Max suggested, but Eleanor seemed lost in thought. She methodically searched the room, checking for hidden compartments or triggers, but found nothing – even a concealed safe behind a sofa was empty.

"Nothing here for us," Eleanor finally conceded, her voice tinged with frustration.

As they departed in the rumbling Vandura, the vacant Viridis building receded in the rear-view mirror, a silent testament to the enigmas they were yet to unravel. The road ahead was uncertain, but their determination remained steadfast.

Upon their return, Eleanor had already been in contact with Wong. "They've ghosted," she announced, her expression a mix of concern and determination. "Viridis Ventures, off the radar. Wong confirms it, they're still out there, just gone clandestine."

Flux, his fingers a blur on his keyboard, echoed her sentiment. "Eclipse Squad's gone dark too. Zilch on the radar. And trust me, if they can hide from Ghost Weaver, they're hiding deep."

Max leaned back, arms crossed, his mind racing through myriad scenarios. "What's this mean for the 8th? Have they called off whatever they were planning, or are we missing something?"

"Negative!" Eleanor's response was instant and firm. "It's the calm before the storm, that's what this is."

Flux, eyes glued to his monitors, bobbed his head in agreement. "Ellie's right, we gotta stay sharp and keep rolling as if the clock's still ticking."

Max, shifting his gaze to Flux, inquired, "Any breakthrough with that locked folder?"

Flux let out a short, wry laugh. "Man, cracking this thing is tougher than getting a straight-up answer out of a politician! By the time we get in, we'll probably be mopping up whatever mess this gonna make."

A notification popped up on Max's phone, snapping him out of his contemplative silence. He clicked it open, his eyebrows arching in surprise.

"Free on the Sunday? Wanna make 50 mil? Pop by for Halwa-Puri in the morning – will reveal all!" The message was from Ahmed Abbas.

Max's expression shifted subtly, his lower jaw dropping slightly as he pieced together the significance of the date. Eleanor, ever observant, caught the change. "Something on your phone, Max?"

"Possibly," Max responded, his voice tinged with a mix of curiosity and scepticism. "It's from Ahmed, a close friend of mine who owns..."

"Abbas Auto Emporium... Yeah, the guy who babysat your Bimmer," Flux interjected with a knowing grin. "Good ol' Ahmed, eh?"

Max was still adjusting to the fact that Eleanor and Flux seemed to know almost everything about him. He fought the urge to question their knowledge and continued. "Right, him, yeah... well, he's just sent me this message."

Eleanor took the phone and Flux leaned in to take a look, their expressions turning analytical. Flux immediately swivelled back to his array of monitors, his fingers tapping away furiously.

"50 million smackers?! That's the kind of cash that should be flashing up in neon on the net, but I'm getting zilch. Nada."

Eleanor, her mind already racing through possible scenarios, handed the phone to Flux. "You're sure this message is legit?" she asked. Flux gave a quick nod.

"Honestly, right now, this seems like the only solid lead we've got," she concluded, turning to Max with a determined look.

"Mind if I tag along? It's been forever since I had Halwa Puri. Hope he has some achaar," she added.

Max chuckled, "Trust me, when Ahmed does breakfast, he doesn't hold back. He'll have All the trimmings!"

As dawn tinged the London sky with soft hues,

Max and Eleanor pulled up outside the Abbas Auto Emporium in West London. The dealership was already buzzing with activity, with Ahmed orchestrating the repositioning of some of his prized vehicles.

He noticed their arrival and hurried over, engulfing Max in a bear hug. "Max, my friend! You made it! And who is this delightful mohtarma?"

Eleanor, brimming with energy, danced around the car to meet Ahmed. With a playful flourish, she extended her hand. "Eleanor Rodrigues, but Ellie will do just fine!"

Ahmed, charmed by her vivacity, took her hand gently and bowed with a flourish of his own. "A pleasure to meet you, Ellie. Welcome to my grand bazaar of motoring marvels!"

"It's absolutely wonderful!" she told him, much to his pleasure. Eleanor playfully raised an eyebrow, "But Ahmed, Max promised me a breakfast of legends. I hope he didn't exaggerate?"

Ahmed's laughter boomed across the forecourt as he ushered them towards his office. "Exaggerate? Max? Never! Please, come in, come in... breakfast just arrived!"

They were led directly to his 'vault' at the rear of the dealership, and towards the library corner, stacked with the best of automotive literature. The smell of freshly delivered breakfast wafted through the air, mixing with the sharp metallic scent of pristinely maintained cars scattered about the warehouse, all under dust sheets.

Arriving at the sofas and table, Eleanor paused to look at the heaving shelves and ran her fingers along the books, pausing at a particularly large volume partially nestled in a box sleeve.

"Stephen Bayley's 'Cars: Freedom, Style, Sex, Power, Motion, Colour, Everything'... the title's nearly as grand as the book itself!" she exclaimed!

"Ah yes, that book is a beauty, but come... first things first," Ahmed interjected as he began unpacking the food. "We can't let the chana masala get cold."

Eleanor, her curiosity piqued by the myriad books and memorabilia, took a seat at the table and eagerly reached for a plate. "You've got quite the collection here, Ahmed. This is incredible!"

Ahmed chuckled, a note of modesty in his voice. "Oh, just a few of my favourite things, Ellie."

Max, joining in the conversation, pointed towards the larger warehouse area. "You should see his personal car collection, Ellie. Though Ahmed, I can't help but notice there are quite a few missing since my last visit?"

"Yes, that's actually what I wanted to discuss with you..." Ahmed's expression turned thoughtful as he passed a small tub of achaar to

Eleanor. Her eyes lit up at the sight of the tangy and spicy pickle, and she almost squealed in delight exclaiming, "Oh, Ahmed, you really know the way to a girl's heart!" That elicited a hearty laugh from him.

Max, grabbed a plate, spooned the steaming hot chickpea curry onto his plate and nabbed a puri. He knew Ahmed too well; the man wouldn't tuck into his own food until his guests had started, but nor would he get into the conversation until he was happily chomping down on breakfast.

Wanting to speed things along, Max broke off a piece of puri, using it to scoop up some curry. The rich, familiar flavours brought back fond memories of their previous breakfast sessions, where they'd talk cars and motorsports until it was time to switch the conversation to where they would go for lunch!

After savouring the taste and washing it down with a gulp of the sweet chai, Max decided it was time to delve into the reason for their meeting. "Ahmed, about that message you sent me last night... how exactly do you plan to make 50 million this Sunday?"

Ahmed, his plate now heaped with food, chuckled heartily. "Abbay, I'm not yaar! But I knew that would grab your attention, huh?" He wiped his greasy hands with a napkin, then fished out his phone, scrolling to the message and sliding it across the table to Max.

The message was bold and direct:

"EXCLUSIVE RACE INVITE!!

PRIZE: 50M EUROS!!!

DATE: 08/08/26

START: Regents St, London, 11:00 AM

* Reply w/ your car reg to enter

* End Point revealed on race day

* High-stakes, NO RULES!

Keep it under wraps. Let's burn rubber and make history!"

Max's eyes widened at the brazenness of the invitation, and he slid the phone over to Eleanor. "This has got to be some sort of sting operation," he mused aloud to Ahmed.

"Exactly my thoughts," Ahmed replied, "but when I checked with some traffic cop friends of mine, none were in the know, or at least hadn't been briefed yet... and then there's what's happening in the trade."

As Eleanor eagerly dug into another helping of curry, Ahmed, delighted by her appetite, passed her more chana masala. "The trade? You mean the car trade? What's been happening?" she asked between mouthfuls.

Ahmed turned to Max, "Well, you remember last time you were here, I mentioned a big spender who bought ten high-end performance cars? He came back," his expression a mix of astonishment and disbelief.

Max, jokingly responded, "Brought back those dodgy cars you sold him, heh?"

"No, yaar. He wanted more. He wanted to see what else I had. I brought him here to the vault, and he started eyeing some of my personal collection..." Ahmed trailed off, a hint of regret in his voice.

Max's eyebrows raised in surprise. "But I thought you said you wouldn't sell your own cars..."

"I did, bhai, but when someone offers you a suitcase full of cash, with figures 50 per cent over the top valuations, it's hard to say no," Ahmed's voice crescendoed as he relived the shock of the offer.

"Max dropped the morsel he was about to put in his mouth, and sat back in his chair, mouth open. "Which ones did you let go, Ahmed," he tentatively asked, dreading the answer and hoping some of his personal favourites from his friend's collection hadn't gone.

"Mostly the ones I had here," Ahmed listed, his voice tinged with a hint of regret, "an Eagle E-Type, my Revuelto SVJ Roadster, the 1992 Honda NSX-R, I shouldn't have let that one go... and even the Revology Bullitt Mustang resto-mod..."

Eleanor looked up suddenly, "the one with the Coyote 5.0 engine?"

Ahmed looked at her, visibly impressed,

"Exactly! Woah, you really know your cars, huh?"

Eleanor flashed a playful grin. "Oh, I'm more than just a pretty face!" she quipped. "But seriously? You had one of those? I would've snapped it up if they hadn't!"

Ahmed's eyes lit up, the salesman in him ever ready. "My dear Ellie, if you want one, just say the word. I can source another for you!"

Max, eager to steer the conversation back to their primary concern, interjected, "So, Ahmed, what's your take? Do you think these purchases have something to do with Sunday?"

"They were after cars ready to hit the road, or ones they could quickly mod up," Ahmed mused.

"Modifications?" Max clarified.

"Exactly," Ahmed nodded. "And you know, Max, this has been going on a while now."

"What do you mean?" Eleanor chimed in, her curiosity piqued.

"Performance parts, you know? Exhausts, intakes, shocks, brake kits, turbos, superchargers, remapped ECUs, even NOS kits..." Ahmed swept his hand in a wide arc as if showcasing an invisible inventory. "They're all sold out, everywhere. It's like a feeding frenzy."

Eleanor leaned back, her mind processing the information. "All those cars, all these parts... that's some serious inventory."

"Indeed, madam," Ahmed replied, "50 million

Euros is no small sum, after all."

Max and Eleanor exchanged a knowing glance. The scattered pieces of the puzzle were slowly aligning, but the complete picture continued to remain elusive.

"You reckon, this is all... what? People getting ready for this alleged race?" Max queried.

Ahmed gave a non-committal shrug, his attention shifting to the Halwa. He heaped the bright orange semolina pudding onto his plate, his eyes lighting up at the sight as he grabbed a spoon.

"That stuff is heavenly," mused Eleanor, her eyes fixed on his plate, chuckling.

Ahmed, noticing her interest, gleefully pushed the tub of sugary goodness soaked in ghee, towards her, "It's delicious Ellie... here take, take..."

As Eleanor began to serve herself a generous portion, she continued the conversation. "But bhai, if it's for the race, why did just one single person buy, what, fifteen cars from you?"

Ahmed appreciated her addressing him as "brother", and if he wasn't already warming to her for her car knowledge, with this respectful and affectionate gesture she had solidified her bond with him.

"Sixteen, actually," Ahmed corrected, offering more chai. "And yes, that's a mystery. I don't get it, perhaps he's spreading his bets, hiring a team of drivers? It's like playing the lottery with multiple tickets."

Eleanor, spooning a mouthful of the sweet pudding, pondered aloud. "But this person had enough cash to splurge on all those cars..."

Ahmed nodded, a hint of pride in his voice. "That much is also true, I alone have made over £10 million from him!"

"Still short of the 50 mil," said Max, "but a fair chunk, especially if you assume they would have bought cars from other sources too... and that's without the mods."

Eleanor, intrigued, leaned forward, "Bhai, can you describe this buyer?"

Ahmed thought for a moment. "Tall, elegant, middle-aged. Very charming," Ahmed took a sip and almost by coincidence both Max and Eleanor lifted their cups too at that moment, "oh... and I think he was French..."

Max and Eleanor nearly choked on their chais. "Quentin Dubois?!" they chorused.

Ahmed, perplexed, shook his head. "No, he said his name was Maxime Lafebvre."

Eleanor spoke into her comms, "Flux, send me a pic of Quentin," almost immediately her phone received an image. She turned it towards an increasingly alarmed Ahmed, "is this him?"

Ahmed peered at the photo, recognition

dawning on his face. "Yes, that's the man, Maxime... or Quentin is it?"

Max and Eleanor shared a look of confirmation. Quentin Dubois had been the mysterious buyer.

Ahmed put down his cup, slid his plate back and straightened in his seat, his voice taking on a serious tone: "Max, what's going on yaar? And Ellie, who are you, really?"

Max sighed, knowing he owed his friend an explanation. He glanced at Eleanor, who shrugged and nodded, simultaneously surveying the warehouse to make sure none of Ahmed's staff were in earshot.

Ahmed sat in stunned silence as Eleanor and Max unravelled the extraordinary tapestry of events that had transpired over the past few days. His expression shifted from disbelief to awe, his jaw slackening slightly, his eyes widening with each revelation.

Max, still grappling with the reality of their experiences, let Eleanor take the lead in recounting their story. She tactfully omitted some of the more intricate details of their operations and downplayed the more violent aspects, yet vividly described their experiences and the machinations of Viridis and Mayor Hartfield.

When their tale concluded, Ahmed was contemplatively silent. He poured more chai, his attention fixed on the steaming liquid, as he absorbed the magnitude of what they told him.

Finally, he raised his eyes to meet Max, who braced for his friend's reaction. "Max, my respect for you has just grown tenfold!" Continuing to hold his gaze, he jerked his head across in Eleanor's direction and spoke earnestly, his voice tinged with apprehension, "But I'm a little afraid of Ellie here now, is that okay?"

"Dude, I totally get that," agreed Max, "I've spent the last few days with her, and I'm still terrified! She's as fierce as they come. But keep the Halwa coming, and she might just play nice."

Eleanor burst into laughter, "Max, stop it!" She turned to Ahmed, reassuring him, "I'm not that bad. I'm tame bhai."

"Yeah, as tame as a tarantula," Max quipped. Their banter helped to put Ahmed at ease, drawing him into their laughter. He theatrically offered the entire tub of Halwa to Eleanor, who gleefully accepted it and leaned back, spooning generous amounts straight into her mouth.

"So, Quentin's bought all these cars, AND he's possibly behind this race. But why?" Max pondered.

"Sterling Carrera might have some answers," Ahmed suggested, watching Max for a reaction. "You know him, right?"

"Who's that?" Eleanor perked up at the mention of the name, but before Max could respond,

Flux's voice chimed in through their earpieces. "Sterling Carrera, founder and organiser of the EuroBall Rally."

"I do have his number," Max confirmed, standing up to make the call. Eleanor, meanwhile, continued to enjoy the Halwa as Ahmed steered the conversation to the now infamous Edison Model A review and the wild events of the car launch that had taken the internet by storm; he was curious to hear all about it.

Sterling Carrera, the vibrant 35-year-old British tech entrepreneur, music producer, and amateur racing driver, was the brains behind the EuroBall Rally. Over the years, his creation had evolved into a highlight of the automotive calendar.

Despite the controversies surrounding its glorification of speed and luxury, the event attracted celebrities and car enthusiasts for a high-octane jaunt across Europe, marked by extravagant parties at each stop. Yet, Carrera had a knack for turning this spectacle into a charitable endeavour, raising millions each year for various causes.

Max had encountered Sterling several times while covering the event and had conducted interviews and profiles of the man in the past. The high-flyer was always a whirlwind of energy, a perfect embodiment of his favourite mantra, "No fun, No fulfilment!" Whether discussing business or indulging in his passion for cars,

Sterling's zest for life was infectious.

To Max's surprise, Sterling picked up the phone almost instantly, bypassing the usual intermediary. "V-Max, my man! Great to hear from you, how have you been?"

Caught slightly off-guard by both the quick response and being answered directly by Sterling rather than an underling or PA, Max replied, "Oh, hey... Hi Sterling! Doing well, thanks. And yourself?" They exchanged a few more pleasantries, with Sterling taking a moment to praise Max's recent Edison Model A escapade, "Dude you totally ROCKED! That was the wildest review I've seen. Just epic!"

Max was still getting used to people referencing that impromptu video. Amidst the chaos of his current life, his channel had exploded in popularity, propelling him into the upper echelons of automotive influencers - a fact that had, frankly, escaped his notice as he'd been rather preoccupied with trying to stay alive among other things. Nonetheless, Sterling's readiness to engage was a testament to this newfound high-profile status.

Max steered the conversation towards the EuroBall Rally. "Sterling, I was hoping to discuss the upcoming event in Regents Street..."

"Say no more, V-Max! You want in? No problemo. Just the launch or the whole shebang?" Sterling's enthusiasm was almost tangible.

Max cut in, "Actually, just the rally start event please Sterling..." he trailed off, realising he needed to tread carefully with his next question.

Sterling didn't miss a beat. "You got it, mate! All-access pass for you. Anything for V-Max T!"

"Sterling... Actually, I need to ask you about something. Have you seen this SMS going around about a race?" Max queried cautiously.

There was an uncharacteristic pause on the line. When Sterling finally spoke, his voice was subdued, almost unrecognisable. "Listen, Max, this thing... it's not us. It's got nothing to do with EuroBall. Mate, are we off the record here?"

Max reassured him, "Yeah, absolutely, Sterling. Off the record."

Sterling's voice lowered further, conveying his unease. "Honestly, Max, it's a nightmare. My insurers are panicking, participants are backing out, sponsors are getting jittery..."

"Can't you just cancel or postpone the event?" Max suggested.

"You know, I did want to do that," Sterling began, "but after talking to the Mayor and even the Police Commissioner, they almost begged me not to!"

"What? Why? I mean why would they want that, given the risks?" Max was perplexed.

"That threw me too, Max. The Mayor said it's great for the city, brings in business, and it's important for showcase events..." Sterling's tone was one of bewilderment.

Max couldn't help but remark, "Seems a bit hypocritical, given her stance against cars."

"Exactly my thought!" Sterling's usual rapid pace returned, tinged with a note of frustration. "Max, I was frankly flummoxed, I was planning to pull the plug, but then she sent some big-name sponsors my way. And now it's like my hands are tied."

Sterling continued, "I thought the police would be against it, you know, due to potential public disorder and all that. I was certain they'd advised me to postpone, and that would be my get-out, right? I went to see Commander Priya Kapoor of the RTPC personally, figuring she'd be sure to demand I can it."

"Commander Kapoor? She's in charge of Roads and Transport Policing, right?" Max interjected.

"Yeah, that's her. Funny thing is, I laid it all out, gave her every reason to shut me down... showed her the secret race message, told her we could end up with a bunch of renegade drivers running riot around her streets; hardcore racers coming out in force for the supposed ginormous prize... you know, complete mayhem, potential disaster, fire... brimstone... the works!"

"And what was her response?" asked Max.

"You ain't gonna believe it Max, it was like total

surreal freaky role reversal or something..." Max was virtually shouting down the phone line. "She was reassuring me! Told me they'd have patrols out, undercover officers, the works." The shock was evident in his voice.

"She was adamant the SMS wasn't a police sting and said they'd clamp down on any racers immediately," his voice lowered a fraction. "Mate, I feel I'm careening down a motorway with no brakes right now!"

Max could certainly sense the exasperation in Sterling's voice. "Listen, let me dig into it, try to find out who's sending out the messages, maybe we can nip it in the bud yeah?"

Sterling was effusive, "Max! Mate, dude... if you can, you will find Sterling Carrera forever in your debt. And anything I can do to help you, let me know yeah?"

"Thanks, Sterling. See you on Sunday."

Max went back and reported the conversation to Eleanor and Ahmed and of course, Flux who was listening in.

Eleanor became serious, "Let's get back, we need to figure out our next move," still holding the tub of halwa, she turned to Ahmed, "Can I get this to go Bhai?"

"Tch, Ellie, wait a few minutes, I'll order you some more fresh halwa!" he offered.

"Oh no, bhai, really, let me just take this..." she

glanced down at the table, "and a few of those puris!"

Ahmed laughed and started re-packing the all the remaining breakfast for her to take.

"Ahmed, are you taking part? In the EuroBall I mean?"

"Are you kidding yaar?" Ahmed's eyes lit up. "I've done it every year for the last five! And I've been building this thing all year for the rally" He gestured towards a car under a cover nearby.

Max squinted, playing his old game of trying to identify the car under the cover. "Wait, is that… no way… did you…?"

He got up and walked to the car. He tugged at the sheet, casting a questioning glance at Ahmed, who, drying his hands on a napkin, ambled over, Eleanor in tow with her food haul. With a nod from Ahmed, Max whisked off the cover to reveal a Jaguar XJC 12, reminiscent of John Steed's car from the 1970s TV action show 'The New Avengers', resplendent in British Racing Green.

Modelled after the 1976 Jaguar XJC two-door coupe, the version used in the TV show had undergone significant modifications to meet Broadspeed's racing specs. What was once an elegantly understated car had been morphed into something much more aggressive. The exaggerated, flared wheel arches flirted with vulgarity but stopped just short, giving the car a formidable presence. The transformation was further defined by the removal of the front bumper, replaced by a wide, prominent grille, and the addition of a blunt black spoiler lip on the boot, lending the rear a sleek, purposeful look.

Max was speechless. "Is this the actual one from...?"

"Nah, the actual car just changed hands for over a million bucks!" Ahmed planted his substantial bulk on one of those equally substantial fenders. "I didn't want a 'Trailer Queen', I wanted something I could actually enjoy driving. Take a guess what this really is?"

Max was confused; Eleanor, however, glanced inside the car and whistled. "The interior is from a Jag F-Type! What have you been cooking up here bhai?"

Ahmed's laugh boomed through the garage. High-fiving Eleanor, he said, "Spot on sister! You beat Max to it!" he teased a sheepish Max. "Yup, it's a carbon-fibre replica body, mounted on a Jaguar F-Type R chassis. Took a lot of surgery, but nice result huh?"

"Bhai, this thing is just gorgeous!" Eleanor's sentiments were genuine.

Max, still in awe, pointed at the car, barely forming words. "Ahmed, I have to review this!"

"You got it," Ahmed beamed. "She's all yours after the rally."

As they headed back out, Eleanor was slightly ahead of them. Ahmed discreetly caught Max's arm, leaning in to whisper while subtly nodding towards Eleanor. "She's a keeper, you know. Don't you dare let this one go!"

Max, half-embarrassed, half-amused, playfully jabbed at Ahmed's belly, "Mate! C'mon!".

Eleanor's smile broadened, a hint of a blush on her cheeks. She'd overheard Ahmed's words through the open comms channel.

About an hour later, back at base, Flux eagerly tucked into the breakfast Eleanor had brought back, nodding in approval. "Yo, you were NOT wrong about this stuff, this is finger-licking good!"

"You should taste the karak chai too," Max told him.

"I'll whip up some for you one day," Eleanor offered Flux.

Max, surprised, raised an eyebrow. "You know how to make Karak?"

"Of course, and I can make this halwa, the chana masala and a lot more besides," she grinned smugly. "I'm quite the chef... when there's time," she responded. Max was beginning to think there was no end to her talents.

"Maybe after all this is over..." he said, "you can show me?" Eleanor just responded with a playful wink.

Between mouthfuls, Flux spoke up, "So what next? The Mayor?"

"Nah better keep hands-off, or we'll piss off Wong," warned Eleanor. "Nah, I'm thinking... Kapoor!"

"That could work, she's got a copy of this folder... probably decrypted," Flux chimed up.

Max was astonished at this revelation, "How do you know that?!"

"Dude, I'm the Ghost Weaver!" Flux laughed. "When I was hooked up to the server, I didn't just download the files, but grabbed the trace logs. It's only been downloaded a couple of times, once to an IP address registered to the Metropolitan Police Force IT network."

"Priya's computer!" Eleanor deduced.

"Exactly," Flux confirmed. "And she likely has the decryption key. We get her laptop, we get the folder's contents."

"Erm... Flux, this might be a dumb question," Max ventured, "Isn't it easier to just break into the folder we have?"

Man, I've hurled everything AND the kitchen sink at that sucker, but it's clammed up tighter than a perp in the box at a high-stakes trial!" Flux exclaimed, shaking his head. "Got a whole bunch of apps chewin' on it, but they're sweating bullets. The thing might spill the beans in an hour, or it might keep its lips zipped till we're knee-deep in it."

"By which time it'll be too late," Eleanor agreed.

"But what are you guys suggesting? That we break into... what... Scotland Yard? One of the most secure police HQs in the world?!" Max asked incredulously.

"No," conceded Eleanor, "but what about Transport for London's head office, the Palestra building in Southwark? She has meetings there most days."

Even as she spoke, Flux had already hacked into the Police Commander's calendar and was scanning details on the building Eleanor had mentioned.

"Yeah, she's due there in a couple of hours," Flux reported, eyes glued to the screen as he dove into the building's blueprint. "Yo, check this, the joint's decked out with some high-tech gear – got a fancy Building Management System, a beast of a CCHP setup chilling in the basement, that's Combined Cooling, Heat and Power, ya dig? Plus, there's this Thermal Store Overload jazz, like a crazy maze of pipes and wires all snaking through the guts of the place!"

Max looked puzzled. "And that means what exactly?"

"It means," Flux grinned, "I've got a plan to get you in!"

"Yeah... about that," interjected Eleanor. "Back

when I was on the Mayor's security detail, I used to spend a lot of time there. They'd spot me a mile off!"

She gestured towards Max, "And as he's trending right now…"

Flux spun in his chair, punching the air with excitement. "Yes! Ghost Weaver's time to shine! Now THAT'S what I'm talking about!"

Two hours later, Flux entered the Palestra. He was wearing a white hard hat, red overalls and a yellow high-visibility jacket with a backpack slung casually over his shoulder. All featured EcoVolt logos patched on, fresh from his 3D printer. In a reversal of roles, Eleanor and Max were set up in the back of his A-Team van, parked nearby, with a bank of computer consoles, monitoring his progress, while Flux posed as an engineer from the building's official energy supplier.

Flashing his fake ID and a winning smile, he was waved straight through security, "Yo, my dudes! Head office sent me to rummage around in your downstairs, you know what I'm saying?" He laughed loudly, "Seriously though, I'm here to make sure that CCHP is humming its sweet old tune!"

"You see this is why I don't let him in the field," Eleanor turned to Max back in the van, they were both listening into to Flux, "It's not that he can't handle it, he just goes and overdoes it every time!"

"Hey, hey! I ain't overdoing it, it's just my character, this EcoVolt guy's got a big personality, a'ight?"

Eleanor and Max grinned at each other. Meanwhile, Flux was already in the basement and had hooked his laptop to the control console for the building's sustainability-focused environmental and power systems. His fingers flew over the keyboard, easily gaining access to the Building Management System and then he initiated a cascading software fault.

It would take at least a couple of hours before the EcoVolt IT guys arrived and futilely tried to resolve it, before realising that a hard reboot would be required. Meanwhile, in the immediate term, the action caused a flicker in the system that manifested as an apparent heat surge in the Thermal Store and triggered the automated alarms.

Transferring control back to Eleanor, Flux bounded back up the stairs, shoving his laptop into his backpack, as he burst out into reception, he could see an evacuation was already in process. "Get everybody out! System's overloading, call 999!" he shouted at the nearest guard.

"Already on it!" the anxious guard responded, turning his attention back to the evacuees, "Exit as quickly as you can please! Leave everything behind. Head to the assembly point. THIS IS NOT A DRILL!"

"I'm gonna head to the roof, gotta shut down that photovoltaic array manually, or it'll keep feeding energy into the system. That could build up pressure and send it into critical overload!" Flux cried.

The guard suddenly even more alarmed turned back to him: "What happens then?"

"Thermal runway man!" Flux brought his hands together and then parted them in an expansive and elaborate gesture, "Kaboom!"

"Mate, you better get up there!" the guard then grabbed his radio to alert his colleagues, "Oi, hustle it up, lads! The engineer's sayin' we're about to have a proper Guy Fawkes' party in 'ere!"

Flux nodded at the guard and turned, hearing him call out "Good luck!"

"Thermal runaway? Really?" Eleanor laughed through the comms.

"If you're gonna make shit up, make it sound like some real scary shit, right?" Flux grunted back, while he ran past the stairwell exit. As he did so, he noticed the crowd evacuating the building; sure enough, among them was Commander Priya Kapoor and her team of senior officers. He scanned the group quickly - no bags, no laptops. Perfect. With a satisfied grin, he veered through a Facilities door and sprinted towards the service lift. Just as he got there, the doors opened with a ping, revealing a group of maintenance workers.

"Quick as you can boys, move it, double time," Flux barked authoritatively and clapped his hands together, "let's hustle!" The maintenance crew, picking up on the urgency in his voice, quickly dispersed in the direction he pointed. Once they were out of sight, Flux slipped into the lift and jabbed the button for the 13th floor.

Moments later, the lift came to a halt and the doors parted to reveal a deserted corridor. Flux stepped out, his steps quick and quiet as he navigated towards his target - the meeting room Commander Priya had been in.

Checking in with his team, he spoke into his comms, "We clear on surveillance, El? Those camera eyes blind?"

The response came swiftly, "You're invisible to them, Flux. It's all running on a loop, just like you set up. Although that means, we can't see you either. So get in, get the file, and get out."

Nodding to himself, Flux moved with purpose along the corridor. He located the meeting room, the door ajar. Inside, the remnants of a hurriedly abandoned meeting were evident – half-eaten biscuits, cooling cups of tea, and pens left mid-scribble. Spotting Commander Kapoor's laptop among the others, he made his move, quickly bypassing the security and copying the crucial folder onto his thumb drive, which also transmitted the data back to Eleanor and Max.

Just as he was about to exit, all of a sudden, the door swung wide open, and he nearly crashed into Commander Priya Kapoor. Flux's heart almost stopped!

"Who are you and what are you doing in here?" Commander Priya Kapoor's voice was sharp, her eyes assessing Flux critically.

In the van, Max and Eleanor were startled to hear her voice. Afraid for Flux, Eleanor switched the camera feeds back to live. Max, beside her, was a mix of confusion and concern as they witnessed Priya and Flux face off. Eleanor had an idea and her fingers raced furiously over the keyboard, her focus laser-sharp.

Flux, only momentarily thrown, retorted with his usual quick wit. "I'm the EcoVolt guy, lady! These badges aren't just for show, you know." For effect, he waved his ID in her face.

"Okay, okay," Priya replied, scepticism colouring her tone. "But why are you in this room?"

Flux raised his voice, feigning indignation. "What am I doing here? The real question, Ms Police Officer person, is what are YOU doing here? This building's being evacuated! You need to get out, now!"

In the van, Eleanor muttered to herself, her eyes darting across the screens. "Come on, come on... which node...?"

Priya, unfazed, stood her ground and reached for her radio. "I need you to sit down and be quiet."

Flux gestured wildly, playing up the urgency. "You're missing the point, lady. We're sitting on a ticking bomb here! We need to move, like, yesterday!"

Priya, however, remained calm and collected. "Oh, I don't think so..." Her hand hovered over her radio, ready to call for backup.

Suddenly, in one corner of the room plaster from the wall stripped away like a zipper being yanked open. A seam appeared, parting to release a jet of hot steam that immediately forced Flux and a now very alarmed Priya to crouch down low.

Back in the van, Eleanor leaned back in satisfaction, grinning at Max. "Who needs thermal runway when you have a makeshift pressure cooker, right?"

"But... how did you...?" Max stammered, having watched the CCTV feed from the room and witnessed the wall explode on cue.

"Spend enough time with Flux, you start learning a few Ghost Weaver tricks!" she boasted.

Back in the room, "You were saying, Miss?" Flux shouted at Priya, his voice filled with feigned concern and urgency.

Priya grimaced at him, snatched her laptop from the desk, and made for the door. As she turned towards the stairwell, Flux headed in the opposite direction. Priya halted and shouted, "Oi! Where do you think you're going?"

"Lady, didn't I tell you? We've got a situation! If I don't get to the roof to release those pressure valves, this place is gonna blow. Now get out of here!" Flux called back, continuing his run.

Priya paused, watching him dash away, weighing her options and deciding whether to believe him.

At that moment, Eleanor triggered more junction nodes in the ceiling above her. As the corridor began to collapse around her, Priya bolted for the stairs, racing down to street level.

"She bangs, she bangs!" sang Eleanor while doing a little victory dance.

"Nice one, Padawan!" Flux congratulated Eleanor as he sprinted through the door leading to the roof access.

"Learned from the best!" she replied.

"Well, the best still needs his ass saving," Flux said, reaching the rooftop. "I'm topside now, gonna evac from here!"

"Response units are incoming. This place will be swarming," Eleanor warned, motioning for Max to start driving the van. "Head to the northeast corner, near the train tracks."

"Got it!" Flux responded, already pulling out his grappling gun. He fired a line from the roof to the raised train tracks, ziplined down, and remotely detonated the cable attachment on the roof to cover his tracks.

"Exit point's a couple of blocks east. We'll meet you there!" Eleanor directed him.

A short while later, Flux was safely back in the van. "Did you get it?" he asked, referring to the transmitted folder.

Max and Eleanor were fixated on a monitor. Flux joined them, and together they watched a computer simulation depicting cars racing out across London from Regents Street, unfurling across the city like ink spilling onto a canvas, corrupting every street with chaos and disarray. The screen showed estimates of damage cost and, more horrifyingly, the number of casualties expected.

When the simulation ended, the numbers stopped at:

Property Damage: £43.4m

Cost to Authorities: £57.6m

Injuries: 2872

Fatalities: 174

The three sat in silence in the replica A-Team van parked under a railway arch, absorbing the gravity of what they'd just seen.

"Carnage," Max finally spoke. "A devastating race, piggybacked on a high-profile rally. The fallout will be catastrophic. The Mayor won't have to convince people to give up their cars; they'll be begging her to take them away."

Max slumped back, exchanging a sad look with Eleanor. "The war on motorists will be won right there and then."

CHAPTER 11

Max was at the wheel of Flux's resto-mod A-Team van, driving back to Northwest London, negotiating through the late afternoon's increasing traffic. Even so, the hum of the Vandura's powerful V8 was more than just a mere soundtrack; it was a lifeline to Max's scattered thoughts. Drawing on the van's latent torque and its confident potency, restored some strength to his spirit, which had threatened to descend back into the despondency he was so familiar with, having at last discovered the contents of that folder.

As he piloted the monstrous machine, feeling its mass judder and resonate over ruts and bumps, it served as a reminder that amidst the chaos that his life had become, cars – the one constant – remained steadfast, solid, and dependable. And now, his apparent nemesis, Mayor Hartfield, was on the brink of obliterating this sanctuary.

He hadn't realised how much he had missed driving until he had gotten his old BMW back; in fact, it was only then that he had realised that it wasn't so much that he missed it; more accurately, it was how much he needed it. He needed the BMW to restore some semblance of normality in his life and to reclaim fragments of his former self. His car made him feel like... well, like himself; complete, in control and self-assured.

Driving was therapeutic, plain and simple. It seemed to empower him as he wrestled with the dual weights of despair and determination in equal measures. The Vandura, a living, growling beast with a soul of its own (Max was certain of it) seemed to understand its driver's mood, purring and growling as if in response to his inner turmoil. And it helped him think.

In the rear-view mirror, he caught glimpses of Eleanor and Flux in the back, engrossed in the data displayed on their computer consoles. Their intense focus and the gravity of their discovery were clear.

Suddenly Max's mind wandered to Dubai, to the possibility of escape from this maelstrom of danger and deception. His channel's sudden viral fame had raised his stock, it could open new doors. It afforded him the chance to leave behind all the madness that threatened to engulf him.

Eleanor somehow became aware of Max observing them, sensing his contemplation. Her voice cut through his musings, like a lighthouse beacon offering lost ships guidance and salvation. "Don't worry Max, we'll figure this out; the war on motorists isn't over yet. There's still a battle to be fought." Her resilience, in the face of what seemed like insurmountable odds, jolted him back from any thoughts of acquiescence he might have been entertaining.

He nodded and returned his focus to the act of driving. Driving, he understood, was his safe place, where the connection between man and machine offered clarity and solace. The Vandura responded to his every command, a powerful ally in a world that seemed increasingly hostile. It was in this moving haven that Max's mind began to clear, and his scattered thoughts began weaving into a coherent plan.

"You fight fire with fire," he muttered quietly to himself, and his mechanical companion, as a new resolve started taking shape. The Mayor's devious plan to orchestrate a social media storm against cars and their drivers could be countered. No, make that pre-empted, especially now that they had the full foreknowledge of her and Viridis' scheme. It meant they had the chance to beat their opponents at their own game.

An irrepressible thought jumped into his head. Sterling Carrera had relayed Commander Priya Kapoor specifically telling him that the SMS message about the race, was not a police sting operation. And indeed, it wasn't. However, what if they caught her saying that it was? But how was that even possible? It wasn't. Unless...

Max called out to the back of the van, "Flux, can you deepfake the Police Commander?" his voice steady now, filled with a newfound purpose.

Flux's excitement was, as ever, irrepressible. "Yo, Max, you kiddin' me? Man, you're talkin' to the Ghost Weaver here! That's like askin' if the sun's gonna rise, bro! Lay it on me, what do we need the Commander to spill?" His lively spirit was contagious, igniting a renewed sense of purpose in Max.

"I need her back in that meeting room you bumped into her. I need her briefing TFL and fellow officers about 'Operation Speedtrap'. I need her confirming that she sent out that SMS, and that anyone taking part will be nicked on the day."

Eleanor turned Max's idea over in her head, "Hmm... you put that out on your socials, with the sort of reach you have, that could very well put off anyone thinking of taking part..."

"But yo, what about Quentin's free-wheeler gang?" Flux queried, leaning into the conversation. "I'm guessing they'll all be Eclipse Squad operatives; they're all trained in advanced and tactical driving. Operation Speedtrap ain't gonna faze 'em one bit!" he asserted.

Max mulled over what Eleanor had said, "There's still a battle to be fought". He recalled a quote from Sun Tzu's "The Art of War" which said, "It is best to win without fighting". In other words, a battle thwarted, is also a battle won, he realised.

"No," he replied to Flux, "for that, we need to turn London's streets into a chessboard with our own pawns and knights, and work out all our moves before they've even played theirs. We need to disable and gridlock... let's call it... 'Operation Immobilise'."

"Ooo... sounds like Max be the man with the plan Ellie; you up for a new playbook?" Flux's voice was tinged with both surprise and excitement.

Eleanor smiled and responded: "Now you know why we needed him, Flux."

The Ghost Weaver, energised by the unfolding plan, stretched out expansively in the confines of the van, his knuckles cracking audibly. He then rotated his neck with a satisfying click, turning back to face his console. "A'ight, time to whip up a Commander Kapoor special! This is gonna be so legit, she'll be second-guessing herself!" Flux announced.

Max glanced back in the mirror and held up his thumb in approval. He gunned the engine as they crossed the North Circular road into Outer London, letting a few more of those 650 horses off the leash. He gripped the wheel tighter, taking comfort from the van's unquestioning responses.

Max felt a kinship with the machine he drove. It was a partnership forged in the furnace of adversity, a union of man and machine against a common enemy, and it felt more profound than ever. It gave him the strength to face what lay ahead. The battle for the streets of London was far from over, and he, along with Eleanor, Flux, and their vehicles were ready to take them back. Vehicles... cars... he was going to need more, a lot more. He continued to formulate his plans, trying to make them as solid and tangible as the tarmac beneath the van's rolling tyres.

The next several hours were a whirlwind of activity as Max, Eleanor, and Flux orchestrated "Operation Immobilise". Max's phone was almost a permanent fixture against his ear as he juggled calls and messages. His first crucial call was to Sterling Carrera. He told him that the SMS was a police sting, and that proof would be coming out soon.

Sterling eagerly took his advice to contact each and every participant of the EuroBall Rally to warn them and insist that no single traffic law be broken during the Rally.

Turning to his next task, Max briefed Ahmed on their findings. Ahmed's reaction was a mix of shock and outrage, yet he was quick to offer his assistance. He promised to provide not only details of all the high-performance vehicles he'd sold to Quentin, but also reaching out to his extensive network of dealers across the South East to track every car the Belgian had bought.

Much to Max's astonishment, when Ahmed returned with his findings, the scale of Viridis's acquisitions was staggering. He reported that at least 40 top-tier sports cars, muscle cars, and supercars had been purchased, amounting to an estimated total of over £30 million.

Finally, Max reconnected with Ajeet Singh, a comrade from the days of rallying against the ULEZ expansion. Ajeet, who owned a construction company, had been severely affected when replacing his fleet of non-ULEZ-compliant vans pushed his business to the brink of bankruptcy. He had organised rolling protests against the ULEZ expansion, in the form of convoys.

"V-Max! Wow, what an honour! You're like super-famous now!" Ajeet's voice boomed with enthusiasm over the phone. After a brief exchange of pleasantries and updates, Max got straight to the point, "Mate, I need you to organize another protest convoy."

"Omigod, I'm already doing that!" Ajeet responded. "I was just about to…"

"No listen… and you might want to sit down for this… I need it to happen THIS Sunday!"

There was a moment of stunned silence on the line before Ajeet recovered. "You're serious? This Sunday? I mean, it takes planning and…"

Max quickly briefed him on the urgent necessity

of their action, explaining the covert police sting coinciding with the EuroBall Rally and its larger implications in the escalating war against motorists. "We'll merge the convoy with the Euroball guys at Regent Street. The aim is to keep the speeds down, to counter any negative publicity that could lead to further restrictive legislation on cars and driving."

Ajeet's hesitance turned to resolve as Max detailed the plan. "Sterling Carrera will handle the police side of things. He's got the Mayor's backing for the Rally, so he has carte blanche to do whatever. We need to make a big impact, and I know we can count on strong participation."

Soon enough Ajeet's tone shifted from alarm to determination. "Max, you can count on me. We'll make our voices heard, and this time, they won't be able to ignore us."

With these conversations out of the way, Max was ready to record some videos. True to his word, Flux's work was impeccable and extraordinary. A CCTV recording of Commander Kapoor's meeting at Palestra appeared to show her briefing her TFL staff and her own officers on Operation Speedtrap. The level of detail in the video was meticulous. Flux even managed to make her appear to hold her phone up, as she read back the SMS they had sent out to ensnare wannabe racers. She was seen drawing up plans to have unmarked police vehicles ready in strategic locations, with liveried patrol cars standing by for support. Even the availability of space in police pounds was discussed, to ensure there would be room to store all the confiscated vehicles.

"That's a nice touch mate," Max exclaimed as he high-fived Flux, "you've outdone yourself," Max said, visibly impressed by the lifelike deepfake. He watched as the video showed Commander Kapoor concluding the briefing with calculated precision, reinforcing the importance of their operation to curb illegal street racing. "When we're through, we'll have sent a message loud and clear; do 21 and you're done!" she concluded, referring to the blanket 20mph speed limit imposed across London.

Max was nodding appreciatively; Flux was grinning and much to their amusement he flicked on some music, a lively hip-hop beat, before breaking into a rap, coupled with a display of old-school breakdance moves and playful freestyling, perfectly in sync with his lyrics.

"Yo, yo, yo, it's Flux in the house,
Ghost Weaver's here, quiet as a mouse.
Deep fakin' scenes, make it all gleam,
Tech wizardry, like a dream.

"They asked, 'Can you fake it, make it real slick?'
I was like, 'Puhleez, I got this trick!'
Flippin' ones and zeros, it's a digital breeze,
Makin' impossible, look like cheese.

Hackin' the mainframe, slidin' through nets,
My skills so fly, got no regrets.

"I'm the Ghost Weaver, keepin' it tight,
Tech magic flowin', all day and night.
From keyboards to screens, I dance and weave,
In the tech world, I'm the one you believe.
With a click and a swipe, I change the game,
Flux, The Ghost Weaver, remember the name!"

He finished by spinning, dropping down and balancing on the inside calf of one leg, then bouncing back up, launching into a short jump and landing with feet planted wide, arms crossed, nodding his head in slow motion and holding the pose for a moment, his expression one of triumph and satisfaction, embodying the persona of The Ghost Weaver – the master of tech wizardry.

Max and Eleanor broke into applause and laughter.

"Man, those moves and that rap – that's pure talent, Flux!" Max exclaimed; his voice filled with admiration.

"Utterly brilliant, Flux!" Eleanor added with a chuckle. "How long have you been working on that rap?"

"Oh c'mon Ellie... you know I'm tight on the mic and smooth my moves!" Flux accompanied this with a mic-drop gesture, and they all burst into laughter again, basking in the light-hearted moment. Max, surprisingly, was the one to snap them back to the mission at hand.

"Right, let's create some fake accounts and seed it out. Facebook, Instagram, X, TikTok... the works!" Max instructed.

Eleanor raised an eyebrow. "Not YouTube?"

"Nah, anything we upload there will be flagged and taken down almost immediately, because the Police will declare it as fake.

"The same will also happen on the other platforms, but it'll take a little longer, and it'll spread like wildfire before anyone can even blink. And once it's out there, it'll be reshared and reposted so extensively, it'll be impossible to contain." Max explained, drawing on his knowledge of how social media content worked. Eleanor listened intently; this was clearly outside her usual realm of expertise.

Flux, meanwhile, nodded in agreement, understanding the mechanics of viral content, "By the time they untangle this vid and prove it's all smoke and mirrors, which they will, it'll be too late. Everyone will have bought into it, hook, line, and sinker. That's how the social media game is played, right?"

Max continued, his voice carrying the weight of experience. "Yeah, on YouTube, people will upload it or share clips when it starts to trend. The key is how to do it so your video doesn't get taken down," explained Max. "So, I'll make a video with a screen grab of the CCTV footage, positioning it as 'unverified proof' of a police sting. Since I'll openly declare that I can't confirm its authenticity, it should stay up on my channel without issues."

Flux backed him up, "The moment that CCTV footage hits the net, it will explode, you can be sure of that!"

Max continued with an air of satisfaction, "And that will be the endgame for anyone thinking of having a go because they think there's 50 million up for grabs. That just leaves us with Quentin's supercar fleet and your Eclipse Squad buddies to deal with."

Eleanor nodded towards Flux, "Yup, we've been working on that!"

Flux, ever the enthusiastic collaborator, chimed in. "Oh yeah, I've got some tricks up my sleeve, and some tech toys that could give us an edge," he said, his eyes lighting up at the thought. "Hey Max, is it cool if I get in touch with your friend Ahmed for some extra muscle on this?"

Max smiled at the idea. "He'd jump at the chance to be part of this; go for it," he encouraged. "Actually, how about we both head over to his place now? I can introduce you, and I've got a second video I'd like to shoot there – in this one, I need to rally the troops for the protest convoy."

Before long, Max was standing outside Abbas Auto Emporium. He had duly introduced Flux and Ahmed who had both stepped off to the side where Flux could brief the latter on Sunday's plan.

Meanwhile Max had positioned his camera in front of the showroom. In the frame, his black 1989 BMW 325i gleamed alongside Ahmed's sensationally crafted replica of the 1976 Jaguar XJC Broadspeed coupe. Arrayed behind these focal vehicles, an assortment of other tantalising high-performance cars had been artfully arranged to catch the viewer's eye.

Max flicked the camera to 'record'. With a confident demeanour, honed by his years as a YouTuber and auto enthusiast, he began his broadcast. The setting, with its array of automotive splendour, formed the perfect backdrop to his message.

"Hey, Turner Wheels family! It's V-Max T here, and today, I'm calling on every motor enthusiast, every freedom-loving driver, and every petrolhead out there. Make no mistake people, we're at war, and I need you – not just to step up – but to drive up!

"Our cars are more than just metal and rubber. They're the heartbeat of our freedom, the pulse of our adventures. And now, they're under siege. Pay-per-mile schemes? Restrictions on our right to drive? No! Absolutely not! Not on our watch. Not in our city!

"We, we band of motoring brothers and sisters, we're not just drivers; we are the staunch defenders of our beloved cars, the vigilant guardians of the open roads. And now, it's our time to roar. It's our moment to take back our streets!

"This Sunday, 8th August, we're making a stand with a protest convoy unlike any other – right in the beating heart of London. Whether you own a classic beauty, a supercar, a sportscar, a mean bike, or a hard-working van, bring it! Your ride is your proclamation. And together, our collective roar will echo through the city.

"We're even uniting with the EuroBall Rally – can you imagine that spectacle? A dazzling array of supercars, sports cars, and yes – actual celebrities, standing shoulder to shoulder with us!

"Regent Street, midday, this is where we etch our names in history. This is where we declare that our passion for cars isn't just a hobby; it's a profound way of life. They want to tax us for every mile we drive? Well, we're going to give them miles they'll never forget.

"We're not merely protesting a policy here; we're standing up for our fundamental right to drive, our freedom to explore. This fight is about choice, about the liberty that comes with owning four wheels and a driving licence.

"So, gear up, ignite your passion, make some noise. Let's show the world what our vehicles truly mean to us. Regent Street, Sunday, 8th

August, at midday – that's where we need to be. Spread the word, tell everyone. Bring friends, family, and anyone who shares our passion!

"But remember – we're sticking to the rules. Obey ALL driving laws. There's a police sting operation that day – and you can find all the details in my other video; I've linked it above and below for you. We're not the hooligans or lawbreakers they paint us as. We're law-abiding citizens who simply cherish our freedom of movement, our civil liberties, and our right to own and enjoy our vehicles.

"So, let's demonstrate our unity, our commitment. Let's show them the largest, most disciplined convoy London has ever seen. Let's make this a historic day, one that they can't ignore. Let's drive for our rights, united. Let's show them that our love for our cars, our bikes, our vans, and our trucks, isn't something they can simply legislate away.

"See you on Regent Street, folks – let's make this count!"

Max uploaded both videos on Friday evening, an hour apart. Timing them strategically late in the week, he aimed to catch Mayor Hartfield and the traffic police chief off-guard. The impact was almost immediate. Within a couple of hours, the videos exploded across the internet, there was even some discussion about the videos on the 10 O'clock TV news shows. The response was so overwhelming that Max had to disable notifications and call-receiving on his phone, which was inundated with a deluge of messages.

Saturday was their final day of preparation, a crucial window to fine-tune their plans before the predicted chaos of Sunday.

As the day of reckoning dawned, London's streets wore an air of eerie calm, almost as if the city itself sensed and braced for the impending uproar. The word had spread. Everyone knew about the 'sting' operation and the protest convoy. The city woke up to a sluggish and cautious start. Businesses opened their doors with hesitation, and pedestrians looked up and down the streets, sceptical and unsure whether to believe everything they saw online.

Meanwhile, the heart of the city, particularly around the West End's iconic Regent Street, began to witness an unusual gathering. Car enthusiasts, motoring fans, and die-hard petrolheads were converging in significant numbers. The excitement was palpable as they anticipated the start of not just the EuroBall Rally, but what also promised to be an unprecedented protest convoy, a tangible pushback against the tightening noose on motorists' freedoms.

The barriers and sponsor displays had already gone up the day before, transforming Regent Street into a spectacle of automotive passion.

The street was restricted to one-way traffic, entering from Piccadilly Circus, as the dazzling array of EuroBall Rally cars lined up in preparation. Marshalls were already struggling to control the throngs of car enthusiasts, the carparazzi, Instagrammers, YouTubers, and those simply eager to witness the automotive event of the year.

Max had arrived early, positioning his BMW E30 at the forefront of the EuroBall Rally line-up, right beside Ahmed's Jaguar XJC. They were waiting for Eleanor to arrive. Eventually, Max spotted a 1987 Brooklands Green Ford Capri 280 approaching and his jaw dropped in recognition – it was Eleanor's car, the one her father had cherished.

He hurried over to greet her as she parked. "This... this was your dad's car, wasn't it? But I thought..." Max trailed off, his voice tinged with sympathy.

"Yeah, I bought it back after he passed... I had to," Eleanor replied, stepping out of the car with a mix of pride and a hint of sorrow. Spontaneously, Max reached out and embraced her, offering a comforting hug. To his relief, she didn't resist but reciprocated, her embrace warm and appreciative. "Thanks, Max, I'm okay," she whispered, a small smile playing on her lips.

"Woah, this thing is an absolute beauty!" Max exclaimed, his eyes scanning the car's classic lines.

They joined Ahmed who was taking a look inside the Capri. "Wonderful example!" he enthusiastically voiced, giving Eleanor an approving fist bump.

Eleanor's smile faded as she surveyed the scene, her thoughts turning to the potential dangers of such a gathering. "It would only take one nutter... and it could all end in disaster," she mused aloud, her gaze lingering on the crowds milling around the impressive array of vehicles.

Max, who was busy scanning updates on his phone, reassured her, "Don't worry, the cavalry is on its way!" His eyes lifted towards Piccadilly Circus, where a growing commotion signalled the approach of a slow-moving cavalcade. A colourful procession of cars, vans, and bikes adorned with protest stickers and blaring music from loudspeakers inched its way towards them.

Eleanor grinned, but her mind was already shifting gears. "I'd better get moving. Flux is starting to identify Quentin's cars; time to get handy!" she said, determination in her tone. She cast a glance towards the BMW. "And you should move your car too, Max, before you get trapped here."

Turning to Ahmed, she expressed her gratitude, "Thanks so much for helping us today, Bhai. It's a big ask, I know."

Ahmed, with a brotherly warmth, put an arm

around Max, "Don't be silly, Ellie," he said with a smile. "For you guys... anything. And for this bugger," he gave Max a friendly thump on the chest, "I would never say no to him for anything!" His laughter echoed down the street, blending with the growing excitement of the gathering crowd.

Max hugged him back in appreciation, "Thanks my friend; you good with the plan?"

Ahmed nodded and addressed both Max and Eleanor, "Yes, yaar, no problem. I'll hang around here, keeping an eye out and listening for Flux in my earpiece. Also, my two top mechanics, Joe and Yusuf, are on standby nearby. I've got them on scooters so they can zip around quickly."

Max nodded in acknowledgment, they all exchanged a quick fist bump, and then Eleanor swiftly hopped back into her Capri, skilfully manoeuvring it through the crowd towards Oxford Circus. Ahmed casually strolled off to blend in with the EuroBall crowd, keeping his eyes and ears open for any renegades or infiltrators.

Max, meanwhile, made a beeline up Piccadilly on foot, straight down the middle of the road, heading directly for the Convoy Leader, Ajeet Singh who was driving a Volkswagen ID.Buzz. Ajeet had eventually replaced his entire fleet of vans with EVs, including the striking ID.Buzz, hoping to avoid future restrictions – only to now face the challenge of pay-per-mile.

The ID.Buzz, with its retro design reminiscent of the classic VW Camper Van, boasted a bright red main body and white upper half, adorned with protest slogans and vibrant graphics. As Max approached, Ajeet spotted him and began honking his horn, inciting a chorus of car horns. They clasped hands as Max reached the side window, Ajeet greeting him warmly, "Sat Sri Akal, Max!" He slowed to a walking pace, but kept the convoy moving.

"Great job, Ajeet! What a turnout!" Max exclaimed, his eyes wide with awe. "I can't see the end of it. Looks like we've got ourselves a proper convoy!"

Ajeet chuckled heartily, "Mate, this is all your doing! Your video was a game-changer – it brought everyone out; wasn't anything to do with me!"

"Nah, mate, I just put the word out," Max replied modestly, slightly embarrassed by the praise. "You're the one who got them here."

Ajeet shook his head in disbelief. "I've never seen anything like this before, Max! Last I was told, there are nearly 500 vehicles behind me!"

Max corrected him with a smile, "Actually, closer to 700." (Flux had been keeping a tally and had informed him of the numbers.)

He gestured towards Regents Street, "Listen,

head that way, but take it slow. There's a massive crowd there for the EuroBall Rally. I need you to extend the convoy up to Oxford Street. We're talking about a mile of road, and I want it packed tight. Double up if you have to, just lock it down. You've got enough vehicles to do it." He handed Ajeet a walkie-talkie, "Keep this on. Don't move on until I give the word."

"I got you bro!" Ajeet responded. He continued moving at the same pace as Max ran back to his BMW and drove it down Shaftsbury Avenue. The pieces of their plan were falling into place, and Max could feel the adrenaline surging through him as he prepared for the next phase of their audacious strategy.

Flux, as usual, had hacked into the extensive CCTV network of one of the most monitored cities in the world. He had quickly identified the 16 cars sold by Ahmed, along with another 20 from the comprehensive list he had compiled. The team had swiftly sprung into action.

The modern vehicles were a breeze to immobilise. Flux, with his digital prowess, had remotely accessed all the Teslas, rendering them inoperable, along with several other models that had left their over-the-air update systems vulnerable. For those cars still reliant on electronics but not connected to the internet, a close-range EMP device would kill them dead.

Eleanor, in her Capri, pulled up alongside

a McLaren pinpointed by Flux and smiled alluringly at the driver, who grinned back. She reached into her bag, pulling out a grey, tablet-sized device. Casually opening her door, she placed it on the ground and kicked it hard with the back of her boot. It slid across the underside of her car, halting perfectly beneath the adjacent supercar. A quick tap on her phone and the device was activated. The McLaren's systems failed immediately, leaving the driver waving his arms in frustration, likely reporting the sudden breakdown to the Eclipse Squad's coordinators.

Ahmed was equally busy, roaming around on foot and employing similar tactics on several of Quentin's performance cars waiting in the side streets off Regents Street. He chuckled to himself at how frequently his shoelaces seemed to 'come undone' near target vehicles.

The older cars, however, presented a greater challenge. When he encountered a 600bhp Chevrolet Nova SS resto-mod he had sold to Quentin, he knew the EMP wouldn't suffice. From his backpack, he retrieved a case filled with small, thumb-sized pellets, each equipped with a tiny trigger button. With a hint of regret, he activated one and tossed it into the Nova's tailpipe where it instantly expanded, effectively blocking the exhaust and immobilising the car. The Nova would be going nowhere now.

His mechanics, Joe and Yusuf, were just as busy.

Armed with portable power tools, they swiftly stripped bolts from the wheels of several parked cars Flux had identified. Without these bolts, the moment a driver attempted to move, the vehicle's chassis would land on its belly. For the faster SUVs, a quick slide underneath to sever a few cables was all it took to leave the drivers scratching their heads for hours.

Max, doing his part, moved from car to car, employing similar tactics. However, he suddenly noticed two of their target vehicles pulling away before he could reach them.

"Guys, they're onto us," Max urgently alerted the team. "Quentin must have sensed something. He's got them moving now."

"Yep, I see them swarming," Flux confirmed from his console. "Nice job, though. We've neutralised 32 cars between you and Ahmed's crew. I've got eyes on five that are on the move, but that still leaves three unaccounted for."

"Got them!" it was Ahmed, "well one of them at least…"

"Go on Bhai," responded Eleanor.

"It's part of the rally line-up. I just walked past the Eagle E-Type I sold. It's been wrapped in a different colour, which is why I missed it at first," Ahmed explained.

"I'm looking through the list on my phone to see if the other two might be on there…" Ahmed continued.

"Hold up, bro," Flux cut in, working frantically. "Cross-referencing the rally entrants now... Yep – entry number 22, the Eagle E-Type, 46 is the Ferrari 288 GTO, and 113 is the Nismo GT-R."

"Well, much as it hurt me to do so, I've stuffed some pellets up the E-Type's exhaust pipes," reported Ahmed. "I can take out the GT-R with a tablet, but the 288... I can't bring myself to touch it. I'll send my guys."

"Flux, the five on the move... what are they doing?" Eleanor inquired.

"They're just cruising around at the moment," came Flux's reply.

Max interjected, "The original plan must've been to sync the fake race with the Rally's official start, but we still have about 10 minutes till the official flag-off..."

"True, but Quentin knows we're taking out his cars by now. He might get desperate," Eleanor added, her voice tense.

"Where are they now?" asked Ahmed, his tone anxious.

Flux paused before answering, "They're around Carnaby Street, Hanover Street, Maddox..." Another pause followed, "El, I think you might be onto something, they're flanking Regents Street..."

Eleanor's voice was firm and resolute, "Gridlock

Flux, do it now!"

The comms went silent as Flux launched his preset programme. He had already infiltrated the traffic control system, and now, all the traffic lights around the area switched to red, freezing the flow of vehicles. "It's working, guys..." Flux's voice crackled through the comms, "They're stuck... ah, except for one, a Lamborghini Urus..."

"Where?" Max's voice was tense.

"Beak Street... oh no... he's breaking away, he's gonna come in hot!" Flux's tone escalated with urgency.

"I'm nearby, in Golden Square. I'll cut him off," Max declared, accelerating hard.

"What? And ruin that beautiful shiny bodywork on the Bimmer? No chance buddy, besides, he's past you already!" Flux told him.

A collective gasp echoed over the comms. The Urus was a massive vehicle; if it crashed into the crowded Regent Street, the impact would be catastrophic.

"Fret not my friends!" Even over the comms they could all hear the A-Team van's mighty motor roar into life, "What you don't know is, I've been parked in Warwick Street this whole time, and I'll pop out in front of him, right about..."

They all heard the LS motor engage, the big tyres spinning, and then a sudden thunderous crashing noise.

"Flux! Flux!" Eleanor shouted frantically.

"Flux are you there? Respond!" Max added.

"C'mon yaar Flux!" the concern in Ahmed's voice was equally clear. But there was total silence.

"Max, can you get to him?" Eleanor's voice was tense.

Max was already sprinting through the gridlocked streets. "Yeah... traffics backed up... I'm on foot... nearly there."

There was still no response from Flux.

"Flux... please..." Eleanor's voice softened, tinged with worry.

"I see the Urus, it's a mess," reported Max, "driver appears to be out cold, knocked out by the airbag... I see Flux's van... oh, he's... he's..."

Suddenly Flux's voice crackled back to life over the comms. "Yo, folks! Worried about me? I'm flattered! You all forgot, this van's a beast! Those front bars aren't just for show – pure reinforced steel baby! I might need new headlights though, damn, those are a bitch to source!"

Eleanor's voice was tinged with concern and relief, "You okay, Flux?"

"Just a bit winded, but I'm fine," he replied, his tone shifting to a more serious one. "A'ight guys, I'm making a path out of here. Max, Eleanor, I'm about to clear a way for you back to the convoy; time to get this party moving, rolling out the red carpet now!"

The relief was palpable among the team. Ahmed quickly caught up with Sterling Carrera and signalled it was time to start. "Gentlemen! Start your engines!" Sterling shouted into his megaphone, and the call rippled down the line of cars. Meanwhile, Max, back in his BMW, radioed Ajeet, "Roll out, buddy! Head towards Tottenham Court Road and keep heading east!"

"10-4, good buddy!" Ajeet replied, his voice tinged with excitement and a playful American accent, "Mercy sakes alive, looks like we got us a convoy! Ain't she a beautiful sight?"

Max chuckled as he navigated the tight back alleys, eventually merging onto Oxford Street and joining the convoy. To his surprise, he was met with an enthusiastic cacophony of cheers, engine revs, and beeping horns. People recognised him and his famous black BMW E30, snapping pictures as he opened the sunroof and windows to wave back.

Unbeknownst to Max, as photos of him started circulating on social media, more cars joined the convoy. Flux excitedly reported that their numbers had swelled to nearly a thousand vehicles. At some point, Eleanor managed to weave her way through and pulled up next to Max in her Capri, beaming and giving him a thumbs up. The sight of the two classic 80s cars together caused an even bigger stir, with more people taking photos of the duo as they passed.

He couldn't wait to see some of those images.

"A'ight team, I got you green lights from here on in. And I reported those four remaining cars to the police for traffic violations. They've all been pulled over," Flux reported with a hint of mischief in his voice. "I know, it's a bit cheeky, but it should hold them for an hour or two at least!" His laughter rang through the comms. "Okay, I'm going dark for a bit. Catch you on the flipside. Stay sharp!"

The convoy snaked its way through to Aldgate, moving steadily towards the Tower of London, and continued eastward towards Limehouse and Canary Wharf. Ajeet's voice broke the radio silence on the walkie-talkie Max had given him.

"Max, are we heading where I think we're heading?" Ajeet inquired, curiosity evident in his tone.

Max couldn't help but chuckle, realising Ajeet had figured out his plan. "Well, if you're going to tell Hartfield to have a heart, why not do it face to face?!" he replied with a hint of mischievous defiance.

Ajeet relayed the message, and a wave of excitement surged along the convoy, all the way back to the EuroBall Rally participants at the rear. The sheer energy of the crowd was obvious as they rolled closer to City Hall.

As they neared their destination, Max, Eleanor, and Ahmed broke away from the main procession, moving to the forefront of the convoy. They turned into the Western Gateway, parking at the front of City Hall. The rest of the convoy followed suit, extending and spreading all the way down to the ExCel Exhibition Centre further east, a stunning display of automotive solidarity and purpose.

This had been the site of V-Max T's now infamous car review of the Edison Model A. The still boarded-up windows on one side of the otherwise immaculate building bore silent witness to his earlier escapades. Though most people had come to believe the chaotic events captured in that video were a carefully choreographed, pre-scripted promotional stunt, rather than the life-threatening escape from the Mayor's assassin it actually was. But then again, people often chose cynicism over confronting the reality that lay plainly before their eyes.

The three stepped out and casually leaned against their spectacular cars, Max on his BMW 325i, Eleanor against her Ford Capri, and Ahmed leaning on the Jaguar XJC, a striking contrast to the futuristic building. They waited as the drivers of the convoy emerged from their vehicles, spreading along the front of the building, their voices uniting in a chant that reverberated off the City Hall's walls: "Have a Heart, Hartfield!"

Ajeet, having parked his VW ID.Buzz, joined

in the swelling chorus, his voice loud and impassioned. Leading campaigner Alex Harrington also appeared, megaphone at the ready.

Then, as if summoned by the clamour, Mayor Hartfield herself emerged from the building, striding purposefully towards the small dock where a sleek boat had just pulled up. "Pretty little yacht that," Eleanor remarked nonchalantly.

The Fairline Targa 38, a luxury sports cruiser, gleamed in the sun, a fitting vessel for a Mayor in haste, accompanied by her personal assistant and what appeared to be an Eclipse Squad operative. They boarded swiftly, and the Skipper wasted no time, steering the boat back onto the Thames with a sense of urgency.

"What the heck, luv?" Alex bellowed in the Mayor's direction, his voice carrying over the water. "Come and face us!" A collective groan of frustration rose from the crowd as the boat sped away, leaving ripples of discontent in its wake. Max and Eleanor shared a knowing look and smiled faintly amongst themselves.

Ahmed turned his attention to his phone. Max, too, was busy checking his device for any news. Eleanor, meanwhile, distracted Ajeet and Alex in conversation, expressing her frustration over the Mayor's hasty retreat in the face of the impressive convoy.

"There's a ton of social media buzz about this convoy and the EuroBall Rally, Max..." Ahmed broke the silence, his voice reflecting subdued excitement over their apparent success.

"Yeah, but were there any incidents?" Max asked, his tone still cautious though hopeful.

"None that I can see. There isn't even a whisper about the little scrape with Flux's van," Ahmed replied, scrolling through his feed.

Max verified Ahmed's observations on his phone. "Looks like we pulled it off, mate!" He looked over at Eleanor who was still chatting with Ajeet, Alex having moved back amongst the crowd. Catching her eye, Max nodded, a silent confirmation of the successful execution of their well-laid plan. She responded with a knowing wink.

Just then, Sterling Carrera pushed his way through the throng of people, his face lit up with a mix of relief and excitement. "Hey gang! How did we do?" he inquired, his gaze sweeping over Max, Ahmed, and the rest of the group.

"You're trending all over social media, yaar!" Ahmed exclaimed, showing Sterling his phone screen filled with posts and hashtags about the rally.

"And the day has been completely incident-free," Max added, his tone carrying a hint of pride. "We owe you a big thanks for your help today,

Sterling."

Sterling clapped Max on the shoulder, his laughter genuine and warm. "Dude, are you for real? It's me who should be thanking you! You've got my eternal gratitude, and trust me, I mean that," he said, his expression turning grave for a moment.

"But seriously," Sterling continued, "if things had gone south today, it wouldn't have just been the end of EuroBall. It could have dragged me down with it. I've got so much riding on this event now. I'm not joking, Max, whatever you need, whenever you need it, you've got a friend in me. Just give me a call."

Max nodded, appreciating the gravity of Sterling's words. He turned back to observe the endless line of cars jammed along the road behind him. "Sorry about this though, your Rally's kind of stuck here for a bit, I guess?"

Sterling Carrera, with his typical flair, thumped his bare chest just visible through the unbuttoned silk Dolce & Gabbana shirt hanging on his well-tone and tanned body, "Hey, this is Sterling Carrera you're talking to!" He spread his arms wide in a grand gesture, gold bracelets jangling on his wrists, "I don't just find silver linings, I create them!" he declared.

Max looked slightly perplexed by Sterling's enthusiasm. Ahmed, sensing Max's confusion, decided to clarify, "Smart boy Sterling here, booked us all into the Sunborn Yacht Hotel, just down the road next to the ExCel... you know the one you raced past in your Edison review?" He gave Max a knowing wink.

Max, keen to steer the conversation away from that day's events, quickly replied, "Oh, that's a brilliant move, mate!"

"And that's not all," Sterling chimed in, "I've arranged for all the Rally cars to be displayed on the courtyard out front!"

"Man, you are killing it right now!" Max exclaimed, impressed with Sterling's resourcefulness.

"Wait till you see the after-party... you're coming right?" Sterling asked.

"Aw man, I really can't... you know... gotta keep churning out that content and all..." he glanced across at Eleanor and Ajeet, "but have you met the convoy leader yet?"

"No, I don't believe I have!" Sterling replied.

"Let me introduce you," Max said, leading Sterling towards Ajeet. "And, er... it would be great if you could invite him instead. He's helped me out a lot today."

Sterling's grin broadened. "I'll make sure he has the night of his life, don't you worry," the millionaire assured Max with a confident nod.

As Sterling, Ajeet, and Ahmed got engrossed in their conversation, Max noticed Eleanor intently looking at her phone, a hint of concern etching her features. Curious, he approached her. "Everything okay, Ellie? We didn't miss anything, did we?"

Eleanor glanced up at him, and instantly her expression transformed. Her eyes sparkled, a broad smile graced her lips, and her head tilted slightly. For a fleeting moment, Max felt a surge of excitement. "No. We're all good. But Max, you were incredible! In fact, I think it's safe to say we shattered the Mayor and Quentin's plan," she maintained his gaze, her voice carrying a tone of triumph. "We won, Max. Today, we really won!"

But her phone pinged again and her business-like demeanour quickly resurfaced. "It's Wong, he's livid... and that's a bridge I really can't afford to burn."

Max's brow furrowed with concern. "Oh, but doesn't he realise how disastrous things could have been today, if we hadn't done what we did?"

"He does, but these guys like to flex their muscles, don't they?" Eleanor exhaled deeply. "Don't worry about it. After you wrap up here, head back to base. I'll go smooth things over with Wong and then join you there."

She moved around to the side of her Capri and opened the driver's door, as she did so, some of the protestors deferentially started making space for her to leave - word had already spread that the mysterious and sexy girl in the awesome

Capri 280 was V-Max T's girlfriend! She blew him a crowd-pleasing kiss, "Max, you saved the day." She waved at the crowd, "This is all you!"

Max watched her drive away, a proud grin spreading across his face. "Time to do some content" he thought to himself. With a contented shrug, he walked to the boot of his BMW, retrieved his camera gear, and headed into the midst of the crowd. As soon as he did, he was warmly embraced and cheered by the enthusiastic protesters.

Several hours later, Max, wearied but still on a triumphant high, pulled up to Flux's place. The shutter rolled open, and he guided the BMW inside, parking it next to the Vandura, which bore the scars of the day's events.

"Aw man, Flux, I'm really sorry about the van!" Max exclaimed as he stepped out of the car.

Flux, ever the ball of energy, bounded over and enveloped Max in a solid bro-hug. "Forget about the van, man, it's a quick fix. I've already ordered the headlight kit... but you!"

Flux stepped back, admiration shining in his eyes, and performed an exaggerated bow. "You're the hero of the day, Max! You did it! You should get some sort of medal for this, except, you know, we don't do medals around here!" His laughter echoed through the garage. "But hey, I do have burgers!"

"Ah, lead the way, Flux!" Max replied, his spirits

lifting at the mention of food. They walked over to the centre of the room, where Flux's tech was set up. The tables were laden with gourmet burgers and fries, a mouth-watering aroma filling the space.

"Ellie not with you?" Flux asked. Max had just grabbed a burger but stopped before taking a bite. "She's not here? She left me ages ago back at City Hall," Max explained, his voice tinged with concern. "Said she got a message from Wong, something about him being pissed off. She was going to smooth things over with him."

"She never checked in," Flux said, scanning one of his console displays. "I've got nothing on her comms, and her phone's off the grid too."

Max set the burger down, a sense of unease washing over him. "What do you mean? Where is she?"

Flux tapped rapidly on his keyboard, sending a secure message to Wong. Almost instantly, a reply pinged back. "Wong says he never sent her any message..." Flux's voice trailed off, confusion etched on his face as he turned to Max. "He didn't see her!" He quickly refocused on his console, his fingers flying over the keys. "Hold on, wait..."

Max leaned in, watching as Flux pulled up a CCTV feed from outside the nondescript café where they had previously met Wong. He watched intently as Flux fast-forwarded the footage. Sure enough, the distinctive nose of her

Ford Capri appeared at the edge of the frame and stopped, parking on the street. Eleanor appeared and entered the café. Moments later, she re-emerged, accompanied by Jake Dalton, the agency operative and Eleanor's former colleague. Max had felt pangs of jealousy the last time he saw them together. He started feeling them again now.

But his jealousy quickly turned to shock as Flux paused the footage, zoomed in, and enhanced the image. They both gasped. There, unmistakably, was Jake Dalton with a gun pressed into Eleanor's side. She was being taken by force.

CHAPTER 12

The chill of the concrete floor seeped through Eleanor's bare skin as she lay there, slowly regaining her senses. Her consciousness fluttered back to life, but her head pounded with the sluggish heaviness of someone trying to emerge from a deep, drug-induced stupor.

She struggled to focus, trying to piece together the fragmented memories of what had happened. The last thing she remembered was Jake, a former mentor, colleague, friend... more than a friend? He had forced her into a car at gunpoint. Wait... it was her car. "Well, that could be a good thing," she thought, or spoke out loud - in her current state, distinguishing between the two was a challenge.

What was happening to her? She vaguely recalled the sharp prick of a needle. A drug. Benzodiazepine, perhaps? A sedative known for its confounding side effects of confusion and disorientation.

As her eyes adjusted to the dim light, the stark reality of her situation began to come into painful focus. She was in her underwear, stripped of her clothes, watch, phone, her earpiece, and any other possessions she had. One of her ankles was chained to a heavy pipe running along the floor of what appeared to be a storeroom in an industrial facility. The faintly visible logo of Albion Cement Works Ltd on a rusted sign confirmed her location as a disused cement factory.

Dust particles floated lazily in the sparse rays of light filtering through a small, barred window high up on the wall. The stale air was thick, pungent, almost tangible.

A door creaked open, letting in a sliver of light that grew steadily, revealing the silhouette of a man framed in the doorway. He stepped inside, the unmistakable shape of a pistol in his hand symbolising the control he wielded. It was Jake. His face, once a source of familiarity and comfort, now wore a mask of cold, detached professionalism.

"Ah... Princess Ellie stirs," he said, his voice tinged with mock affection, yet carrying an undercurrent of steely detachment. The familiar tone, once a source of comfort, now sent a shiver of foreboding down her spine.

"Dalton?" Eleanor feigned fuzzy disorientation, her voice barely above a whisper. "Jake... is that you?"

"Yes, it's me, sweetheart," he replied, his tone flat

and unemotional. She dragged herself up and stumbled toward him, only to be jerked back harshly as her chain tensed. She crumpled to the ground, a sense of helplessness washing over her.

But Jake didn't move to assist her. He simply stood there, his gun arm extended, a sardonic smile playing on his thin lips. Her act had confirmed that the man she once trusted implicitly was now officially a hostile. Eleanor shifted tactics abruptly.

"What are you doing, Jake?" Her voice was sharp, laced with disbelief and a profound sense of betrayal. Her mind raced, eyes flicking to the doorway, fingers feeling for any give in the clasp around her ankle, quickly surveying the room for any advantage. Anyone else might have missed these subtle actions, but not Dalton. He almost nodded, an unspoken approval of her discreet actions.

"Just doing my job, Ellie. A new job, that is." His voice was a low, menacing whisper as he moved a fraction closer. "Pays much better than the old gig."

"Your job?" Eleanor spat back, anger flaring in her voice. "To kidnap and drug a friend?"

Jake's expression remained impassive, his shoulders shrugging with an ease that belied the seriousness of the situation. "You know how it is, Eleanor. In our line of work, loyalties shift.

Opportunities arise."

Waves of bewilderment pulsed painfully through Eleanor's brain, each one irregular and jarring. She tried to steady her breathing, to centre her focus and restore a semblance of self-control. Shivering in the cold, she folded her arms, rubbing her shoulders for warmth. "Where are my clothes?"

Jake's voice dripped with amusement. "Oh, come now, Ellie. Who knows what little gadgets Flux might've hidden in the seams? I even checked your bra and panties, just in case."

Eleanor shot him a look of outrage. "Come now, gorgeous," he grinned, his tone cutting, "you know I've seen it all before."

Her voice trembled, "How could you do this to me, Jake? I thought... I thought we had something."

Jake paused, his gaze meeting hers for a fleeting moment. A flicker of something – regret, or maybe sorrow – crossed his face, but it was gone as quickly as it had appeared. "It's not personal, Ellie. It's just business."

Fighting back tears of frustration, she told herself it was just the drugs' effect. "And what about us, Jake? Was that just business too?"

"Us?" he scoffed, his voice laced with contempt. "I was just bored, darling. You know how dull those long stake-out missions can be. You've got to find some way to pass the time, right?" His wink was like a slap.

Her heart ached with the pain of betrayal, the sting amplified by the narcotic stupor. The man she had once trusted, perhaps even cared for, was now a stranger, an adversary. Swallowing hard, she forced herself to focus. "What do they want with me, Jake? What's your new employer planning?"

Jake's attention shifted towards the door. "Why don't you ask her yourself?" he replied.

Eleanor's struggle to stay focused felt like wading through treacle. She shook her head, attempting to clear the fog enveloping her mind. As she looked up, the unmistakable visage of Mayor Victoria Hartfield coalesced in the doorway. Victoria stepped in, her presence exuding an aura of cold, calculated menace. She regarded Eleanor with a look that was part disgust, part indifference.

"You've been quite the thorn in our side, Eleanor," Victoria began, her voice a silky, menacing purr. "Still, it's rather convenient you've joined us. You're an integral part of Plan B!"

Eleanor's gaze never wavered. Despite the drugs coursing through her system dulling her usually sharp wit, she managed a derisive chuckle, "What happened to plan A? Stalled on the start line, did it?"

The Mayor's expression soured visibly at the

jibe. Eleanor pressed on, "I hope you have valid warranties for all those cars you bought."

Victoria's lips curled into a disdainful smile. "Your attempts at defiance are quite wearisome," she retorted. "But since you're curious, your little escapades were merely a hiccup."

"What is Plan B?" Eleanor demanded, her voice trembling despite her efforts to sound defiant.

Victoria's eyes glinted with malice. "Oh, you'll see soon enough. In fact, you'll have a front-row seat... I do so enjoy a bit of audience participation."

As she spoke, Victoria reached into her handbag, pulling out a packet of Virginia Slims. She elegantly extracted a thin cigar, then produced an elaborately bejewelled lighter. Just as she was about to light it, Jake loudly cleared his throat. Victoria glanced at him, annoyance flashing across her face before she reluctantly placed the items back in her bag. Eleanor observed this exchange in her stupefied state, unable to decipher its significance.

The Mayor turned back to Eleanor, "Tch... Enough of this mundane chit-chat!" she declared, waving her hand dismissively. "I only graced this dreary place to gloat. I bid you adieu." She bestowed upon Eleanor one final, withering look before turning away with a dramatic flourish.

"I took out two of your best operatives. What

makes you think I won't score a hat-trick?" Eleanor retorted, her voice regaining its edge, "You've underestimated me before."

Victoria spun around theatrically, her laughter exaggerated and staged. "Luck, my dear! Bold, brassy, and, to borrow a plebeian phrase, 'jammy' luck. So don't flatter yourself, luvvy!"

Her expression then morphed into one of mock mournfulness. "Though I must admit, I do miss Stahl," she paused, a faraway look crossing her features, "he was quite... erm... capable," she mused, a self-satisfied smile playing on her lips. Shaking off her reminiscence, Victoria's gaze sharpened as she addressed Eleanor again. "But you, you can't kill Jake, can you? Because of your... how shall I put this? Past amorous entanglements?"

Victoria's eyes then lingered on Jake. "Though frankly, Jake, I can't fathom what you saw in this pitiable little creature when you could do so much better," she said, her tone laced with insinuation. A coquettish smile flickered across her face, guileful eyes hinting at rewards for Jake that went beyond mere financial gain. It was a calculated move, designed to reaffirm his allegiance, dangling the tantalising prospect of untold pleasures.

She briefly turned her attention back to the half-naked girl, lying helplessly on the floor, chained to the wall. A look of utter disdain contorted

Victoria's heavily made-up face, a face that put Eleanor in mind of a pantomime dame.

And the dame was still hamming it up, "I mean, just look at her. She's so... she's so brown, eww!" Victoria shuddered with disgust, her bigotry laid bare. Eleanor's skin crawled in revulsion. A surge of fury propelled her towards the Mayor, but the chains yanked her back to the ground with a jarring thud. The sudden movement caused Victoria to recoil and Jake to instinctively raise his gun.

"Why do we even allow such people in our intelligence services? How can we trust their allegiances?" Victoria sneered, her words dripping with contempt.

"That's rich," Eleanor spat back, her voice laced with scorn, "coming from someone who's betrayed Londoners and sold out to international corporations!" She turned to Jake, her eyes blazing, "And as for you..."

"My dear Eleanor," Victoria interjected with theatrical insincerity, "I assure you, I have only the best interests of the proles at heart..." She paused, a melodramatic affectation in her tone. "Oh, sorry, did I say proles? I meant the darling little people who adore me." With a grandiose gesture, she swept out of the room, "Goodbye and good riddance, Ms Rodrigues."

Eleanor blinked, her focus returning to Jake, who stood there with an unsettling, almost lascivious look. "What are you staring at, you arsehole?!" she shouted, her voice a tumult of rage and frustration.

Jake's expression was dark and distant. "I'm just taking you in one last time," he said softly, a hint of melancholy in his voice. "If it's any compensation, you were one of the best agents I've ever worked with... A shame you couldn't be turned," he added wistfully. "This is the end, Ellie." With those final words, he turned and left, the sound of the locking door echoing like a death knell in Eleanor's ears.

Eleanor's heart pounded with a mix of rage and fear. Her eyes darted around the stark room, desperately searching for any avenue of escape. But her hopes dwindled – the windows were placed too high, the door was robust, and the chain was mercilessly tight around her ankle. She was trapped.

Her mind whirred, sifting through the fog of drugs, grappling for a solution to this waking nightmare. Her gaze settled on the pipework across the room, snaking into the wall, likely leading to storage tanks. The adjacent plaques, which would have identified the contents of the pipes, had been deliberately erased.

She waded through the fog in her head, trying to theorise about the potential substances within the pipes: solvents, ammonia, nitrate compounds, oxidisers. Together, they could form a lethal, explosive combination. Even the mere concentration of cement dust, if disturbed and ignited, could combust.

Her attention was drawn to a small black box mounted near the pipes, conspicuously newer and cleaner than its surroundings. A remote detonator - the realisation hit her like a wave. Depending on the chemicals still stored at the facility, any explosion would scatter particulate matter, toxic gases, and harmful chemicals into the air, drastically exacerbating pollution levels. Investigators combing through the aftermath would trace the blast to this room, where her DNA would be found.

But her befuddled mind stumbled over the logic, it wasn't quite adding up. Her DNA would lead nowhere; there were no official records of her, and the Agency would never disclose her identity, not even under pressure from the Mayor. She would be just a 'mysterious woman' in the news. What purpose would that serve?

Then, a chilling thought pierced through her confusion. It wasn't her DNA they were after. Realisation dawned on her, a sense of despair creeping in. As the drug's effects deepened their hold, her thoughts blurred, and darkness enveloped her once again.

Back at Flux's tech-laden den, he was replaying the footage from the nondescript café, studying it intently. "Alright, check it out – he whisked her away in the Capri. And guess what? That's the first slice of good news we've snagged!"

"How so?" Max peered over, curious.

"Encrypted transponders, my man," Flux replied with a swift turn to another screen. "I've kitted out all our rides with these bad boys. Ghost tech – nobody but the Ghost Weaver himself can track 'em!"

"All our cars?" Max raised an eyebrow.

"Oh, uh, yeah man, I put it on yours too... hope you don't mind buddy?" Flux shot him a quick, apologetic grin.

Max quickly responded that he didn't, but in his head mulled over the implications of spies secretly tracking his car without his knowledge, but then concluded that he should just be grateful those spies were his friends.

Flux's eyes were back on the screen. "Bingo! Staples Corner Business Park Industrial Estate – that's where the Capri's at. Looks like an old cement factory."

"Should we bring in Wong?" Max asked tentatively.

Flux paused, mulling it over. "I'll shoot him the café scoop and drop Dalton's name, but let's face it, Wong could be playing us too." He faced Max, a serious edge to his voice. "Straight up, the only cats I trust to pull Ellie out of this mess are right here in this room. You game?"

"Let's roll," Max responded instantly, determination in his voice, only to be shadowed by a hint of doubt. "But hey, Flux, you gotta be my GPS in this maze, you know what I mean? This isn't my usual turf."

Flux clapped a hand on Max's shoulder, his confidence radiating like a beacon. "I got you, brother. You and me? We're like the A-Team," he declared with a grin, pointing towards the van, "We even got the ride." He imitated Mr T, "Hey man, these suckers gonna pay!" he said, slamming his fist into the palm of his other hand.

Flux worked with a focused intensity, loading extra gear into the van in preparation for the mission. The drive to the old Albion Cement Factory took about forty minutes, during which Flux was busy setting up and prepping the equipment. Max parked the Vandura in a shadowy side street, a strategic spot of darkness away from the street lights, with a clear view of the plant's entrance.

"A'ight Max, it's showtime," Flux declared as they surveyed the facility through the van's windscreen. "We're gonna glide in smooth, keep it low-key, snatch our girl, make like ghosts and vanish! Time to gear up, partner."

Max shed his brown leather jacket and donned black overalls, topping them with a dark tactical vest. Flux, with practised hands, attached mics, sensors, and cameras to Max's gear. He then handed Max a helmet equipped with a 360-degree camera and a dark visor featuring an internal heads-up display. Finally, despite Max's hesitation, Flux passed him a SIG Sauer P365 pistol. "You know how to handle this?"

Max shook his head. "No, mate. I really don't. I don't think I could... maybe we leave it?" he implored.

Flux wasn't having it. He ran through a quick, hands-on tutorial on gun handling and firing. "In case things get hairy," he said, sliding the pistol into Max's holster and adding extra cartridges to his vest.

Gripping Max's shoulders, Flux locked eyes with him. "Listen, if Eclipse Squad goons are in there, they won't think twice about putting two in your chest." He firmly placed Max's hand on the side holster. "If you're cornered, use this. You got me?"

Max nodded, a slow, reluctant agreement. "But what if they're not Eclipse Squad?"

Flux shrugged nonchalantly, swivelling back to his screens. "Shoot or be shot, my man. We're in the jungle now, you feel me?"

He lifted a VR headset. "With this, I'll see and hear everything you do," he said, pointing to the sensors on Max's suit. "Actually, I'll see even more with all this data feeding in." Leaning in, Flux added, "I'm with you every step, brother.

We're in this together, but don't lose sight of why we're here..."

"...to get Ellie back," Max completed, his resolve solidifying. "Don't worry, Flux. I haven't known her for long, but I promise you, she means more to me than my own life!" Max's voice carried a weight of sincerity, echoing what Eleanor had said to him.

Flux flashed a knowing grin and winked. "Oh, I'm hip to that, brother!" He then turned his attention to a box of drones he had brought along.

Max caught the implication and seized the moment, "Really? That obvious?"

Flux, working on the drones, glanced back with a smirk. "Dude, I've been extensively trained in the art of human observation by the best behavioural analysts the CIA got..." he chuckled, "but trust me, it didn't take any of that to see you got it going on for her!"

"I haven't got a chance though, have I?" Max mused, half to himself. "She's leagues above me. I've never met anyone quite like her."

Flux, activating a few of the drones, replied over the rising whir of rotors, "Our Ellie's one in a million, for sure. That's why we're gonna get her back." He shouted, "But there's one thing you've got, man, something she values more than anything..." He slid open the van's side door, releasing the drones into the night. "Trust! She trusts you, Max. And that's hard currency in our world."

Max's thoughts swirled as he absorbed Flux's words. Perhaps Eleanor wasn't as unattainable as he thought. If anyone knew her well, it was Flux, the man she called brother. Yet, at that moment, she was physically beyond reach, and for once, it was up to him to be her knight in shining armour, or rather dulled black armour. He almost made himself laugh at the thought as he stepped out of the van, ready to take on whatever the night was about to throw at him.

Flux turned back from the monitor, his face a blend of focus and anticipation. "A'ight, here's the sitrep – the joint's quiet, which is the good. The bad? A couple of goon-mobiles parked out front. I count four, maybe five assholes. No fear, we ain't going in the front entrance." He tapped a gadget on Max's utility belt. "Head around the west perimeter, and use this baby to cut through the fence – it's an ultrasonic cutter."

He grabbed the VR unit and waved to Max, "Remember, I'm with you every step. Now go be the hero, man!"

As Flux slipped on the VR headset and slammed the van door shut, Max felt a sudden rush of isolation. The familiar streets of London now felt alien as his heart raced, beating as rapidly as it did that first time he was shot at in Trafalgar Square. Yet, beneath the fear, a grim determination took hold.

He jogged along the fence on the opposite side to where the guards were parked, Flux's voice guiding him through his earpiece. "A bit more, dude... yeah, right there. Use the cutter here – button's on the back. But hey, watch where you point that thing; it will slice your leg clean off!"

Flux wasn't joking. The cutter hummed to life, slicing through the fence like a hot knife through butter. Once inside, Flux's aerial guidance led him to a side building. "The car's there!" Flux advised.

Max found it: Eleanor's Ford Capri, unscathed amidst the desolation. Max tested the car door. "Locked!" he whispered into the mic.

"Under the rear bumper, behind the left overrider," Flux instructed.

Max's fingers found the spare key hidden there. "Got it," he confirmed, slipping the key into his pocket. "So, I guess it would be a fair assumption that if Ellie is here, she'll be in the building next to her car?"

"Fair assumption!" Flux's voice crackled through the comms. Max moved towards the door, but Flux's sharp command halted him. "Freeze, Max!"

Max immediately stopped. "Look up, on the lamp pole next to you. Camera facing the door..."

"Yeah, I see it," Max confirmed. "But all the

cameras in this joint are supposed to be dead, right?"

"True, but check out this one. It's clean, shiny and new. That cable plug? It's way too fresh. This camera just went live," Flux explained, his tone laced with suspicion.

"Can't you hack into it?" Max asked, scanning the camera.

"Nah, man. It's off-grid. Linked directly somewhere. There's no way in," Flux sounded regretful. "Just stay out of its sight. Circle the building, and let's find out where else there are cameras."

Max complied, cautiously edging around the building. Nearing the north corner, a faint sound caught his attention. Before he could report it, Flux was already in his ear. "I hear it too... sounds like tapping. Get closer, I'll crank up the mics."

Pressing his ear against the cold concrete, Max listened intently to the rhythmic tapping. "Is that... Morse Code?" he ventured.

"Definitely is! That's gotta be El. Clever girl!" Flux praised.

A glimmer of hope sparked in Max at the thought that Eleanor might still be alive. But then, a wave of frustration hit him. "I don't know Morse Code."

"You don't need to, let me translate," Flux said, quickly deciphering the message.

"-... B

"--- O

"--- O

"-... B

"-.-- Y

"Then a space

"- T

".-. R

".- A

".--. P

"BOOBY TRAP. Oh… oh damn."

Flux had Max move to different spots, using this to triangulate the source of the sound. He soon pinpointed it to the bottom of the East wall, probably from some metal piping inside. "A'ight, let's get a bird's-eye view," Flux muttered, sending his drones on a silent, lightless sweep. Equipped with infrared cameras, the drones scanned the windows about two and a half metres off the ground, but despairingly, all the rooms appeared empty.

Max pointed out that if Eleanor was tapping a pipe along the wall, it would be directly below the windows and she wouldn't be seen. Flux switched the drones to thermal imaging, running another sweep. This time, a drone picked up a heat signature of a small device on the wall opposite in one of the rooms. "Third window, Max... but hold up, don't do anything. Remember, she's warning us about a booby trap."

The window was barred, with broken glass and a tiny gap at the top – just enough for Flux's drone to slip through. Inside, the drone hovered, careful to stay out of the detonator camera's range. Flux patched the feed into Max's helmet visor. Both of them gasped as the camera revealed Eleanor, half-naked, curled up in a foetal position, her wrist faintly twisting as she continued discreetly tapping out her message.

Max scanned for a door without a camera trained on it. "Hold up, Max. Just hold," Flux's voice crackled through, a mix of caution and urgency. Max stood still, every fibre of his being yearning to rush in to get Eleanor.

Flux sent in a fresh drone from his van, this one was carrying a few small trinkets; an earpiece, a tiny box with what appeared to be a lens in one side and Eleanor's favourite lipstick. "C'mon princess, Santa's coming to town, and he comes bearing gifts; you're gonna be all made up," Flux mumbled to himself, his voice betraying his tension. He expertly manoeuvred the drone, releasing the earpiece first. It bounced off Eleanor's cheek, landing close to the wall.

A short while earlier, Eleanor had started to shake off some of the effects of the drugs. Having realised that she was bait, she had started tapping the message as discreetly as she could.

Nonetheless, her mind was still a little scattered. Plus, after the shivering had subsided her body had become numb and stiff from the cold, she could barely feel her legs and feet.

When the earpiece struck her chin, she was engulfed in confusion. She looked up, her fuzzy mind conjuring the image of a gigantic moth looming over her. A surreal thought crossed her mind – after years of dodging bullets, was she about to meet her end from the sting of a colossal lepidopteran? As she stared in bewilderment, the blurry 'moth' morphed into a more familiar shape - a drone!

Her mind started to clear. She looked around and spotted the earpiece, she slid it discreetly into her ear, keeping it hidden from the detonator's camera. "Flux, is that you?" she whispered.

"Yeah, Ellie, we're here. I'm in the van, and Max is right outside your…" Flux began, his voice crackling with excitement and relief.

Eleanor cut in urgently, "NO! Get Max out now. Both of you, leave! It's a trap. They want Max here. If he enters, this place will go up like a barrel of gunpowder!"

"Don't be ridiculous, Eleanor. We're not leaving without you," Max interjected, his voice firm.

"Retreat, retreat!" Eleanor insisted. "This is a no-win scenario!"

But Flux was not swayed, "I don't believe in the

no-win scenario! And I am NOT losing my sister today, uh uh! Look sharp, I got another couple of trinkets coming your way."

Eleanor cautiously moved to catch the next items – a tiny box with a lens and her favourite lipstick. "Really, Flux?" she murmured, a mix of amusement and disbelief in her voice.

"C'mon, little sis. You gotta look sharp when you're up in the Mayor's grill, telling her she just got owned... again!" Flux quipped, trying to lighten the mood.

Despite her anxiety and fear for Max's safety, Eleanor allowed herself a small smile at Flux's comment. Meanwhile, he greenlit Max to use the ultrasonic cutter on the door lock and let himself in. Max made his way to the door of the room Eleanor was being held in, but stopped just in time to stay behind a camera pointing at it.

There were no movement detectors inside, just the detonator camera. Flux used his drones to scan the room and create a comprehensive 3D image. He instructed Eleanor to position the tiny box to face the detonator camera. She slid it under her body, and once in position, pressed the tiny button to instantly activate a holographic projection, bisecting the room, and continuing to show the camera an unchanged view.

Behind the projection, Eleanor was finally able to move unseen. She instantly painted her ankle clamp with the lipstick and used the laser cutter to slice it off. Despite her efforts, the numbness in her limbs made standing impossible. "Stay low for now," Flux advised.

In the corridor, Max worked the ultrasonic cutter on the wall adjacent to the door, ensuring he remained hidden from the camera's sight. He carved a gap just wide enough for Eleanor to crawl through. Getting the message, she had crawled towards the opening. When Max pulled away debris to open up the gap, he finally laid eyes on her. Covered in dust and cement, her once black underwear now dusted grey, she pulled herself toward him on her elbows, her hair dishevelled but her eyes shining with recognition.

As she reached him, she wrapped her arms around his torso, burying her face in his chest. "I told you to get out," she murmured, looking up at him, her hand gently touching his cheek. "They plan to blow this place up with you inside. Frame you for it."

Flux's voice crackled in on the comms, "The pollution from that place would've hung around for days. Mayor Vicky's playing dirty – hitting two targets with one move." Flux drew a sharp breath almost impressed with the strategy. "She's pushing her agenda and trying to discredit V-Max T!"

Max was only half-listening, having lifted his visor, his gaze was locked with Eleanor's.

The relief and joy of seeing her safe were overwhelming, he had never anticipated becoming so obsessed with someone. He started moving his face closer to hers, and she reciprocated by curling her arm around his neck, they came close enough for their breaths to mingle, lips almost brushing only to be interrupted by Flux's urgent call. "Guys! Heads up!"

"Oh damn, so sorry Flux," Max had completely forgotten that Flux was on the VR and seeing everything.

"No, it's Jake! He's closing on your location! Exit the way you came in, Max. He's storming in the front door," Flux's voice crackled with urgency.

Max turned to Eleanor; concern etched on his face. "Can you walk, Ellie?"

Eleanor grimaced, attempting to push herself up but faltered. "I was drugged; and my legs aren't cooperating... need to get circulation back..."

Max swiftly supported her up, keeping a firm hold as she clung to his jacket and utility belt. But they were too slow and their escape was thwarted. Jake's bellowing laughter echoed from the other side of the corridor. "What a sight you two make!" he jeered.

They turned around to confront their adversary. In the dim corridor, backlit by the yellow-orange glow of the street lamps outside streaming through the door window. Max stood tall, his overalls and flak jacket adorned with cameras and sensors, a matte black helmet on his head, its dark visor flipped down. Beside him, Eleanor clung tightly, her body caked in dirt and grime, her hair wild from her ordeal.

Jake advanced towards them, stepping over the debris from the wall, his gun steadily aimed forward. In his other hand, he brandished zip ties, his taunts echoing through the corridor. "What do we have here? The cyborg and the slut!" he sneered, tossing the zip ties at their feet. "Tie yourselves up, lovebirds. I'll make sure you're snug before I take off. Gives you a bit of time, doesn't it? A final moment together - consider it a parting gift."

"I'm guessing you're nearby Flux?" he spoke a little louder, though he didn't need to as Flux was listening with increasing alarm. "My boys will be paying you a visit real soon, Ghost Weaver. And hey, maybe switch off those cameras? Let's give these kids some privacy."

Then, in a bizarre and unsettling display, Jake gyrated his hips crudely, "Oh, Max, you're in for a treat. Ellie's got some moves... I should know. After all, I was her teacher!"

Max felt an impotent rage coursing within him, but he was acutely aware of his limitations. He still had the SIG in the holster, but he knew he wouldn't be able to draw and fire it before Jake did, plus he lacked the skill and the cold-bloodedness to take a life. He cursed himself for not giving it to Eleanor. Their predicament seemed inescapable, and even Flux had fallen ominously silent. Suddenly he noticed Eleanor tensing in his arms; a simmering volcano on the verge of eruption.

"You're one sick bastard!" she hissed, gently pushing Max back and staggering towards Jake with unsteady determination. "And you're bluffing."

"Bluffing?" Jake's voice was cool, mocking. He pressed the nozzle of his Glock against her skin, right over her heart. "You sure you wanna go out THIS way?" he glanced down at the pistol as if to suggest he was about to pull the trigger.

Eleanor, though trembling, spoke with a surprising calmness. "Two things, Jake." She stood her ground, pushing against his gun arm. Her voice was steady, the drug's effects finally waning. "First, you can't have bodies with bullet holes here – it won't fit your little narrative."

She leaned in closer, her face was contorted with fury, a defiant frenzy lighting up her dark eyes, and she pretended to sniff him, twisting her mouth as if encountering an awful stench. "You're rotten to your core Jake, like the smell of rotten eggs that's been lingering in the air. Or is it the sulphur and what, ammonium nitrate that you've laced the air with in here?"

A flicker of concern broke through Jake's smug

façade as Eleanor pressed on, "That's a potent cocktail, and it means you won fire that gun in here. You love your own skin too much."

Suddenly Eleanor let out a feral scream startling both Jake and Max. It was a raw, desperate cry bursting forth out of pent-up rage and desperation. "I'll end you myself!" she roared, her eyes blazing with fury.

With a sudden burst of energy, she lunged forward, her movement swift and unexpected, her left hand clamping around his gun hand swinging it away and down, as she balled her right hand and brought it up in a shattering blow under his jaw, her fist tearing against his stubble, drawing blood. The impact disorientated Jake momentarily, but he recovered quickly, relinquishing the gun he knew he couldn't use, relying instead on his greater height and superior strength to try and pummel Eleanor into submission.

The fight erupted into a violent dance of blurred fists, elbows and knees. Eleanor, fuelled by fury, ducked under his swings, her stiffened limbs moving awkwardly yet effectively. Drawing on everything her Jeet Kune Do training had taught her, she delivered a vicious elbow strike catching Jake in the temple and staggering him. He retaliated with a crushing knee to her abdomen, she gasped, pain and fury mixing in her eyes, but she didn't falter.

Her numbness was a double-edged sword; it made her movements clumsier than she would have liked, but with her pain receptors deadened, she was hitting harder than she normally would. Each strike was delivered with reckless abandon, her skin tore, her fists bloodied, but she felt nothing except sheer unadulterated rage.

A palm strike to his nose, a blocked knee to his groin, a brutal ballet of violence. Jake grabbed her, throwing her hard against the wall, but Eleanor pushed through the pain, using the wall to catapult back at him with renewed ferocity. A series of fast, bone-crunching strikes to his ribs winded him, and as he reeled from the relentless onslaught, he repeated his brute force move of slamming her hard against the wall, this time pinning her there with the weight of his body. His bloodied lips twisted into a grotesque grin.

She felt the cold, hard wall against her bare back. With whatever strength she could muster, she willed her obstinate feet to slide out and brace against the opposite wall, stepping up against it, while at the same time she wrapped her arm around Jake's neck. Bringing her body to a horizontal position and in a swift, fluid motion, she rotated, leveraging her weight with the momentum gained from the wall. Jake stumbled back, tripped on the debris scattered on the floor, and lost his footing.

She brought Jake down, while simultaneously

twisting sharply, applying all her force in a calculated direction. There was a sickening snap as Jake's neck broke just as his body impacted the floor. The struggle ended abruptly, his body going limp in her grasp. Eleanor's breath came in ragged gasps, her heart pounding her chest. She released him and rolled away. Lying still for a moment, taking deep steadying breaths.

Max stood, mouth agape, momentarily frozen as he witnessed the ferocious struggle. A mix of awe and horror washed over him. Snapping back to reality, he moved towards Eleanor but paused, a thought striking him. He approached Jake's lifeless form and, with a mixture of dread and determination, removed his blazer. Wrapping the oversized garment around Eleanor, he lifted her exhausted body into his arms and leapt over Jake's corpse, dashing towards the entrance. Eleanor's voice was faint, all he heard was a whisper: "Hat trick..." She teetered on the edge of consciousness.

"Get to the Capri and get out, Max!" Flux's urgent voice came through the comms, accompanied by the sound of the van starting. "I've got hostiles closing in, I'm rolling out too!"

Max swiftly unlocked the Capri's passenger door, gently placing Eleanor in the seat and securing the belt around her. He slid into the driver's seat, tossing his helmet into the back. As he did, he noticed Eleanor stirring, her fingers brushing the door card. "Daddy, you'd have been proud..." she murmured softly.

"He definitely would've been, Ellie," Max replied, his voice firm with admiration. He started the 2.8-litre V6 engine and engaged first gear. "You're incredible. Now, let's get you safe." He revved the engine, side-stepped the clutch and executed a spin-turn, racing towards the exit, slicing through the open gate. Only one car remained outside, it was empty – the other, Max realised, must have gone after Flux.

As he drifted the Capri onto a road leading away from the industrial zone, two police cars screeched to a halt ahead, blocking his path. Max braked hard, the car halting at an angle. Commander Priya Kapoor emerged from one of the police cars, gun in one hand, megaphone in the other. "Game over, guys. Give it up," she commanded.

"For what?" Max shouted back, feigned disbelief in his voice. "We haven't done anything!"

Eleanor sharpened as her awareness started to come back. She pulled the borrowed blazer tighter around her and assessed the situation. At that moment, the cement plant erupted in a massive explosion behind them. Astonishingly, Priya remained unmoved by the blast, a smug grin spreading across her face. As the dust settled, she aimed her gun at them. "I'd say I have reasonable grounds now!"

Max and Eleanor exchanged a look of realisation – they were being framed.

CHAPTER 13

It was a stand-off. Distant sirens confirmed that emergency services would arrive within minutes, responding to the raging inferno now engulfing the old cement factory; thick, black smoke streamed into the air above. The flames cast an ominous glow across Commander Priya Kapoor's face, who probably triggered the massive explosion remotely herself.

It wouldn't be long before the area was swarming with more police cars. Priya, with a menacing authority, commanded, "Switch off the car and step out." her voice brooking no opposition. A self-assured grin etched on her face, she lowered the megaphone and raised her Glock 17, aiming squarely at them. Her silent message was clear – she was done talking.

Behind them, the hellish scene continued to unfold. The fire turned the air red and crackling hot, as if they were at the gates of hell itself. Debris was still falling from the sky while glowing fiery embers swirled to the ground like a snow shower gone grotesque.

The Capri burbled, a slight shimmy in the body. Max gripped the leather-bound three-spoke RS steering wheel, his knuckles white. Eleanor, beside him, dishevelled and dirty from her ordeal, now wearing Jake's oversized dark blue blazer, had regained her composure. Her eyes, sharp and calculating, darted around, assessing their dire situation.

"If we're taken, the Mayor will win; but chances are, we might live," Eleanor's whisper cut through the tension, her tone controlled yet urgent. "Kapoor wants us to run though, she'll try to take us out permanently... corpses are easier to get confessions out of."

Max continued to stare ahead, the grimace on his face confirmed he didn't like either of those options. He too was letting his mind race. They'd come too far, been through too much. His eyes flicked momentarily to the Capri's instrument panel, watching the rev needle quiver just below 1000 rpm. He imagined it spinning around the dial in fury. The leather-trimmed Recaro seats seemed to embrace him, offering a silent reassurance.

Max's gaze returned to the Police commander, her sneer an open challenge. Behind her, stood two fully liveried Police Ford Mustang Mach-E GT pursuit cars, their presence ominous. He recalled their specs: dual motors, about 480bhp, 860Nm of torque, and a 0-60mph acceleration capability in just under four seconds. With a range of around 300 miles, these electric beasts wouldn't run out of juice anytime soon, especially with more police cars likely to join the fray.

"This Capri of yours..." he said to Eleanor, "felt a little frisky, you've done something to it?"

Eleanor rattled off the modifications: "Bilstein shocks, Mintex brakes, faster rack, Janspeed exhaust, better airflow, remapped ECU. We're pushing about 200bhp," she listed, her voice a mix of pride and urgency. "plus Flux added a one or two little optional extras for me." Max flashed a look across at her just in time to catch a hint of a smirk.

At that moment, Flux's voice crackled through the comms, his tone playful yet alert. "Yo, did someone just say my name?!"

Eleanor's concern was evident. "You good, Flux?"

"Better than good, I'm A-OK! They lost track of me – I'm the Ghost Weaver, remember? I'm holed up at Brent Cross Mall, tapping into the traffic cams as we speak. You've got blues and twos coming at you, yellows and reds from all sides. Whatever you're planning, better do it quick!"

Without glancing across, Max extracted the SIG from his holster and handed it to Eleanor, keeping the movement discreet. She accepted it with practised ease, her fingers deftly checking the cartridge, priming the gun for action.

Max drew a deep breath, reflecting on how surreal his current predicament was. Just eight days earlier, the notion of engaging in a high-speed pursuit through London, battling trained police pursuit drivers in advanced EVs, while at the wheel of a 40-year-old, lairy rear-wheel-drive sports car, would have seemed imbecilic and ludicrous. And yet, here he was... contemplating exactly that.

His hand shifted to the slender gear lever, firmly slotting it into reverse. He looked across at Eleanor, who had glanced down and observed his gear selection. She nodded her approval and by confirmation, methodically cocked the gun and slowly rolled down her window in preparation.

With a decisive stomp on the accelerator, the Cologne V6 roared, and the Capri's rear wheels scrambled for grip, the whole vehicle shuddering with wheel hop as it jolted backwards. Eleanor, with calculated precision, fired warning shots into the ground ahead of Commander Priya, forcing her to run back to the patrol cars and take cover.

Max whipped the Capri into a J-Turn, snatching first gear and squirmed down the road, past the raging fire and straight into the path of a stream of fire engines and ambulances racing in from the opposite direction. Eyes wide, senses sharp, Max's reflexes took over, weaving through the maze of fire engines and ambulances that parted in startled disarray. The Capri danced perilously close to calamity, yet miraculously emerged unscathed, pulling a big power slide onto Edgware Road heading West.

Behind them, the police pursuit was momentarily hampered by the emergency responders, allowing Max and Eleanor a fleeting but crucial lead.

"Sweet move, Max!" Flux's voice crackled through the comms. "But watch your six, the boys in blue are sniffing around. Lucky for you, their screens at HQ just went on a little unscheduled vacation. Oops! Looks like someone forgot their virus protection update, huh?"

Max couldn't help but smirk at Flux's remark. "Nice work, thanks Flux!"

"Stay off the main roads, man!" Flux advised urgently. "They'll box you in faster than you can say 'traffic jam.'"

"Roger that!" Max responded, just as the Capri soared over an overpass, landing with a solid thump. A police Mach-E appeared from the left, but Eleanor was ready. Pointing the SIG, she forced the driver to back off, but even as he slowed, she fired at the tyre and made sure that particular Mach-E would take no further part in the pursuit.

As she was leaning out, she heard the police pursuit drones overheard. "They got eyes in the sky Flux!"

"Standard stuff..." Flux's voice was calm but busy. "Need a minute or two to scramble their sensors."

"Don't worry," Eleanor responded, "I'll do it the old-fashioned way!" Unclicking her seatbelt, she wrapped the strap around her right leg, hooked her left foot under her seat, and slid half out of the door on her back, firing shots into the sky. A large police drone smashed into the ground just in front of the Capri forcing Max to swerve in avoidance.

The sudden movement caused Eleanor to lose purchase with her left foot, and she slipped further out. Max instinctively caught her flailing foot and anchored it under his left leg. Eleanor's aim remained true, downing two more drones that crashed harmlessly to the side and behind. She pulled herself back into the car and grabbed a fresh magazine off Max's jacket to replace her spent cartridge.

Max drifted the car off the A5, slicing through onto Station Road towards Hendon. Abruptly, another police Mach-E surged in from the right, gunfire erupting from its window. Priya, Glock in hand, was taking aim from the passenger seat. Eleanor slid back out, perching on the edge of her door, and leaning over the roof so she could shoot back at the Commander's pursuing car. Again, her return fire wasn't intended to harm, just to deter, and it worked – the police car fell back.

She slid back into the Capri and much to Max's surprise, pulled down the ashtray compartment under the dashboard, except it was now a digital screen. As she manipulated the controls, the Capri's rear number plate flipped open, revealing an EMP emitter. A pulse shot out, and Priya's Mach-E coasted to a stop, rendered lifeless.

But their reprieve was short-lived. At that instant four other police cars, burst out of a side street directly in front of them. Two peeled to the right side, with one holding point and another squeezing to the left.

"They're going to try and box us in Max!" Eleanor warned.

"Do you have one of those EMP guns at the front?" Max asked hopefully. Eleanor shook her head. "Tell you what..." determination clear in Max's voice, "fire it up anyway!"

Eleanor re-engaged the EMP pulse, and as she did so Max braked hard, flicked the wheel right, then hard left, and yanked the handbrake. The Capri nose-dived, the rear vaulted around, streaming smoke from tyres desperately trying to hold onto their sidewalls. The car launched into a 180-degree arc. The EMP pulse fanned out, disabling the police cars in a single, swift motion. Eleanor let out a triumphant whoop!

However, Max winced as he realised the lights had gone out on some of the houses nearby too. "Sorry for the blackout, folks," Max muttered, half to himself, as he steered the car down a side street, following Flux's guiding voice. Some people would be missing the evening news, but it was all bad news anyway, so maybe he had done them a favour, he reconciled himself.

With the traffic cameras disabled, the Capri became a ghost on the grid, invisible to the reinforcements. Flux's own drones patrolled the skies, countering police surveillance and carving out a safe path for them. Eleanor, finally allowing tension to ebb away, wound up the window and sank back into her seat with a relieved exhale. She placed her gun on the centre console, then reached across to wrap an arm around Max, suddenly planting a soft kiss on his cheek.

Max's adrenaline was surging, his senses electrified by the rush of outmanoeuvring the high-performance police pursuit vehicles in a car chase. Eleanor's touch, as ever, was instantly soothing, his trembling subsided. Her intimate nearness immediately calmed and comforted him. The kiss was an unexpected, sweet surprise. He stole a glance at her, his grin irrepressible and wide.

As Max returned his focus to the road, he could feel the warmth and affection in Eleanor's dark, expressive eyes tenderly observing him. In that brief moment, he longed to lock stares with her, to delve deeper into her thoughts, to understand the myriad emotions playing in her mind and in her heart at that exact moment.

She snuggled against his shoulder, murmuring, "My hero," before slumping back in her seat, snapping up the SIG and returning to her vigilant watch. It was like a switch had been flicked. She returned to sentinel mode, eyes darting in keen surveillance, her mind tactically evaluating escape routes should they be needed.

As she did so, she felt a weight in the blazer, realising only now that there was something in the inside pocket. She pulled out a smartphone. "Was this Jake's phone?"

Max glanced across, completely oblivious that along with the jacket, he had also snagged the dead operative's smartphone. "I'm guessing yes!"

Eleanor looked at it thoughtfully, "Hmm... could be useful. Flux?"

"I hear ya, plug it in and download before they try to burn it, I'll break into it back at base. I'm rolling now." Eleanor immediately connected the phone to the computer console in the would-be ashtray and a progress bar confirmed it was downloading the contents."

As she did so, Eleanor's attention momentarily shifted to her hands. For the first time, she noticed her knuckles, bruised and bloodied from the deadly battle with Jake. She flexed her fingers, wincing slightly at the discomfort now coming to the fore. Exhausted, she leaned back in her seat, her breath deep and weary. Despite her fatigue, she didn't let go of the SIG, her hold firm even as she finally drifted towards a fitful doze. Well, it had been a long day.

The next morning at City Hall, the same space where the disrupted Edison car launch had taken place, a press conference was about to begin. An air of urgency and anticipation filled the room. Journalists from all the major newspapers, TV and radio channels, as well as smaller local outlets, filled the room, cameras and recording equipment primed and ready. The atmosphere was thick with the scent of brewing coffee, and the low murmur of assembled reporters discussing the explosion at the Albion Cement Works Ltd Facility in Staples Corner Business Park. The atmosphere grew charged as PR staff confirmed Mayor Victoria Hartfield was about to grace them with her presence.

Running her customary ten minutes late, the Mayor made her entrance, a vision of polished sophistication. Dressed impeccably, she was the epitome of Hollywood glamour fused with commanding political authority. Her charisma was evident as always, she knew the power of her presence and how to deliver her words with the weight they warranted.

The Mayor's Head of PR approached the podium, signalling the assembly to quiet down in anticipation of Hartfield's address. Victoria glided onto the stage with an air of effortless grace, captivating the room instantly, her presence an alluring mix of allure and authority, instantly captivating, wielding an X-Factor other politicians would kill for.

"Ladies and gentlemen of the press," she began, her voice a perfect blend of sternness and charm, "as you are aware, a tragic incident occurred last night at the disused Cement Factory in Staples Corner, sadly claiming the life of one security guard, and resulting in serious and life-threatening toxic pollution streaming into our beloved city's air. Rest assured, the cause is being rigorously investigated.

"However, our immediate concern is the public's health. So, I am declaring a public health emergency. I am issuing instructions to all residents in the areas spanning from Edgware to Harlesden, and from Harrow to Wood Green to stay indoors and to wear masks if they must go out. These instructions will remain in force until further notice." As she spoke, maps detailing the affected zones illuminated the screens around the room. "Detailed maps and safety guidelines will be distributed to you shortly."

A rumble of voices circulated across the gathering, there were flashes from cameras, and some journalists leapt to their feet with a barrage of questions.

Victoria responded by simply raising a hand to command silence. The room quickly fell quiet as she continued. "This distressing incident at the Albion Cement Works Ltd Facility only highlights the critical battle against toxic air pollution - a battle I am dedicated to winning for the health and wellbeing of all Londoners.

"This is precisely why I championed the road user charging scheme, set to revolutionise our approach to environmental preservation. Each and every vehicle, with no exemptions of any kind, shall have to pay for the privilege of using the hallowed roads of our glorious capital city."

A TV reporter, unable to contain herself, interjected, "Mayor Hartfield, can you clarify how the pay-per-mile system will address incidents like the factory explosion?"

Victoria's eyes flickered with a touch of annoyance. "While the pay-per-mile initiative is not a panacea for every environmental challenge, it represents a significant stride towards diminishing the city's overall pollution levels. Each mile not driven is a victory for cleaner air."

Another voice cut through, a reporter from a prominent London newspaper. "Mayor, there's considerable speculation regarding the ULEZ. Will the new road-charging plan supersede ULEZ charges?"

Leaning slightly on the podium, with a dramatic exhale, Victoria responded, "To be unequivocally clear, The ULEZ charges are not going anywhere," she paused to let that sink in before continuing. "Let us not forget, we are in a battle for better air!"

"We are currently in the process of meticulously refining our policies. As of January 2027, let it be noted that only those vehicles that conform to the Euro 7 Emission standards, which have been available since earlier this year, along with zero-emission vehicles, shall be accorded the privilege of exemption from the daily levy of £12.50.

"This exemption is to be implemented in tandem with the pioneering, and globally-leading variable distance and emissions-based pay-as-you-drive tariffs. Both are slated to come into effect simultaneously."

Her declaration sent a wave of surprise and shock rippling through the crowd. Camera shutters clicked frenetically, while journalists from TV and radio stations hurried to broadcast the news.

A local radio presenter, positioned near the stage, directed his microphone towards the Mayor, his tone pressing. "Isn't this effectively double-charging motorists, particularly in these challenging economic times? Won't this policy make it even harder for businesses in London? Basically... are you trying to fleece us all for just trying to get around?!"

Victoria's patience visibly waned. "Darling, life isn't always fair, and this great city isn't cheap!" she snapped back, her tone sharp yet composed. "But the right to breathe clean air is fundamental. We are tasked with making difficult decisions for the greater good. It's time for us to collectively contribute."

The press conference had devolved into a maelstrom of questions, the Mayor's PR team struggling to regain control. Yet, Victoria Hartfield stood her ground, unflinching and resolute against the media's assault. Her responses, laced with a hint of tetchiness, were nonetheless delivered with the perfectly articulated sincerity of a veteran actress and the calculated evasion of a seasoned stateswoman.

In the midst of the press kerfuffle, a sudden movement caught everyone's attention, as a hand went up to snatch one of the roving mics. The tall man in the brown leather jacket stood up and stepped forward. The immediate vicinity around him hushed as some of the journalists recognised who it was, whispers of, "No way, isn't that the Edison review guy," echoed in his ears.

The man announced himself, "V-Max T of Turner Wheels here," he spoke confidently, a hint of challenge in his voice as he addressed Mayor Hartfield. "But of course, you know who I am, don't you, Mayor?"

Mayor Hartfield's perfectly practised impassive but faux-sincere expression, wavered for just a fraction of a second as she saw him. A swift, sharp glance to her security team conveyed a silent, seething question: "Who the hell let him in here?!"

Composing herself with practised ease, the Mayor retorted with a veneer of sweetness that barely masked her irritation. "Mr Turner, this is a press conference, not a car meet, have you lost your way today?" Her words, laced with a patronising tone, barely concealed the undercurrent of tension that had suddenly gripped the room.

Undeterred, Max launched into a volley of accusatory questions. "Mayor Hartfield, were you directly involved in the fire at the cement factory last night? Was it not just an orchestrated event to bolster your environmental policies?"

"Mr Turner, accusations of such a grave nature demand concrete evidence. As it stands, they are mere conjecture. The incident is currently under thorough investigation." the Mayor replied coolly.

Max pressed on, "And what of the alleged scheme to wreak havoc on London's streets? Your attempt to discredit motorists and car culture? Didn't you plan for there to be carnage on the streets of London yesterday, with a tally of nearly 200 deaths estimated?"

The Mayor's jaw dropped fractionally, and her veneer of patience began to crack. "Your flair for weaving dramatic tales is noteworthy,

Mr Turner, but completely misplaced in this context. There is no basis to these fantastical claims. Perhaps you're in the wrong profession - a screenwriter for my next film, maybe? I'll be sure to recommend you to my producers." Her words, tinged with sarcasm, elicited chuckles, though primarily from her own team.

Max wasn't flustered. "What about your connections to international corporations profiting from greenwashing policies? Why don't you tell everyone how you've been awarding contracts for public transport services to companies linked to these corporations? You know, mates of yours."

The Mayor's response was icy. "My administration makes decisions for the public good. Allegations of corruption are not only unfounded but offensive," she leant slightly forward on her podium and fixed him with a threatening stare, "And let me remind you, Mr Turner, that any insinuations of corruption are taken with utmost seriousness and investigated with full rigour. I hope you have good lawyers Mr Turner."

Max grinned back, completely unfazed, displaying a level of self-assured boldness he would never have believed himself capable of mustering just a few days ago. The force of his tone was undiminished by the Mayor's implied warning. "What about your involvement in kidnapping, and attempted murder, chiefly... mine?!"

The Mayor's response was swift. "Mr Turner, have you lost possession of your senses, or would you stoop to any depth to get views for your channel? Is this another dramatic ploy like the chaos you created in my building with your reckless stunt?" Her arm swept across the room, indicating the boarded-up windows, her voice inadvertently rising in pitch.

Max shot back, "This?! This was because you sent someone to kill me!"

The Mayor's facade of control shattered, her voice escalating to a near-shriek. "Lies! I was not the one that instructed Stahl to kill you!!"

Max's eyes narrowed; none of the news reports about the Edison cars incident mentioned Stahl, in fact, it had been reported that there were no injuries or casualties, as Wong had covered up what really happened. Max seized upon her unintended revelation: "Interesting. I never mentioned the name 'Stahl'. How would you know that, Mayor?"

The Mayor fell silent, finally flummoxed, her poise crumbled, her silence speaking volumes. The brief pause was all it took for the media to leap into action, bombarding her with a torrent of questions. The room erupted into chaos; the air charged with outrage and the whiff of political scandal and criminality.

Max, sensing the urgency of the moment, swiftly clambered onto his chair, still clutching the microphone. "Everyone, please, just a few more seconds of your time please!" he implored, his voice resonating throughout the room.

Behind the Mayor, her Head of PR, panic-stricken, was frantically gesticulating at the AV team, signalling them to cut Max's microphone. Unbeknownst to her, a slight, athletic woman with brown skin, clad in black and sporting impenetrable sunglasses and dark red lipstick, held sway over the control desk. Her enigmatic smile belied the gun she discreetly brandished, ensuring the staff's compliance. Leaning in, she whispered instructions without losing her smirk, "Turn up his mic."

The Mayor stared at Max, feigning anger, but now visibly struggling to conceal the growing fear that gripped her. She was acutely aware that both her careers as an actress and a politician were unravelling before her very eyes, and that too on a public platform. It was manifesting as her worst nightmare. She was literally dying on stage!

"I have proof, I have evidence, and it's all just gone live on all my channels," announced Max. "Plus I'm sharing everything with all of you right now. Just open your AirDrops and get ready to receive!"

Unnoticed by anyone, a lanky Afro-American in

a red Phillies hat, who had been quietly sitting in the audience and observing the chaos, was poised with a tablet in hand. He hit 'send', and instantly, phones around the room began to ping with incoming data.

The Mayor finally recovered her voice, and how; she screamed in fury at the security, "What the fuck are you lot doing?! Get him out of here. Now!!"

A scuffle broke out as security guards converged on Max, attempting to wrest the microphone from his grasp. The room devolved into pandemonium, journalists scrambling for their devices, hastily reviewing the newly received evidence, broadcasting live, and recording impromptu updates.

At the podium, Mayor Victoria Hartfield's facade of composure crumbled. Her voice rose in a crescendo of fury, lashing out at any subordinate within earshot as she desperately tried to salvage the rapidly deteriorating situation.

Amidst the uproar, a sudden shift in the footage on the large screens commanded everyone's attention. The image of Mayor Hartfield appeared, captured aboard a boat during a hasty retreat from City Hall, as the convoy had arrived to confront her.

What she hadn't known at the time, was that the boat she was on was the Gemini, and it belonged to Flux! When he had gone dark earlier in the day after ensuring the convoy was on route to City Hall, it had been to go retrieve his boat, a Fairline Targa 38, moored at Limehouse Basin.

As the Mayor and Quentin's plan to turn the EuroBall Rally event into an automotive disaster of unprecedented scale crumbled, and with a massive convoy blocking her way out of City Hall; Max, Eleanor and Flux had correctly anticipated that she would resort to a fast boat for a quick escape. All Flux had to do was intercept the call and turn up instead. She and her team jumped on the Gemini, no questions asked, assuming it to be the boat they had summoned. Something else they didn't realise was that Flux's vessel was festooned with hidden microphones and cameras.

On the large screens, footage showed Mayor Hartfield in a volatile FaceTime call with Commander Priya Kapoor. Her fury was palpable as she berated the Police chief. "What the absolute fucking hell Priya? Are you totally bloody useless? Why didn't the race happen? Where are the crashes, the injuries and deaths that I needed to bolster my anti-car policies?!"

As she fumed, the Mayor took a deep drag from her Virginia Slims cigar, her anger simmering. "Imagine the financiers' reaction when they learn of this debacle!" she continued, her voice laced with venom.

Commander Kapoor bristled, but was no less

exasperated, "It was Max Turner! He screwed up everything!" she yelled back.

The Mayor's voice grew colder, more diabolical: "Our contract requires us to deliver, right now we're looking like a pair of utterly incompetent cows. You more than me, Priya."

She was unrelenting and continued unabated, "You do realise that you were always just a token appointment, don't you? 'Let's get a gay, Asian woman in and we'll tick three boxes in one go. It'll add colour to the photo-call' they told me! I'm sorry, I know you can't help being what you are, but it does make you more execrable and..." the Mayor's tone switched from flippantly racist to menacing, "...expendable!"

Without giving the fuming Commander a chance to respond, she delivered a final ultimatum and hung up, "Move to Plan B now; and find a way to pin this on Turner. I won't tolerate any further failures!"

As the screen faded to black, the room erupted in a collective roar of stunned outrage. The journalists were visibly appalled by the Mayor's unveiled ruthlessness and particularly her overt racism. Victoria was mortified. She suddenly gathered herself and feigned mocking laughter, "Oh, what a masterful piece of fabrication, Mr Turner. Such theatrics, if that was really me, I'd get an Oscar for that performance!" However, nobody, not even her staff, laughed with her this time.

"The original file has been sent to all of you," Max announced to the gathered journalists, "you're most welcome to analyse the heck out of it!"

Before anyone had time to respond or ask questions, another video popped up on the screens, this one depicted a dimly lit room with a half-naked girl lying on the floor, as two other people came into the frame, everyone collectively leaned in, captivated by the shocking scene.

Max's earlier decision to take Jake's blazer had proven fortuitous beyond measure. Flux, upon hacking into Jake's phone, had discovered that the feed from the detonator camera at the factory was directly linked to it. Remarkably, the entire sequence was stored on the device. The standard protocol would have been to remotely wipe a deceased operative's phone, but it had most likely been assumed that the phone was destroyed in the factory fire.

Flux chose a particularly telling segment from earlier that evening, featuring Eleanor while she was still unconscious from the drugs. As she was facing away from the camera, and the footage was grainy, she couldn't be identified from the footage.

The two people coming into view were Jake, unknown to anyone at the press conference, but the second was unmistakably, the Mayor of

London, Victoria Hartfield.

Jake was briefing her, "The tanks have been refilled with toxic chemicals, the air's laced with sulphur and ammonium nitrate," he detailed meticulously. "This place is rigged to blow at the first sign of Turner's presence, and rest assured, it will send toxic crap spewing into the air, good and proper."

"Darling, do ensure you don't botch this," Mayor Hartfield warned with a chilling tone. "I require a scenario where people are inhaling abhorrent substances until they're transforming into hirsute Neanderthals sprouting babies out of their mouths and speaking in freakish tongues… you know like the last horrid lot that came over on those little boats!"

Even Jake was seen to flinch in revulsion at her comments, but he remained professional. The Mayor wasn't done, "This needs to be extraordinarily effective, my dear. I require a public so desperate, they'll be clamouring for me to extinguish anything that emits even the faintest whiff of unpleasantness."

She moved closer to Jake, poking a finger at his chest as she continued, "We're orchestrating a disaster of epic proportions here; anything less and well, my patrons will not be amused. They'll be serving my arse on a silver salver. While you, darling, will be unceremoniously discarded, and your bits will be thrown to the scavenging strays in the back alley!" She glanced down to his lower region and tutted, "And that would be such a tragic shame, wouldn't it, my dear?"

Jake tried to reassure her, "Don't worry Ma'am, one way or another, this place will go nuclear tonight."

The video feed abruptly ended, plunging the room into a stunned hush. Mayor Hartfield, her façade of control shattered, desperately yelled at the security guards to apprehend Max. However, her commands were ignored as new orders crackled through the guards' radios, redirecting their attention to her.

A wave of surprise and disbelief swept through the hall. Journalists clamoured to document every second of the Mayor's dramatic downfall, their cameras capturing the moment as she was led away by security.

Amidst the chaos, Flux slipped in next to Max, his voice low. "Solid work, my man!"

Max gestured towards the Mayor being escorted out. "Wong?" he inquired.

"Oh yeah, he about to have some words with our favourite thespian! It's gonna take a while too. Life at least I reckon." Flux replied with an air of satisfaction.

"And the Eclipse Squad?" Max queried further.

"Out of play, Viridis must have pulled them." Max nodded in acknowledgement. "Dude, I'll be in your ear if you need me…" Flux said, noticing some of the journalists turning back towards Max, having realised the futility of trying to get any comments from the arrested Mayor, or her staff. "Though it looks you gonna be here a while."

Max nodded as he steeled himself for the media barrage he knew was imminent. He realised he had to face them to ensure the veracity of the evidence he had given them. He, Flux and Eleanor, had meticulously prepared his narrative, to ensure every pertinent detail withstood scrutiny, while omitting any mention of Flux and Eleanor specifically.

It would be a tricky bit of narrative, not least because it meant he would have to take more credit for everything that had occurred (and he hated that), whilst at the same time carefully side-stepping anything that could implicate him in criminality.

He took a deep breath, and just as the media closed in around him, he caught a glimpse of Eleanor blowing him a kiss and disappearing into the crowd with a smile that lasted long enough to fortify him with the necessary resolve. Still, vindication was a sweet, sweet balm that would provide more healing than all those years of therapy ever did.

"We have questions…" they said.

"And I have answers," he replied, "all the answers

you need."

He opened his arms wide as if to welcome them, "But first, I have a statement to make." He cleared his throat, aware that his next words carried the weight of his entire journey, a journey fraught with danger and revelations that had shaken him to his core. As he began to speak, his voice was steady, strong, and resonating with profound conviction.

"Ladies and gentlemen of the press, and everyone watching, you may know me as Max Turner, V-Max T of Turner Wheels. As a motoring journalist, I've always championed the joy of driving. Yet today, I stand before you not just as an automotive enthusiast but as a concerned citizen alarmed by the path our society is taking.

"We've been sold the narrative of saving the planet, a cause we all support. But let's remember, the planet is a pretty resilient old thing. It's really us that needs saving. We need to tread more gently on this Earth so it can continue to sustain us; that much is a given. I mean a cleaner, greener world for all, well who doesn't like the sound of that, right?

"However, beneath this noble goal, a darker agenda has been brewing, one driven by profit, not the environment.

"This sustainability narrative is being manipulated by powerful entities, turning our environmental concerns into a tool for profit. They're making money off our misery, simple as that. Do not forget, the green industry is expected to be worth $10.3 trillion by 2050! This is a high-stakes game at play and we're merely the pawns.

"They're playing this game by manipulating facts to shape public opinion. But they underestimate the power of truth, and the resilience of public spirit. We've uncovered some of their deceit, just a fraction. But it's enough to reveal their readiness to trade our freedoms for their financial gain.

"Let me stress, what all this is really about is some big players making big bucks, while our freedoms literally get parked at the kerb

"Be in no doubt, this is a battle for our rights, for our freedom to choose how we live, how we move. It's not about opposing environmental protection; it's about ensuring our path to a cleaner world doesn't erode our freedoms. And let's not forget, these are freedoms that were fought for, that we sacrificed a great deal for; these freedoms are sacred.

"We can't just, without question and analysis, let our pursuit of a greener future rob us of the joys and freedoms that give life its flavour. I mean c'mon, life is about living not merely surviving.

"It shouldn't just be about adding years to life, but life to years! And I don't know about you, but those rare moments I get to drive a great car, on an awesome road on a beautiful day, that experience adds a lot of life to my years!

"Nobody wants to live on a flooded ball of mud, drained of its resources and incapable of sustaining us anymore; of course not! And who doesn't want clean air for themselves and their children to breathe?

"But, we've got to ask the tough questions. We've got to demand honesty from those in charge. It's not about being anti-environment. It's about making sure our journey to a cleaner world doesn't strip away the very things that make life worth living.

"The fight has to be against those who exploit legitimate concerns for personal profit. Those who seek to deny us our independence and happiness under the pretence of trying to extend our lifespans.

"I mean what if they do? What then? We live longer? Longer for what? More years trapped in our homes because we can't go anywhere, do anything, see anyone? That is not living.

"Understand that you and me, the ordinary people, are all in this together. Be in no doubt that the war on motorists is real. But we're fighting for more than just the right to drive; we're fighting for the very essence of what makes life worth living.

"Let's ensure that our march towards a greener

future is also a march towards preserving our freedoms; one mile at a time."

As Max concluded, a hush fell over the crowd. He could see the impact of his words reflected in the eyes of the journalists, the bystanders, and the camera lenses that captured this moment. He knew that the fight was far from over, but in this moment, he might just have given people pause for thought before rushing headlong into a future where we are all imprisoned indoors, charged with assaulting the planet and destroying our own health. We might end up living longer, but would we want to?

In the ensuing days, Max's life became a whirlwind of interviews and media appearances. Amid this frenzy, a realisation dawned upon him - he had indeed made an impact, igniting a much-needed discourse. Perhaps, he pondered, his role in this story had reached its conclusion. Maybe it was time to embrace a new beginning.

A week later, Max Turner pushed away his long-emptied cup of coffee and stood up with a sense of finality, snapping up his passport and boarding pass from the table. Ahmed Abbas, Flux Jaxon and Eleanor Rodrigues all rose to their feet as well. It was time for their final goodbyes. As they stepped out of the concourse café, Max reached into his pocket and hesitantly took out his beloved BMW's keys, "I almost forgot Ahmed," he dropped the keys into his friend's hand. "Take care of her please".

Ahmed smiled reassuringly, "Don't worry Max, she'll be waiting for you when you get back or... you know I could easily get her sent out to you in Dubai, just say the word!"

Max nodded silently and reached out to embrace Ahmed in the tightest of hugs he could muster, "Stay well yaar," Ahmed implored, close to getting emotional, "and don't go ghosting me again nah?" Ahmed implored.

Acknowledging Ahmed's request with a shake of his head, Max then turned to Flux. "And talking of ghosts, as for you, Mr Jaxon," he began, his voice laden with respect and gratitude, "it's been an absolute privilege and honour, my friend. You truly are a legend."

Flux pulled Max into a heartfelt bro-hug. "Takes one to know one, dude. Stay sharp out there!"

Tactfully both Ahmed and Flux remained standing at the café while Eleanor accompanied Max towards the departure gates, her arm linked with his. They moved in a comfortable silence, each absorbed in their own thoughts. As Max paused at the threshold of the security checkpoint, he turned to Eleanor, words caught in his throat. "Eleanor, I... I..."

She gently cradled his face in her hands, pulling him down for a tender, lingering kiss. Stepping back, her eyes locked onto his. "You don't need to say anything, Max, I understand. Just go on be the awesome person you are!"

Max exhaled, a mix of disbelief and admiration in his voice. "Me? I'm just me, but you... you're something... something extraordinary... you're unlike anyone I ever met in my life... Ellie, I don't know how to..."

"Shut up Max!" Eleanor interjected softly, embracing him one last time. As she began to turn away, her attention was suddenly drawn to a TV screen broadcasting BBC World News. Max's eyes followed hers to the screen to see what had made her pause.

In the aftermath of his revelations, the whole Mayoral office had been immediately disbanded subject to extensive investigations, and a caretaker administration had been installed.

The breaking news on the monitor was announcing the appointment of a caretaker Mayor. The news ticker caption read: "Tech millionaire Sebastian Alastair Van Houten appointed as Interim Mayor". The news footage showed him being introduced at a press conference and posing for pictures. However, what had caught Eleanor's eye, and now Max's, was what he had in the lapel hole of his sharply tailored suit.

It was a green rose, exactly like the one they had found on Quentin Dubois' abandoned desk. Eleanor and Max turned to face each other and spoke as one, "Viridis!" they uttered in unison.

Flux and Ahmed came running up to join them. "You guys saw it too?" Flux asked. Although he could see from their faces that they had. They stood together, absorbing the implications of this new development, the weight of the discovery hanging heavily in the air.

Max let out a deep, contemplative sigh as he stared at his passport and boarding pass to Dubai. Finally, he pocketed the passport but tore up the boarding pass. He then held out his hand to Ahmed. "Yaar, I'm gonna need the keys to the Bimmer back."

About the Author: B. C. Guy

B. C. Guy is the chosen pseudonym of Shahzad Sheikh, a seasoned motoring journalist known to many as the BrownCarGuy. With a career spanning 35 years, Sheikh has made significant contributions to the automotive journalism landscape, both in the UK and the Middle East.

Sheikh's journey in this field is marked by several noteworthy achievements. He holds the distinction of being Saudi Arabia's first car journalist. His editorial prowess was further established during his tenure as the Editor of the Middle East edition of Car Magazine. Additionally, Sheikh played a pivotal role in launching the Parkers Car Price Guide website and was co-founder of Motoring Middle East in Dubai.

Currently, Sheikh continues his passion for cars and storytelling through freelancing and creating engaging content for his BrownCarGuy YouTube channel and various social media platforms. His personal connection to the automotive world is underscored by his choice of vehicle, a classic black 1989 BMW 325i.

"The ULEZ Files" emerges as a compelling narrative born from Sheikh's extensive, on-the-ground coverage of the Ultra Low Emission Zone (ULEZ) policies, the protests they sparked, and the lives they impacted. As a dedicated automotive journalist, Sheikh has devoted substantial time and resources to understanding and reporting on this critical topic, bringing an unparalleled level of authenticity and depth to this work of fiction.

More than just a riveting thriller, Sheikh's novel reflects his thorough research and numerous interviews with protestors, experts, and those directly affected by the ULEZ expansion. "The ULEZ Files" offers readers a fictional, yet eerily plausible future, delving into the implications of unchecked environmental policies and the enduring resilience of community spirit.